SCIENCE

THE DEFINITIVE GUIDE

SCI

ENCE
THE DEFINITIVE GUIDE

CONTENTS

The popular image of science is one of complexity and equations, computers and test tubes. At heart it is just a simple habit of observing the world around us and looking for qualities and events that are predictable and consistent. There are countless realms of existence, especially in human affairs, that refuse to be analysed, tested with experiments or arranged into tidy data. Science cannot tell us the meaning of our lives, nor guide us towards what is morally right or unforgivably wrong. We have to decide those matters for ourselves; but science is the sturdy platform that anchors our feet while we test the farthest and most perplexing limits of our curiosity.

Modern scientific research is so wide ranging yet so intricately detailed that most professionals have to specialize in a particular area, such as physics, chemistry or biology. These familiar subjects are themselves subdivided into niche specialisms: microbiology, particle physics, biochemistry, astrophysics and so on. These are just convenient ways of parcelling out the work that scientists perform, just as we have to invent practical filing systems in an office, or even on our home computers, to prevent us from being swamped by the mass of data. Nature makes no such distinctions. As this book makes clear, everything that exists is interconnected with everything else.

Your journey through the following pages should also show you that science is not necessarily about hard-and-fast answers. For instance, when the media alerts us to a possible disease risk or a food poisoning scare, the reporters demand to know whether or not some kind of epidemic is about to occur. Responsible scientists can only answer in terms of risks and probabilities. None of them will ever be in a position to say that an epidemic is definitely on its way. The same applies to our current concerns about climate change. Arguments rage on both sides of the debate. Certainties are rare. All we know for sure is that if we do nothing in this generation to alleviate the effects of atmospheric pollution, species extinction and rainforest destruction, the next generation is more likely to suffer.

Science is a perpetual process of debate, analysis and reconsideration, but that is not to say that it cannot be trusted as truth. It is easy to imagine that Galileo proved the ancient astronomers 'wrong' when he showed that the Earth orbits the Sun rather than the other way around. Yet they were not wrong, so much as less right than their successors. When we get up in the morning, the Sun rises in the sky, and when we prepare for bed it sinks over the horizon. That mental model of the relationship between us and the Sun still works for most of us – up to a certain degree of precision. It was only when Galileo made detailed and complex observations of the night sky that he became dissatisfied with the accuracy of that model as an explanatory device or predictive tool.

Isaac Newton provided a magnificent mathematical framework for the behaviour of physical objects that has never been equalled – again, up to a certain level of accuracy. Albert Einstein showed that Newtonian calculations are not reliable when applied to extremely large objects, like stars and galaxies, or ultimately fast ones, like waves of light. Likewise, our generation no doubt exploits many scientific models that future generations will improve upon.

Beyond its practical applications, science is a quest to discover our place in the scheme of existence. Our ultimate ambition is to find a unifying concept, a Theory of Everything that makes sense of all our different strands of knowledge. For instance, we do not yet understand the precise origins of life, nor how DNA first appeared on the Earth. We are trying to discover the relationship between unimaginably small things, such as subatomic particles and photons of electromagnetic energy, and massive objects like stars and galaxies, and the gravity that shapes them into the universe we inhabit.

Perhaps the greatest puzzle is how we can be aware of our own thoughts. Consciousness tells us that a universe exists beyond the bounds of our own skins, yet we have no good theory to explain the vividness of that sensation. Nor do we know if that universe is the sum total of all there is, or just a fragment of the totality. In addressing the deepest puzzles of science, we are not even sure how to ask the right questions. No doubt the next generation of curious minds will make wonderful discoveries that we could barely imagine today. Our present task is to safeguard their future opportunities.

EARTH

In the year 1654, James Ussher, Archbishop of Armagh,
Primate of All Ireland and Vice-Chancellor of Trinity College in
Dublin, was highly regarded as a theologian and scholar. After
scouring the length and breadth of Britain and Europe for biblical
and historical manuscripts, he asserted that the Earth came into
being on 23 October 4004 BC, giving the planet an age of slightly
less than 6,000 years.

A century later, another godly man, the geologist James Hutton, was fascinated
by granite outcrops in his Scottish homeland, and demonstrated that the minerals
in the hard grey rock must once have been molten. He also understood that
sedimentary rock, created by erosion and flowing water, took long ages to form.
Above all, he showed that successive rock layers ('strata') hinted at many different
histories for the Earth's surface across unimaginably vast spans of time. In 1785
he concluded that the Earth was eternal. It had 'no vestige of a beginning, no
prospect of an end'.

In 1862 another Scotsman, William Thomson (later ennobled as Lord Kelvin),
was renowned for his understanding of heat energy and the scale of absolute
temperature later named in his honour. He thought the Earth must have formed
'more than 20 and less than 40 million years ago'. This was not what Charles
Darwin and supporters of evolutionary theory wished to hear. For his scheme to
work, Darwin needed even more time to have elapsed: hundreds rather than tens
of millions of years. Thomson felt sure that the Sun could not have burned, nor the
Earth retained its heat, for so long.

The missing factor was radiation, the fierce energy from within atoms that
powers the Sun and replenishes the Earth's inner heat. In the first decade of
the 20th century the New Zealand-born physicist Ernest Rutherford discovered
that atoms had nuclei, and gave us the concept of radioactive 'half-life', in which
exactly half the atoms in a radioactive lump of material decay into non-radioactive
forms over a specific time. In some cases the half-life is measured in moments;
in others, millennia. Rutherford compared the mass of long half-life radioactive
minerals in natural rock against the proportions of decay products embedded
alongside them, and calculated that the Earth must be 500 million years old.

Today the timescales that geologists deal with are numbing in their
magnitude, but not, as James Hutton thought, eternal. The Earth is four and a half
billion years old. We have identified the 'vestige of a beginning' and we know, too,
that there is indeed 'the prospect of an end' some five billion years into the future.

Universe

1 The term that applies to everything that exists in the physical world, from galaxies to stars, planets, moons and asteroids. Based on our current scientific understanding, the universe began in a single, gigantic explosion some 13.75 billion years ago.

Local group

2 The largest structures in the universe consist of clusters of galaxies loosely held together by their mutual attraction, and by hidden gravitational influences of 'dark matter' distribution. The galaxy in which our Sun resides is part of a 'local group' composed of approximately 30 galaxies. Three of them are particularly large, and have characteristic spiral shapes. Our galaxy, known as the Milky Way, is one of those three.

Galaxy

3 Our Sun drifts near the outermost tip of one spiral arm of the Milky Way. It is just one among approximately 200 billion other stars in this galaxy. The Sun is classed as a 'yellow dwarf' star of average size, very stable in its behaviour, and with sufficient hydrogen fuel in its core to keep it shining for roughly 10 billion years. The Sun has approximately half its lifespan remaining.

Our solar system drifts at one end of a spiral arm towards the outer perimeter of a typical galaxy within a universe so vast, there is no easy way for us to grasp the distances involved.

THE EARTH ORBITS THE SUN at a distance of 93 million miles (150 million kilometres). This is a convenient yardstick for comparing distances in and around the solar system. The Earth–Sun distance is known as an Astronomical Unit (AU). To get an impression of what an AU really means, think of the Sun as a large sunflower and the Earth as a little blue ant about 45 feet (15 metres) away from it. Pluto's average distance from the Sun is about 40 AUs. The outermost realms of the solar system, where lonely comets lurk, is somewhere around about 100,000 AUs in diameter. Beyond that already vastly distant realm, even the AU loses its descriptive power as a measure of distance. We have to turn, instead, to the fastest-known entity in the universe – light. It travels one AU in eight minutes. When measuring distances in the broader universe, we need to think in terms of millennia, not minutes.

The speed of light in a vacuum is 186,282 miles (299,792 km) per second. In one year, an unimpeded photon will travel 5,865,696,000,000 miles (9,460,800,000,000 kilometres).

Numbers of this size become hard to deal with when written down as simple numerals. For convenience, Astronomers call this special distance a 'light-year'. The next nearest star to us is Proxima Centauri, 4.2 light-years away. The distances between stars are almost impossible for us to grasp. Imagine if our Sun were the size of an orange. On that scale, Proxima Centauri would be another orange-sized object more than a thousand miles (1,600 kilometres) away.

Our local galaxy, the Milky Way, contains about 200 billion stars. From one side of the galaxy to the other, the distance is 100,000 light-years. The light that we capture in our telescopes from stars at the galaxy's perimeter was first emitted while neanderthal humans roamed the earth. The next nearest galaxy is Andromeda, 2.5 million light-years away. No human-scaled idea can encompass the distances between galaxies. The known universe contains at least 100 billion galaxies. Light from the most distant galaxies has taken nearly 13 billion years to reach us. That light first shone when the universe itself was still young.

Solar system

4 We cannot be sure if ours is a typical solar system, replicated many times elsewhere in the galaxy, or unique in giving rise to life. Certainly the Earth is fortunate, occupying an orbit that is close enough to the Sun that the planet is kept warm, but not so close that it overheats, nor so far away that it freezes. This privileged orbit is known as the 'Goldilocks zone' after the famous fairytale.

SEE ALSO

■ **The Sun**
page 20

■ **Solar System**
page 144

OUR ORIGINS

The Earth emerged out of the almost vanishingly tenuous wreckage of dead stars drifting through the depths of space. All the matter on this planet was created inside stars that no longer exist.

THE EARTH and its parent Sun owe their origins to the violent deaths of earlier stars that existed long before our solar system took shape. All stars eventually die, and the chemical products of those deaths gradually find their way into new forms.

The nuclear processes inside a star can be be more varied than just the fusing of hydrogen nuclei into helium nuclei, especially in the case of stars substantially larger and hotter than our own Sun. Under the extremely high temperatures and pressures within the core of large stars, helium nuclei can also be fused into carbon. This paves the way for the 'nucleosynthesis' of further chemical elements. More helium nuclei fuse with the carbon nuclei to make oxygen, and then with oxygen to make neon. Carbon and oxygen fuse to make silicon, while pairs of silicon atoms fuse to make iron.

Stars larger than our Sun tend to die a quick and bright death. The hydrogen fuel eventually runs out and the outward pressure of heat and energy generated by the core falls dramatically. The star suddenly collapses in on itself under the pull of its own gravity, creating an immense explosion, called a supernova. This hastens the last, dying atomic fusion reactions, very rapidly creating elements heavier than iron. Then the force of the explosion scatters these products far into space.

With the exception of hydrogen, the primordial building component of the universe, every atom on Earth (including all those that make up our bodies) is far older than the planet itself.

We are the products of an ancient supernova; or more likely, several supernovae whose remnants merged gently over billions of years to create the vast cloud of dust and gas ('nebula') from which our Sun and our Earth eventually coalesced.

Occasional supernova explosions in adjacent star systems will have sent shock waves through the nebula, causing random concentrations of dust, around which the first microscopic seeds of our world were generated.

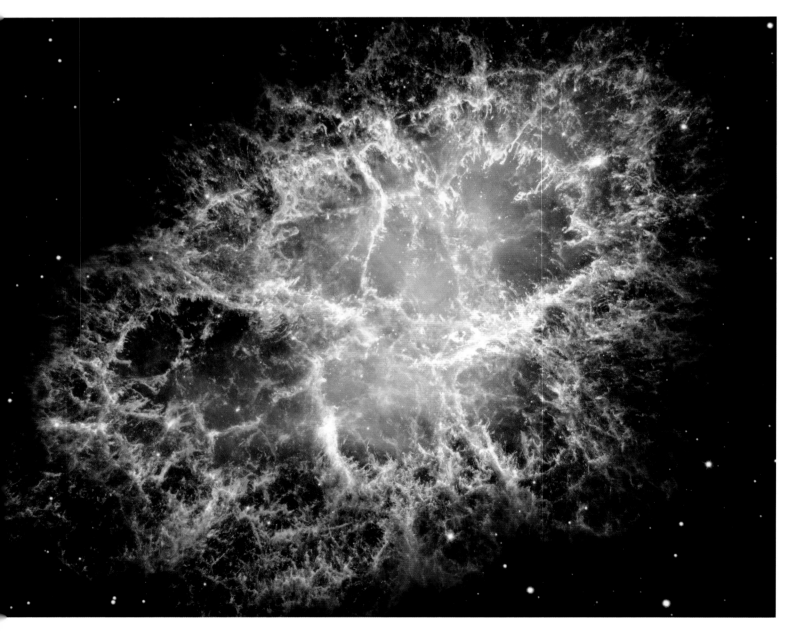

◄ **The Crab Nebula**, one of the most intensively studied phenomena in the Milky Way, is a supernova remnant, the wreckage of an exploded star that has scattered its material far into space. The actual explosion was recorded as a very bright yet seemingly short-lived star by Chinese and Arab astronomers in the year 1054.

► **The Orion Nebula** is the nearest star-forming region to Earth, approximately 1,500 light years away, and located within our spiral arm of the Milky Way galaxy. It can be observed through a telescope by looking towards the constellation of Orion. The nebula is 24 light-years across. At least 700 new stars are coalescing within it.

Formation of solar system
Dust and gas under the gravitaional influence of the newly formed Sun gathered into an 'accretion disc' from which other clumps of matter coalesced. These small masses, known as planetesimals, often collided. The larger accretions drew more loose fragments into them, gaining mass to become full-sized planets. This artwork shows the Earth being bombarded by rogue planetesimals, which it then absorbs into its growing mass.

Violent beginnings
A particularly unstable period in the Earth's early history, from about 4 billion to 3.8 billion years ago, is known as the Late Heavy Bombardment. Drifting through nearby space was a vast amount of debris left over from the solar system's formation. Rogue planetesimals and rock fragments frequently collided with the Earth, repeatedly smashing the crust.

Subsequent wind, rain and erosion has smoothed away most traces of these catastrophes, but we only have to glance at the countless craters on the airless moon to see what the young Earth suffered. With destruction came the possibility of creation. Some asteroids and comets falling on the Earth may have contained chemical compounds that contributed to the emergence of life.

THE EARLY EARTH

Our little home world is a product of violently creative events that began long before our Sun,
or any of the planets in our solar system, reached their present maturity.

FIVE BILLION YEARS AGO, a star-forming nebula drifted through our region of the galaxy. Somewhere within this immense yet ghostly-thin cloud, a seemingly insignificant clump of matter coalesced, gaining mass until it began to exert its own gravitational force, extremely weak, yet just strong enough to attract nearby atoms and molecules. This mass, or protostar, grew to the point where its gravity became strong enough to pull in more material from ever greater distances: tens, then thousands, and eventually many millions of miles. Dust and gas from the surrounding nebula became concentrated into a spinning plate-shaped structure known as an accretion disc, with the protostar – our embryonic Sun – at its centre.

Even as the Sun gathered mass, some of the chemical debris in the accretion disc began to cluster in miniature, and much cooler, versions of the protostar process. Small worlds, known as planetesimals, began to form. When these collided with each other and their wreckage recombined, larger structures emerged and consolidated into the planets and moons that exist today.

One of those worlds became our Earth. It began life around 4.6 billion years ago as a hot, chaotic sphere of molten metals and silicates, but over time the various materials began to divide according to density, with the heaviest metals, such as iron, sinking into the Earth's core, and the lighter materials, such as silica, floating upwards towards the planet's surface. After approximately 100 million years, the outer surface cooled sufficiently for a thin rocky shell, called the crust, to form.

The primordial Earth

As the crust cooled, weak spots allowed molten material from beneath to burst onto the surface through volcanoes. At the same time these eruptions hurled out massive amounts of carbon dioxide, ammonia and methane, creating the early atmosphere. In addition the volcanoes threw out water, in the form of super-hot steam, which condensed into clouds, then cooled still further to fall as rain. So emerged the first shallow seas of liquid water on the Earth's surface. At the edges of those ancient seas, simple blue-green algae emerged as the first forms of life.

SEE ALSO

■ **Solar System**
page 144

THE EARLY ENVIRONMENT

If we could be transported in a time machine to the young Earth, we would find a toxic and hostile world quite unlike the one we know today.

THE EARTH'S EARLY ATMOSPHERE was not remotely the same as the air that we breathe now. It was created largely by volcanoes, belching out compounds based around hydrogen: methane (hydrogen and carbon, CH_4), ammonia (hydrogen and nitrogen, NH_3) and water vapour (hydrogen and oxygen, H_2O), with carbon dioxide adding to the unpleasant brew.

Ultraviolet radiation from the Sun rearranged this mix, breaking up water molecules to liberate oxygen, which in turn attacked ammonia to liberate nitrogen. Even more water vapour emerged as a by-product of these processes, but quantities of lone hydrogen atoms were left unpaired. Lighter than any of the surrounding gases, the free hydrogen drifted up through the atmosphere and was eventually lost to space. Gradually the atmosphere transmuted almost entirely into carbon dioxide and nitrogen, with water vapour clouds delivering torrential rains: the origins of the first seas.

Most of the ingredients for life were in place. After all, even something as complicated as a human body is made up principally from just four elements: hydrogen, oxygen, carbon and nitrogen. Together, these account for 96 per cent of our body weight. The remaining four per cent is taken up by calcium, with hints of sulphur, sodium and traces of iron, copper and magnesium. All of these were available to primitive biology from the moment that the wind and rain, and the ebb and flow of the new oceans, first began to wear away at the Earth's mineral-rich crust.

▼ Planet-wide volanic activity created the early atmosphere, a sickly brew of methane, ammonia and carbon dioxide, spiced with sulphurous gases. Vast amounts of water vapour were hurled into the noxious air, falling as torrential rain to create the primitive oceans.

▲ Wreckage from the formation of the solar system hit the young Earth frequently. Most of it would have been in the form of rocky asteroids, but occasional icy comets may have delivered some of the basic chemicals necessary for life to take hold.

Stromatolites are dense, matted layers of mineral deposits made by microscopic blue-green algae. The oldest known stromatolites, such as these examples in Western Australia, date from 3.5 billion years ago, proving that life established itself while the earth was still young.

Life takes hold

Though we cannot say exactly how, or where, the first organisms emerged, we can be sure that they took hold with startling rapidity soon after the Earth was formed.

By around 3.8 billion years ago, surprisingly soon in the Earth's long history, the oceans supported a great mass of blue-green algae, 'prokaryotic' single-celled organisms lacking a cellular nucleus. There were no other more complex organisms to prey upon them, so they lived and died in relative tranquillity across countless generations. The main threat to the algae's survival was solar radiation, not predation. Pigments in their cells protected them against ultraviolet rays, while letting in beneficial wavelengths of light for a primitive kind of photosynthesis, enabling the algae to break apart water molecules from the surrounding ocean and exploit the hydrogen in their internal chemistry. Much of the oxygen was expelled. The blue-green algae belonged to a class of

microorganism known as anaerobic, or 'oxygen-hating'.

The product of these first biological entities was a form of atmospheric pollution as destructive as any eco-horror we may fear today. After a billion years and more of global domination, the blue-green algae gradually became a victim of their own success, pumping out vast quantities of oxygen gas and changing the Earth's atmosphere into a lethal mix that they could no longer tolerate. This was the origin of the oxygen-rich atmosphere that we breathe now.

As individuals, the primordial blue-green algae were too fragile to leave much in the way of distinct fossils. But they didn't lead solitary lives. At least some species grew in vast, dense mats consisting of trillions of individuals. They left mineral traces that are still found today, in the form of stromatolites, rock-like accumulations dating from more than 3.5 billion years ago.

THE SUN

In the 4.5 billion years since its birth, the Sun has converted four million tons of hydrogen into energy every second, yet the amount of available hydrogen is still so great that it should be able to sustain this process for another 5 billion years to come.

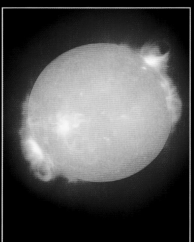

SUN **STATISTICS**

Mass 2,000,000,000,00
0,000,000,000,000
,000 tons
(2 x 10²⁷ tons) or
about 330,000
times the mass
of the Earth

Diameter 870,000 miles
(1.4 million km)

Age 4.5 billion years

Average distance from the Earth 93 million miles (149.6 million km)

Luminosity 390 billion billion megawatts

Composition 91.2% hydrogen, 8.7% helium, 0.1% other chemical elements

Surface temperature 5,500 degrees Celsius

Temperature at Core 15 million degrees Celsius

Core density 12 times that of solid lead

Rotation period around its north–south axis 25.6 Earth days

IN THE HEART OF THE SUN, unimaginable gravitational pressures, a trillion kilograms per square centimetre, squeeze hydrogen nuclei together until helium is formed, in a process known as fusion. The mass of helium that emerges from this process is 0.7 per cent less than the mass of hydrogen that goes into it. That 'missing' mass is liberated as energy. The pressure in the solar core is 300 billion times greater than the atmospheric pressure on the Earth's surface, while the density is a dozen times greater than that of lead. Particles of electromagnetic light energy (photons) are bounced around inside the core for millions of years before finally working their way up to the surface. Then at last they escape.

Solar flares Vast clouds of electrically charged subatomic particles are continually blasted away from the Sun. These violent bursts, which often eject the equivalent of 20 billion tons of matter, are properly known as Coronal Mass Ejections (CMEs). The swarm of particles travel across space, interacting with all the planets and moons in the solar system, including the earth. The electrical charges in the 'solar wind' are responsible for creating auroras high in the earth's atmosphere. They can also disrupt computers and interfere with national power grids and orbiting satellites.

Temperatures in the Sun's atmosphere, the corona, are at least 2 million degrees Celsius, far greater than those at the Sun's surface (the photosphere). The corona is threaded with powerful and fast-changing magnetic fields that constantly twist and distort into new patterns. Positively and negatively charged subatomic particles spiral at very high energies along the magnetic field lines.

It takes solar radiation a mere eight minutes to reach as far as the Earth, in the form of heat and infrared heat, ultraviolet and visible light, and a small proportion of X-rays and radio waves.

The corona The Sun's atmosphere extends far into space, and – mysteriously – is much hotter than the surface.

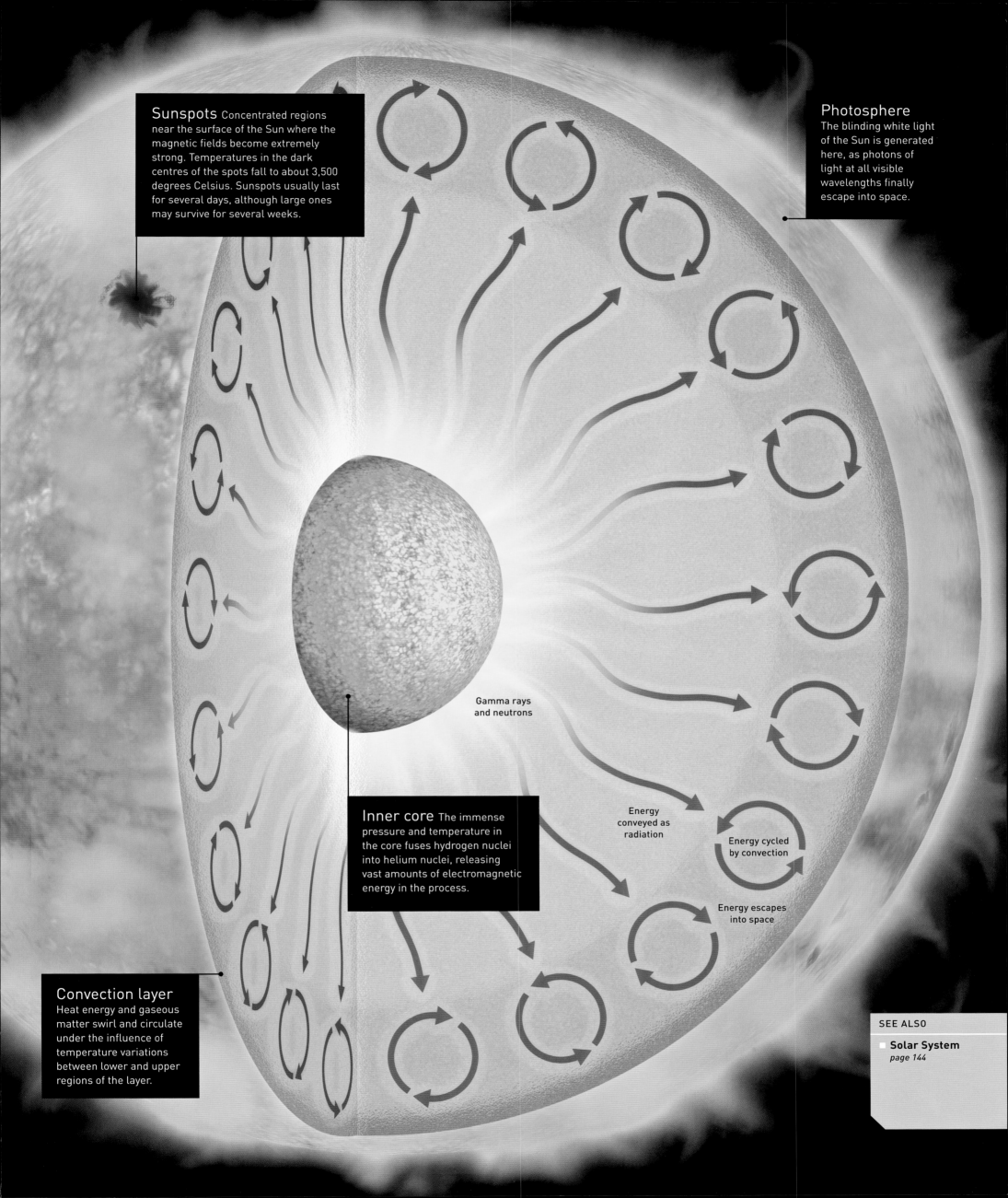

Sunspots Concentrated regions near the surface of the Sun where the magnetic fields become extremely strong. Temperatures in the dark centres of the spots fall to about 3,500 degrees Celsius. Sunspots usually last for several days, although large ones may survive for several weeks.

Photosphere
The blinding white light of the Sun is generated here, as photons of light at all visible wavelengths finally escape into space.

Gamma rays and neutrons

Inner core The immense pressure and temperature in the core fuses hydrogen nuclei into helium nuclei, releasing vast amounts of electromagnetic energy in the process.

Energy conveyed as radiation

Energy cycled by convection

Energy escapes into space

Convection layer
Heat energy and gaseous matter swirl and circulate under the influence of temperature variations between lower and upper regions of the layer.

SEE ALSO

■ **Solar System**
page 144

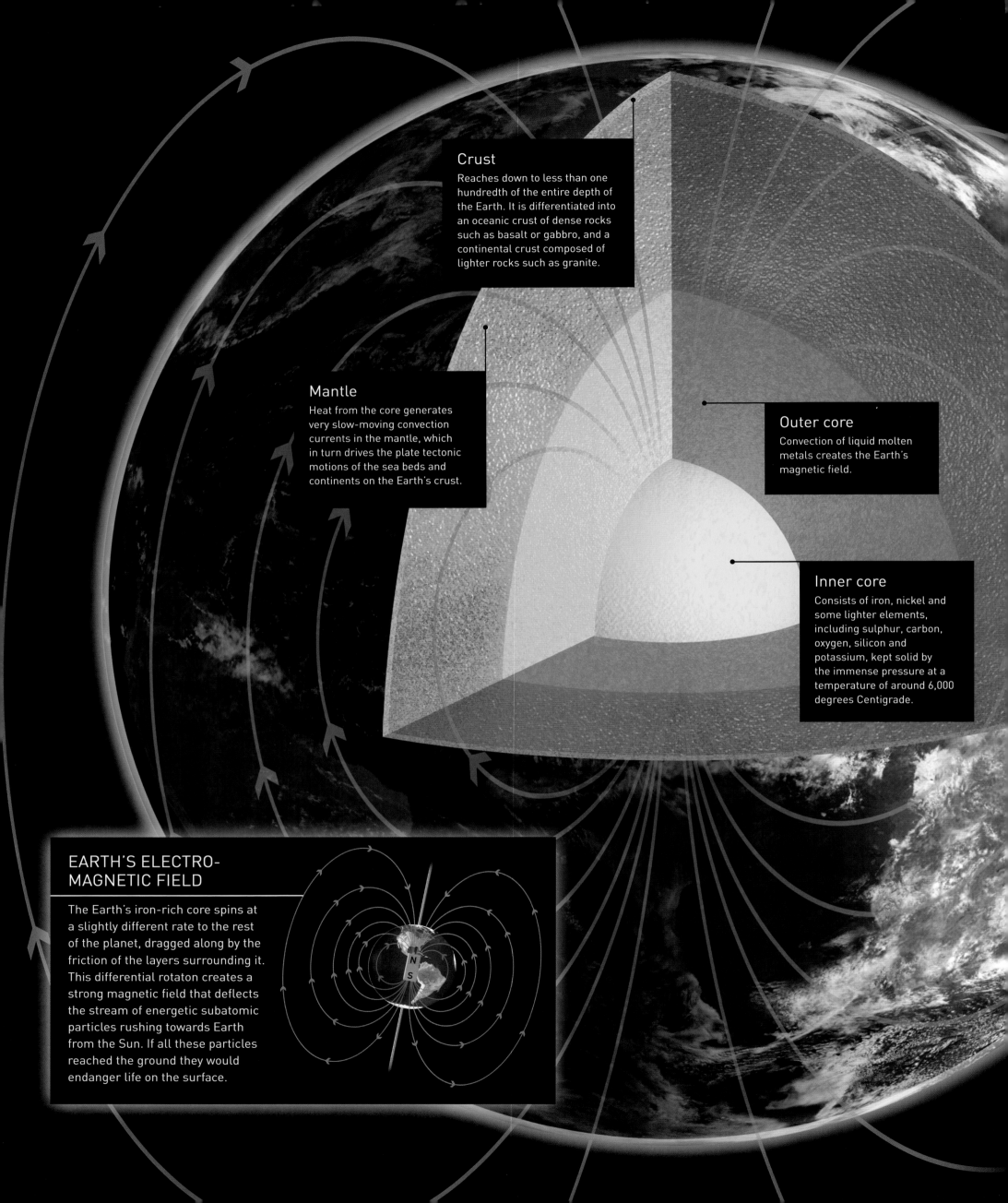

Crust

Reaches down to less than one hundredth of the entire depth of the Earth. It is differentiated into an oceanic crust of dense rocks such as basalt or gabbro, and a continental crust composed of lighter rocks such as granite.

Mantle

Heat from the core generates very slow-moving convection currents in the mantle, which in turn drives the plate tectonic motions of the sea beds and continents on the Earth's crust.

Outer core

Convection of liquid molten metals creates the Earth's magnetic field.

Inner core

Consists of iron, nickel and some lighter elements, including sulphur, carbon, oxygen, silicon and potassium, kept solid by the immense pressure at a temperature of around 6,000 degrees Centigrade.

EARTH'S ELECTRO-MAGNETIC FIELD

The Earth's iron-rich core spins at a slightly different rate to the rest of the planet, dragged along by the friction of the layers surrounding it. This differential rotaton creates a strong magnetic field that deflects the stream of energetic subatomic particles rushing towards Earth from the Sun. If all these particles reached the ground they would endanger life on the surface.

INSIDE THE EARTH

The solid ground on which we stand is not so permanent as we like to believe. Our planet is restless and ever-changing, both inside and out.

EARTH HAS AN INNER CORE of solid iron with an outer layer of iron and nickel in super-hot liquid form. Day by day, the core rotates one third of a second faster than the rest of the Earth, equivalent to an extra quarter-turn every century. This colossal dynamo generates the magnetic field familiar to us from our use of magnetic compasses. Surrounding the outer core is the mantle, a thick and hot layer of rock that is neither quite solid nor completely molten. It swirls and deforms extremely slowly, like partially molten plastic.

The Earth's surface is a thin skin, known as the crust, floating above a complex and restless inferno. The crust is what we stand on: literally, the ground beneath our feet. It seems reassuringly permanent and solid, yet it is extremely brittle, and it represents barely one per cent of our planet's total volume. The Earth's diameter at the equatorial belt is 7,920 miles (12,750 km). The thickness of the crust ranges from as little as 3 miles (5 km) at the bottom of the world's deepest ocean trenches to no more than 61 miles (100 km) amid the highest mountain ranges. The average thickness of continental crust is about 24 miles (40 km). If this planet were an apple, the crust would be no thicker than the apple's skin. A hard skin or crust of 'extrusive' igneous rock forms when hot spots of material in the upper layers of the mantle are melted into a viscous liquid that breaks through onto the Earth's surface and cools down into a solid form. Above ground, this molten flow emerges as red-hot lava spewing from volcanic fissures. When flowing underground through caves or channels between rocks, the lava takes a slightly different form, known as magma.

Two categories of igneous rock, basalt and granite, make up most of the Earth's crust. Basalt is produced by lava flowing out of volcanoes or other fissures in the crust. Rich in magnesium and iron, it is the most common type of rock. Most of the floors of the world's oceans are basalt. Granite is produced by a more complex 'intrusive' igneous process, when magma flowing deep inside the crust interacts with pre-existing solid rock, and then cools while still underground.

Convection in the mantle is driven by heat from the core

Subduction reabsorbs surface rock

VOLCANOES

A volcano is any opening in the Earth's crust that allows molten rock (lava) and hot gases from beneath the surface to break through. The flanks of a volcano are built by the flow of lava spilling down the sides. Very energetic volcanoes may erupt with sudden violence, blowing off large fragments of crust at the point of greatest upwards pressure and leaving a huge crater, known as a caldera. Volcanic activity was far more widespread when the Earth was young, because the planet's newly formed outer crust of rock was much thinner and weaker than it is today. Most of the water in the world's oceans was originally expelled as hot gas from ancient volcanic eruptions.

Ash cloud

Lava flow

Side vent

Magma chamber

Flank

PLATE TECTONICS

The great continents, Africa, the Americas, Europe, Asia, Australia
and Antarctica, are resting on much larger sections of the Earth's crust, known
as tectonic plates. These, in turn, are always on the move.

THERE ARE SEVEN major tectonic plates on the Earth (accounting for the seven continents and the Pacific Ocean) and many more minor ones. The mantle immediately beneath them is constantly recirculating, causing the plates to drift very slowly. The movement amounts to no more than a few centimetres per year, but over great spans of time, measured in hundreds of millions of years, the Earth's landscape has been utterly transformed, with rifts appearing between plates as they tear apart from each other, and mountain ranges pushing upwards where plates collide.

For hundreds of millions of years of the Earth's early history, the continents were part of one large super-continent, which scientists call Pangaea (a Greek word meaning 'all lands'). Around 200 million years ago this land mass began to break apart into the continental plates that we know today. They have drifted ceaselessly, and will continue to do so long into the future, but our generation will not have to redraw any maps because, by the standards of a human lifetime, the rate of drift is extremely slow.

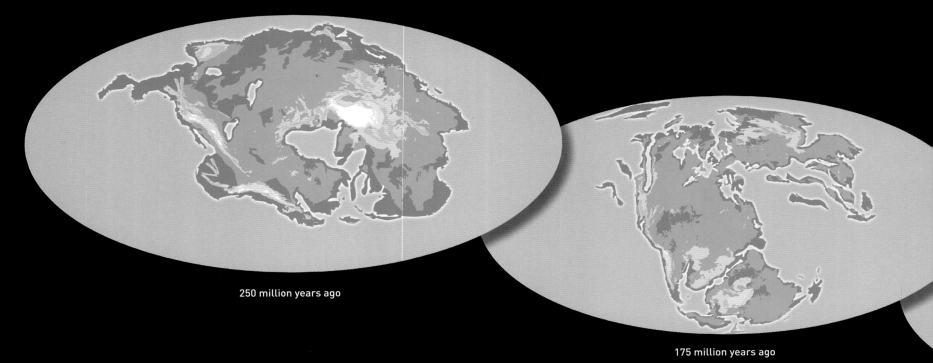

250 million years ago

175 million years ago

The drift of the tectonic plates over 250
million years shows that the position of
the continents today is just temporary.

Fault lines are those regions of the Earth's crust where the restless movements between tectonic plates are most likely to cause violent disruptions, such as earthquakes and volcanoes. Volcanic eruptions are sometimes associated with regions of the underlying mantle rather than the crust. Chains of volcanic islands are created as a tectonic plate slides over a hot spot.

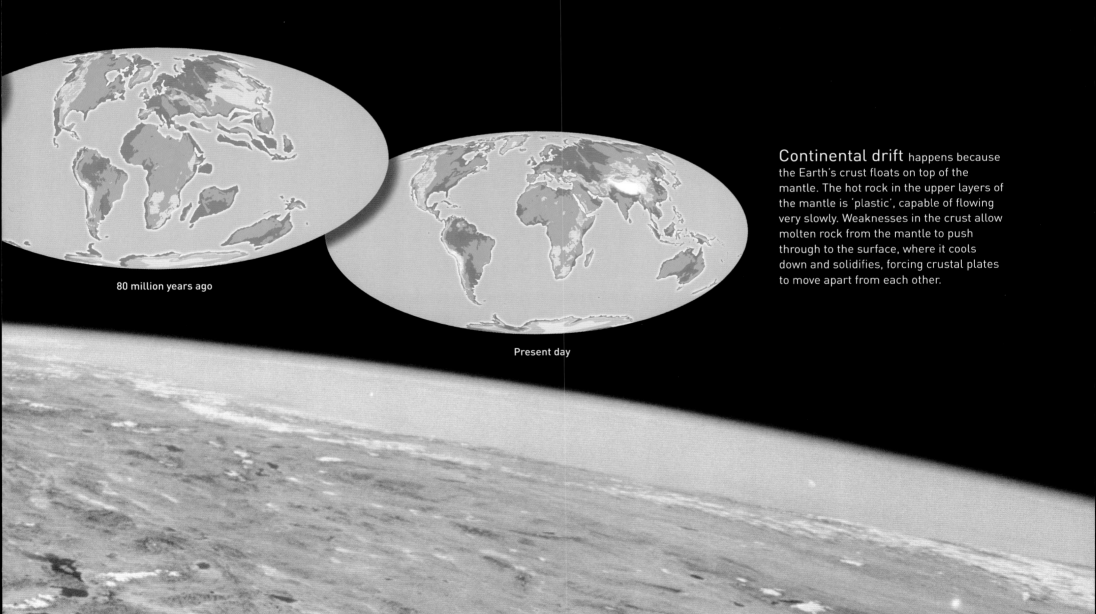

80 million years ago

Present day

Continental drift happens because the Earth's crust floats on top of the mantle. The hot rock in the upper layers of the mantle is 'plastic', capable of flowing very slowly. Weaknesses in the crust allow molten rock from the mantle to push through to the surface, where it cools down and solidifies, forcing crustal plates to move apart from each other.

THE RESTLESS EARTH

Various cataclysms have reshaped the Earth to such an extent that little of its ancient crustal face remains. The underlying forces have not lost their power to cause further massive change.

SATELLITE SCANS OF STRESSES in the Earth's crust are derived from pairs of overlapping radar images taken weeks, months or even years apart. Computers identify the tiniest differences in altitude and lateral shifts over time, highlighted by minor variations in the data between one scan and the next. The notorious Hayward and San Andreas crustal faults in California are closely monitored for any signs that new earthquakes might be imminent. Most shifts in the crust are caused by harmless variations in groundwater levels, but Californians cannot be too careful. San Francisco and Los Angeles will never be free of the significant possibility of catastrophe. Earthquakes are notoriously difficult to predict, and geological upheavals can happen with terrifying unexpectedness. In 1995 an earthquake in southern Japan killed 5,000 people. In 2010 at least a quarter of a million people died when the Caribbean island of Haiti was struck by a massive series of tremors. Recent volcanic eruptions in Washington State, Sicily and the Philippines show that the Earth's mantle still escapes from time to time onto the surface as magma. Our world has not yet settled, and will continue, long into the future, to reform itself.

The greatest disaster may yet be to come. A tremendous force is building up beneath the ancient crater, or 'caldera', of the huge volcano in Yellowstone Park, Wyoming, USA. The volcano's last major eruption was about 640,000 years ago, but it has continued to exhibit a certain restlessness at frequent intervals ever since then. Now the crust around it is rising by up to three inches (seven centimetres) a year. A great mass of molten rock, possibly as wide as the city of Los Angeles, is being forced from the mantle into the magma chamber beneath the volcano. The crust could weaken next week, next month, next year. It might hold for many centuries. We simply cannot be sure. Volcanologists are not predicting an imminent emergency, but if that great mass and pressure of lava ever does burst through to the surface, it may well cause havoc on a similar scale to the explosion that killed off the dinosaurs.

An earthquake lasting just a few seconds can destroy even the strongest buildings. This concrete car park in Northridge, California, must have seemed reassuringly solid until an earthquake struck the town in 1994, killing 72 residents. Recent earthquakes in Chile, India and Haiti have killed or injured hundreds of thousands of people.

Divergent plate boundary

When tectonic plates move apart, magma from the mantle flows to the surface and hardens, filling in the gaps torn open by the diverging plates to create ridges. The weight of this new crustal material presses down between the plates, forcing them yet further apart. Then the ridge between them collapses along its central axis to create a rift.

▲ Great Rift Valley landscape, Kenya

Convergent plate boundary – subduction

When plates converge, one plate typically works its way underneath the other one (subducts), and its leading edge melts as it encounters the mantle.

▲ Chile, South America

Convergent plate boundary – uplift

Where two plates meet and neither plate is subducted, they simply force each other upwards, creating mountain ranges.

▲ The Himalayas, Asia

Transform boundary

Where the edges of tectonic plates try to slide sideways against each other, cracks known as fault lines typically appear. The plates are locked together by friction, but eventually the tension between them becomes so enormous that the friction is overcome, and the plates on either side of the fault move with extreme suddenness, one moving forward while the other jolts in the opposite direction. The result is an earthquake.

◄ The San Andreas fault, USA

SEE ALSO

■ **Plate Tectonics**
page 24

THE EARTH'S SURFACE

The sudden fire and fury of volcanic activity can reshape the affected landscapes in a matter of days, or even hours, but the slower and less immediately obvious influences of wind and water can have an even greater impact over the long term.

ONE OF THE MOST FAMILIAR sediments we encounter is sandstone, made from small, rounded grains of the minerals quartz and feldspar loosely compressed into water-absorbing rock that can easily be broken with a hammer. Limestone and chalk, also very common sedimentary rocks, are made from the mineral calcite (calcium carbonate) derived from countless trillions of microscopic sea organisms whose dead shells dropped to the floors of ancient seas and accumulated over vast spans of time.

Go for a walk in the country, then look at the dirt on your boots. It is easy to dismiss simply as 'mud', but it almost certainly contains clay, one of the most important types of sediment. Clay is just the familiar name for a wide variety of materials derived from the erosion of many different kinds of rock into very fine grains. Clays are rich in silicon, with aluminium, magnesium, sometimes iron, and almost always with the additional presence of hydrogen and oxygen. Some clays form as flat sheets, like stacked roof tiles. Water passes easily between the layers. When clay dries out, it easily flakes away in the wind. The resulting dust can travel great distances, enabling clays of different kinds to accumulate elsewhere and combine into yet more complex forms when water arrives to mix them up.

At the atomic level, wet clay can act as a catalyst, enabling chemical reactions on its surface without itself being changed. Clays on the edge of ancient seas, and in muddy river estuaries, may have played a crucial role in the origins of life on Earth. All the soil used to grow food crops and grasses, flowers, trees and other plants contains clays.

Metamorphic rocks are formed when movements in the Earth's crust bury existing rock strata, subjecting them to enormous pressure and changing their characteristics, but without actually melting them. Quartzite, a hard, weather-resistant rock, is derived from sandstone heated and pressurized until the grains of quartz sand become fused. Shale and slate (used for roof tiles) come from layers of clay compacted together in characteristic flat sheets. Marble, one of the most popular materials for upmarket builders, is metamorphic rock formed from limestone.

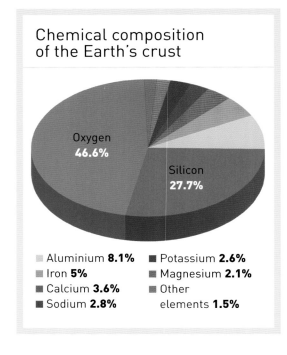

Chemical composition of the Earth's crust

- Oxygen 46.6%
- Silicon 27.7%
- Aluminium **8.1%**
- Iron **5%**
- Calcium **3.6%**
- Sodium **2.8%**
- Potassium **2.6%**
- Magnesium **2.1%**
- Other elements **1.5%**

▲ **Metamorphic rock** Gneiss typically contains banded mineral layers that have been flattened by tremendous heat and pressure.

▶ **Igneous rock** Basalt columns are formed by the rapid cooling of molten magma when it encounters sea water.

Sedimentary rock Something rich and complex happens when air and water encounter crustal rocks, slowly eroding tiny fragments and washing them into streams and rivers, eventually to settle at the bottom of lakes and oceans as sediments. Layer after layer ('strata') of sedimentary materials are deposited on top of preceding ones, and eventually the colossal weight of the uppermost strata presses down on the deepest, which slowly compress into hard rock.

ROCK CYCLE AND EROSION

Just like all other materials in the natural world, rocks are subject to cycles of formation, change, destruction and reformation. Igneous rocks that reach the Earth's surface are exposed to wind, ice and rain, causing them gradually to disintegrate into fine grains. Rivers play a major role in transporting these erosion products over large distances and depositing them in new locations, where they accumulate in layers. When compressed, the layers harden into sedimentary rock. Over time, this is folded back into the Earth's crust, where it is transformed yet again.

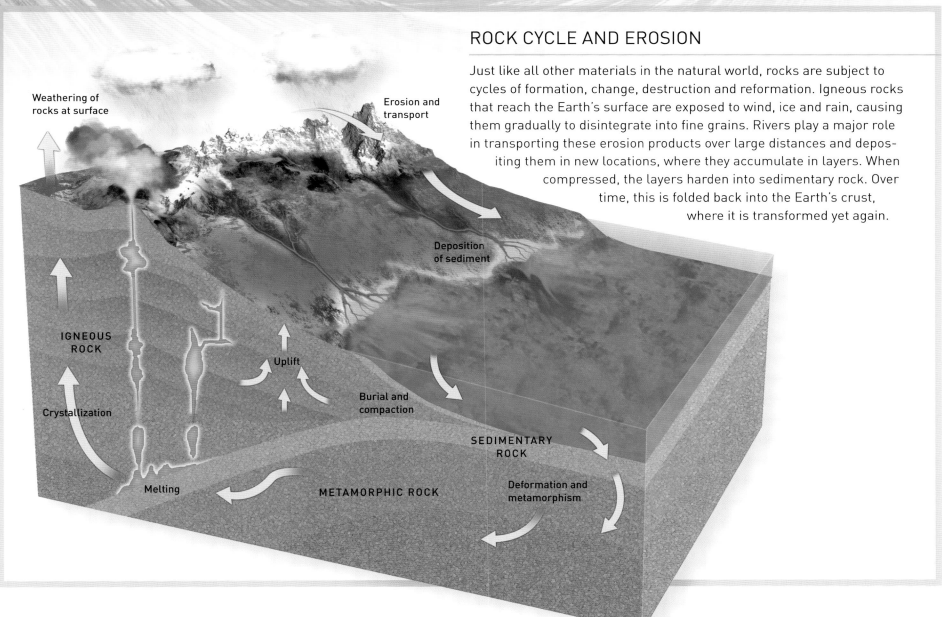

Weathering of rocks at surface

Erosion and transport

Deposition of sediment

IGNEOUS ROCK

Uplift

Burial and compaction

Crystallization

SEDIMENTARY ROCK

Melting

METAMORPHIC ROCK

Deformation and metamorphism

Highest place

1 Mt. Chimborazo

LOCATION Ecuador

- Remnants of an inactive volcano
- The peak is covered by glaciers

FACT The ice is mined as a resource

Mount Everest in the Himalayas is the tallest mountain above sea level, but Chimborazo's peak is further away from the centre of the Earth than Everest's.

Lowest place **on the surface**

6 The Dead Sea

LOCATION Bordered by Israel and Jordan

ALTITUDE 1,300 ft (396 m) below sea level

The high percentage of salt and other minerals in the Dead Sea make it less 'watery' than other seas. You'll never sink in the Dead Sea because the minerals make the water so dense you just bob on the surface like a cork.

Largest river

3 The Amazon

LOCATION South America

- 3,900 miles (6,280 km) long
- Average width 25 miles (40 km)

FACT Africa's Nile river is longer but less voluminous

The Amazon is responsible for one-fifth of all the fresh water discharged into the world's oceans. During the rainy seasons, the river triples its land coverage.

Hottest place

7 Ethiopia

LOCATION Dallol, Ethiopia

- Dallol is near the only volcanic crater below sea level
- The daytime temperature averages 34.4 °C

Widest valley

8 Great Rift Valley

LOCATION East Africa

- 100 miles (160 km) wide
- 4,000 miles (6,400 km) long

FACT Extends into south-west Asia

Largest waterfall

9 Victoria Falls

LOCATION Zimbabwe

- 360 ft (108 m) tall
- On the Zambezi River

FACT Flow halves in the dry season

Wettest place

2 Tutunedo

LOCATION Colombia

- Tropical rainforest
- 30 ft (9 m) of rain annually
- 280 days of rain per year

Driest place

4 Atacama Desert

LOCATION Chile

- Virtually rainless all year round
- Dry for more than 20 million years

FACT Ancient lakes evaporated

Coldest place

5 'Ridge A'

LOCATION Antarctic Plateau

- Life barely exists here
- The skies are almost always clear
- The temperature is –70 °C

The water at Victoria Falls plunges such a distance that it is turned into fine spray by air currents before it reaches the bottom.

THE EARTH TODAY

This is the only planet we know of that boasts such an incredible range of landscapes and climatic conditions, from majestic mountain peaks and volcanoes to plunging ravines, vast and arid deserts, icebound plateaus, deep oceans and lush, dense forests.

THE EARTH is so friendly towards life because, on average, its climate tends to remain incredibly stable over vast spans of time. There is plenty of sunlight available for warmth, and the surface is very obviously rich in water. Forests, grasslands and freshwater rivers abound – but on closer inspection the climate can be immensely variable at a regional scale. There are vast areas of the planet where conditions are very harsh, being either unbearably hot or unbearably cold. Those are just the most obvious extremes of localized unpleasantness that the Earth can offer. Yet life thrives almost everywhere.

Even at the bottom of the world's deepest ocean, where sunlight never penetrates, strange creatures have been discovered that are capable of withstanding water pressures equivalent to the weight of 50 Jumbo Jets applied to a volume the size of your head. Strangely enough, some places on dry land are less suited for life than those terrifying watery depths. There are scorched deserts that haven't seen rain for millions of years, while the exceptionally cold and extremely dry terrain in certain Antarctic regions meets its match only in the lifeless wastelands of Mars.

Largest cave

10 Hang Song Doon

LOCATION Vietnam
- The roof is 650 ft (198 m) high
- First discovered in 1991

FACT Contains an underground river

Lowest place on the Earth

11 Challenger deep

LOCATION Mariana Trench, Pacific
- 7 miles (11 km) below sea level
- Created by tectonic subduction

FACT Primitive life forms thrive here

Largest active volcano

12 Mauna Loa

LOCATION Hawaii
- 33 recorded eruptions since 1843
- Most recent eruption in 1984

FACT It will stay active for 500,000 years

Global water volume

Global air volume

Best preserved impact crater

13 Meteor Crater

LOCATION Arizona, USA
- 50,000 years old
- One mile (1.6 km) across
- 550 ft (168m) deep

Global water and air volume

In this conceptual artwork, the total volume of all the water on Earth, including the oceans, the ice caps and freshwater lakes and rivers, is represented by a transparent sphere, while the total volume of atmospheric gas is shown in pink. The spheres show the finite and surprisingly limited nature of our most basic environmental resources. As the atmosphere extends outwards from the Earth's surface, it becomes markedly less dense. Half of all the air content exists within just the first 3 miles (5 km) of altitude.

CLIM

CLIMATE

A powerful hurricane on the other side of the world might seem unconnected with the duck pond in your local park, but over time, that small body of water must eventually feed its little influences into a hurricane somewhere. The water will evaporate on a sunny day, altering the humidity of the local atmosphere; the cool temperatures locally will affect convection currents in the air, and they in turn will affect a larger breeze somewhere else, which will eventually contribute to building the hurricane – and all in ways that are becoming mathematically comprehensible to us. Within the seeming chaos of the climate lies a deep order. What we cannot do is predict how the climate will behave, because we can never hope to gather enough individual bits of data to feed into our equations. We would need to know the strengths and directions of every last puff of wind on the entire planet, plus all the temperature and humidity variations, and much else besides.

In the winter of 1961, Edward Lorenz, a meteorologist at the Massachusetts Institute of Technology (MIT), was pioneering computer models of weather systems. This was in the days of large, slow, cumbersome computers with paper printouts rather than graphics screens. Inputting the data was tedious in the extreme. Lorenz ran a dozen equations representing particular climate character-istics: temperature, pressure, humidity and so forth. The equations were self-reflexive in that the answers from one would influence the starting values for the others during each iteration of the computing cycle. Typically Lorenz would input the starting values to an accuracy of six decimal places and then set the computer to work, but the rough-and-ready graphics of the printout showed the answers rounded to three decimal places.

One day Lorenz repeated an earlier run, because he wanted to re-examine a certain section, but to save time, he just fed in the initial data to an accuracy of three decimal places. He assumed that so small a difference would have little effect on the outcome. He was wrong. Instead of approx-imately replicating the earlier run, the new printout showed a completely different pattern. It was as if Lorenz had expected to type in the ingredients for a gathering storm and had ended up with a cloudless sunny day, just because of a less than one-thousandth part discrepancy in the data.

Climate experts sometimes talk of 'the butterfly effect' to convey the importance of Lorenz's discovery. When a butterfly flaps its wings, it creates just a few of the billion-fold movements of air that, many weeks or even months later, feed a mighty storm. If the butterfly sleeps, that storm may not happen. Weather forecasts are approximations that become increasingly less reliable the further ahead we try to look. Even so, we are learning to see the climate as an interconnected whole rather than just a collecton of different weather systems.

In the late 1960s, as NASA scientist James Lovelock pondered the differences between the inert Martian atmosphere and our own much more dynamic one, he realized that a fine balance exists on Earth as a result of constant feedback between living and non-living systems. He showed that the oxygen-rich composition of the air is maintained with extraordinary precision: so precise, in fact, that it could almost be compared with homeostasis, the fine-tuned process of biochemical feedback that regulates the metabolism of a living organism.

SEASONS AND TIDES

All of human history has been influenced by repeating seasonal cycles of warm and cold, while our ocean navigators have long known how to predict the rise and fall of sea levels.

A COMMON MISCONCEPTION is that the Earth comes closer to the Sun in summer. In fact, its orbit is nearly circular. It is not the relatively minor variations in Earth–Sun distances during the year so much as the tilt of the Earth's axis that really counts. The Earth's north–south axis is not perpendicular relative to the plane of its orbit. Instead it is tilted by an angle of 23.5 degrees. No matter where the Earth happens to be on its year-long orbit, its axis always points from south to north towards the same distant star, Polaris. This means that sometimes the Earth's northern hemisphere is tilted towards the Sun, and sometimes away from it. Seasons depend on the angle of the Sun's radiation as it penetrates the Earth's atmosphere. When the northern half of the planet is tilted away from the Sun, the rays strike obliquely, and their journey through the atmospheric haze is lengthened. Much of the heat is absorbed before it hits the ground. This is what causes winter. In summer, the planet's

tilt allows solar energy a shorter and more vertical path through the atmosphere. More heat reaches the ground, and temperatures rise.

The phases during which the tilt of a hemisphere switches one way to the other, either Sunwards in summer or away from the Sun in winter, are known as solstices. Halfway between the solstices, the Earth's tilt is not strongly pronounced either way. At these times, called equinoxes, both hemispheres receive similar levels of sunlight. Equinoxes deliver the mild autumn and spring seasons. A northerly axial tilt towards the Sun is always answered by a southerly tilt away from it, and vice versa. This explains why one hemisphere of the Earth always experiences summer at the same time as the other endures winter.

Tides are created by the gravitational pull of the Sun and moon on the Earth's oceans. Because the moon is so much closer to the Earth than the Sun, it has the greatest tidal effect. There are

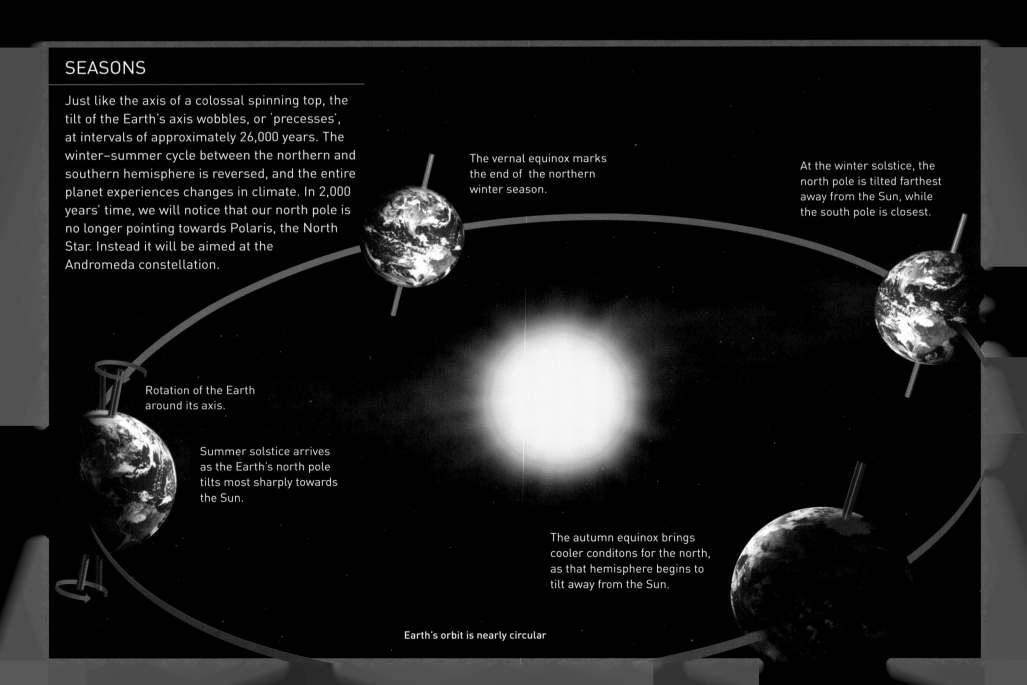

SEASONS

Just like the axis of a colossal spinning top, the tilt of the Earth's axis wobbles, or 'precesses', at intervals of approximately 26,000 years. The winter–summer cycle between the northern and southern hemisphere is reversed, and the entire planet experiences changes in climate. In 2,000 years' time, we will notice that our north pole is no longer pointing towards Polaris, the North Star. Instead it will be aimed at the Andromeda constellation.

The vernal equinox marks the end of the northern winter season.

At the winter solstice, the north pole is tilted farthest away from the Sun, while the south pole is closest.

Rotation of the Earth around its axis.

Summer solstice arrives as the Earth's north pole tilts most sharply towards the Sun.

The autumn equinox brings cooler conditons for the north, as that hemisphere begins to tilt away from the Sun.

Earth's orbit is nearly circular

approximately two tidal cycles per day during which sea levels rise and fall.

Tides are caused by the gravitational interaction between the Earth and the moon. The moon's gravity tugs at the waters of oceans on the side of the Earth that happens to be facing the moon at any given hour. This causes a slight rise in the height of the water. Meanwhile the Earth itself is pulled very slightly away from the water on the opposite side, causing a high tide there as well. Most stretches of ocean coastline will experience a high tide every 12 hours and 25 minutes or so. A third and very substantial gravitational pull has to be factored in when predicting tide cycles: that of the Sun upon the Earth. Spring tides occur when the Sun, moon and the Earth are in line, and neap tides when the Sun, Earth and moon form a right angle.

A complete transformation of the boundary between land and sea occurs as tides sweep in or out. The middle strip in this photo shows a coastal town at low tide, with wet sand exposed by the retreating sea water. The central channel is carved by fresh water flowing from land into the sea.

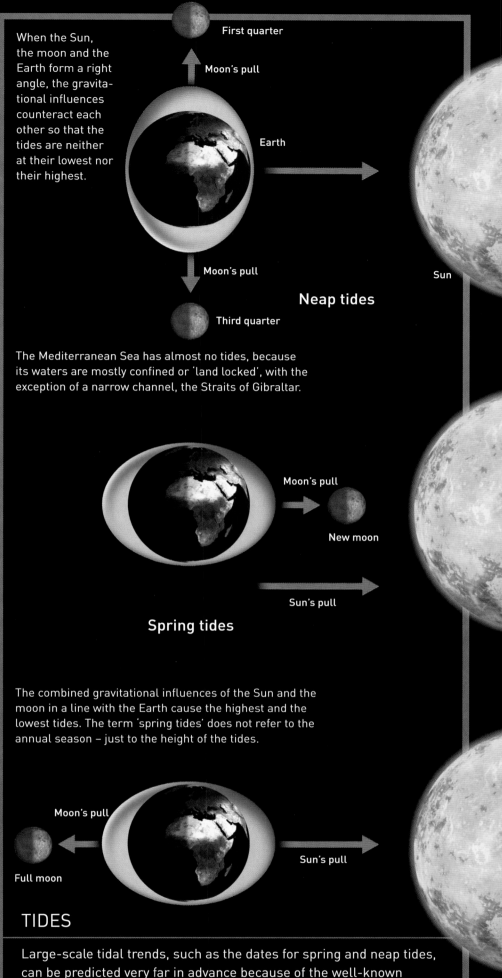

When the Sun, the moon and the Earth form a right angle, the gravitational influences counteract each other so that the tides are neither at their lowest nor their highest.

First quarter

Moon's pull

Earth

Moon's pull

Sun

Neap tides

Third quarter

The Mediterranean Sea has almost no tides, because its waters are mostly confined or 'land locked', with the exception of a narrow channel, the Straits of Gibraltar.

Moon's pull

New moon

Sun's pull

Spring tides

The combined gravitational influences of the Sun and the moon in a line with the Earth cause the highest and the lowest tides. The term 'spring tides' does not refer to the annual season – just to the height of the tides.

Moon's pull

Full moon

Sun's pull

TIDES

Large-scale tidal trends, such as the dates for spring and neap tides, can be predicted very far in advance because of the well-known astronomical data about the movements netween the Sun, the Earth and the moon. However, the rotation of the Earth will bring different oceans and different stretches of coastline into play for any given date that one tries to predict. The depth of an oceanic region is also a factor in determining how those waters will behave during spring or neap tides. Predictive tide tables have to be compiled on a very localized basis.

SEE ALSO

■ **The Moon**
page 148

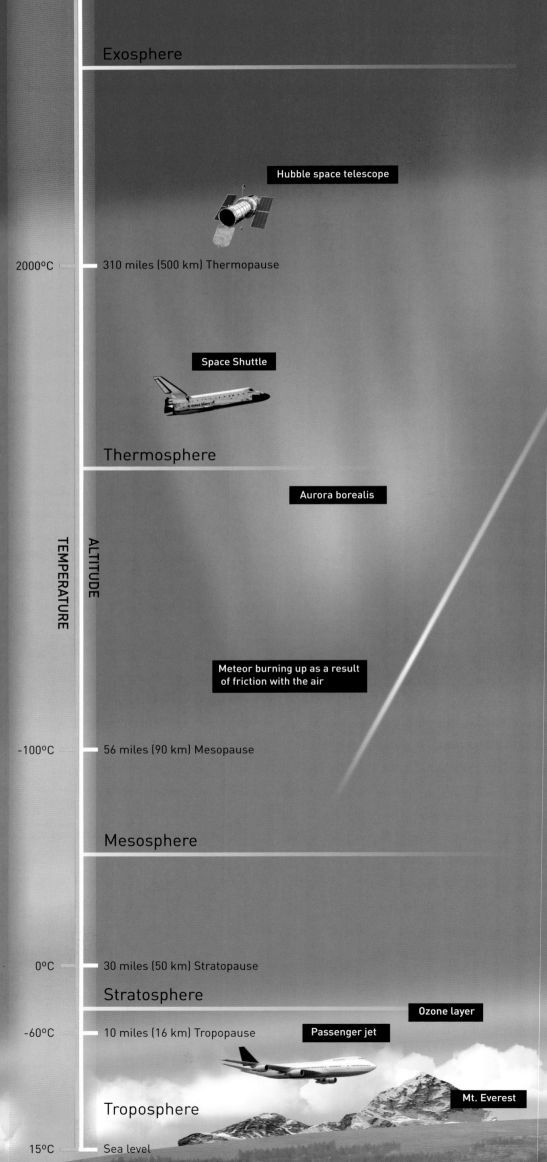

Exosphere

Hubble space telescope

2000°C — 310 miles (500 km) Thermopause

Space Shuttle

Thermosphere

Aurora borealis

TEMPERATURE

ALTITUDE

Meteor burning up as a result of friction with the air

-100°C — 56 miles (90 km) Mesopause

Mesosphere

0°C — 30 miles (50 km) Stratopause

Stratosphere

Ozone layer

-60°C — 10 miles (16 km) Tropopause

Passenger jet

Mt. Everest

Troposphere

15°C — Sea level

Exosphere – The region at the outermost extremes of the atmosphere where occasional stray atoms escape into the almost pure vacuum of space.

Thermopause – The transition layer between the thermosphere and the exosphere.

Thermosphere – reaches from approximately 60 miles (97 km) above the Earth's surface to outer space. Temperatures in the thermosphere can reach thousands of degrees Celsius, because the molecules of atmosphere at these extreme altitudes have no shielding against incoming energy from the Sun. However, the thermosphere would feel extremely cold to us because those molecules are so thinly scattered. Too few would touch our skin for us to feel their warmth.

TEMPERATURE AND ALTITUDE SCALES

From ground level upwards, the air temperature plunges as the atmosphere thins out at ever higher altitudes, up to the tropopause. Further up, in the layers where the air thins into a near-vacuum, temperatures start to climb once again because there is no longer enough air to diffuse the pure, ferocious energy of sunlight.

Mesopause – this boundary between the mesosphere and the thermosphere is the coldest layer of the atmosphere.

Mesosphere – extends from 30 – 50 miles (50 to 80 km) above the Earth's surface, and is very tenuous, yet still thick enough to slow down meteors hurtling into the atmosphere, where most of them burn up before hitting the ground.

Stratopause – the transition layer between the stratosphere and the mesosphere.

Stratosphere – extends from approximately 9 – 30 miles (15 to 50 km) above the Earth's surface. Airliners fly in this region because it is very stable. Ozone exists in the upper regions of the stratosphere, absorbing most of the harmful ultraviolet radiation from the Sun.

Tropopause – the upper boundary of the troposphere, above which the temperature begins to increase with altitude.

Troposphere – the layer immediately above the Earth's surface, reaching to an altitude of between 7 – 30 miles (11 and 50 km), and accounting for nearly 80 per cent of the atmosphere by mass. Most weather events occur within this layer. At the upper boundary of the troposphere is a narrow transition zone known as the tropopause. Uneven solar heating of different regions of the troposphere causes convection currents and winds. Warm air from Earth's surface rises, while colder air descends. Rising currents of air lose their warmth by the time they reach the tropopause, at which point the convection process extends no further.

THE EARTH'S ATMOSPHERE

The thin, invisible layer of gas surrounding the Earth shields us from the vacuum of space and protects us from excessive solar radiation. It is thickest near the surface and thins out with height until it eventually becomes indistinguishable from the vacuum of space.

IN THE LATE 1950S, AS the Space Age began, many scientists thought that there should be a clearer distinction between the atmosphere within which aircraft can fly, and space, where only rocket propulsion works. The Fédération Aéronautique Interna-tionale (World Air Sports Federation) adopted the Kármán line, an imaginary dividing layer at 62 miles (100 km) altitude. This is now commonly considered as where the Earth ends and outer space begins. But this is just a product of the human imagination. We have only to look up on a cloudless night to see that there is no real difference between where our sky ends and the surrounding vastness of the cosmos begins.

In normal light, air is as transparent as glass. Why, then, does a cloudless sky look so blue? Sunlight of all electromagnetic (EM) frequencies reaches the upper layers of the atmosphere, but then the molecules of gas, plus suspended water vapour, dust and ice crystals, scatter the EM wavelengths in different ways. The long, widely spaced red wavelengths slip between the blocking particles, but the short, compact wavelengths

at the blue end of the spectrum are absorbed or scattered. Ultraviolet radiation at very short wavelengths plays an important role in the chemistry of the upper atmosphere, slamming into molecules and disrupting them. In the optical region of the spectrum, blue light arriving from the Sun is bounced and scattered by the water vapour, causing the sky as a whole to appear blue in daylight hours. When the Sun sets, and its light makes its longest and most oblique journey through air, vapour and dust, almost all of the blue light is scattered and only the red light reaches our eyes. That's why sunrises and sunsets look so beautiful.

Composition of the Atmosphere

Leaving aside the one component that we can actually see – the water vapour in clouds – the atmosphere consists of:

78% nitrogen
21% oxygen
0.9% argon
0.04% carbon dioxide
Neon, helium, krypton
and **ozone** also exist in extremely small quantities

The other significant component is water vapour, which can vary from 0% to 4% of the total atmospheric content, depending on local and seasonal variations

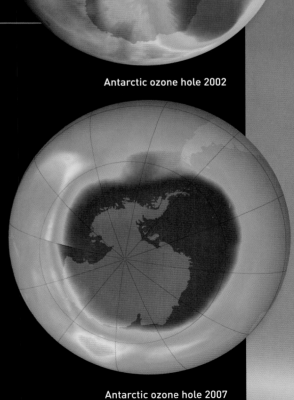

Antarctic ozone hole 2002

OZONE LAYER

Within the stratosphere, a fragile scattering of ozone molecules exists between 12 and 30 miles (19 to 48 kilometres) altitude. Ultraviolet radiation (UV) streaming from the Sun causes atmospheric oxygen molecules made from two atoms to split apart and recombine in a three-atom molecule called ozone. For at least a billion years, the 'ozone layer' has prevented harmful levels of UV from reaching the Earth's surface. UV is energetic and capable of disrupting the complex chemistry within living tissues. Increased UV exposure heightens the risk of skin cancer in humans. In the 1980s it was confirmed that chlorofluorocarbon (CFC) chemicals used in refrigerators and aerosol sprays can escape from the ground and rise into the atmosphere, where they destroy ozone, creating a seasonal 'ozone hole' above the Antarctic. In 1987 an international agreement was implemented to ban the use of CFCs.

Scientists on the Ross Ice Shelf in Antarctica launch a helium balloon into the air currents generated by winter storm systems in the stratosphere, known as polar vortexes. The south pole vortex increases the influence of CFCs in the atmosphere and creates a seasonal ozone hole. The existing CFC levels should fade over the next few decades.

Antarctic ozone hole 2007

WEATHER

The fall of snow on a mountain and the sweltering humidity of a tropical jungle are interconnected facets of a global weather system. The dominating force is the exchange of temperature and pressure between cold air and warm.

AT THE EARTH'S EQUATORIAL REGIONS, heat from the Sun penetrates less obliquely through the atmosphere than at northern or southern latitudes. As a consequence, less of the heat is absorbed or dissipated by the atmosphere before it reaches the Earth's surface. This is the simple and stark explanation for the hot weather that we traditionally associate with the equator. As warm, light air rises higher into the atmosphere, it leaves a partial vacuum, a region of low pressure, underneath it. Cooler air surges inwards to fill the void. In cooler climes, cold air sinks because it is heavier than the surrounding atmosphere, and its descent compresses air beneath, creating high-pressure zones. As the displaced air is forced outwards, currents of wind result. Basically, any difference in temperature between one region of the atmosphere and another will cause differences in air pressure, and therefore winds will blow.

Global wind patterns move restlessly between different hemispheres and at different heights in the atmosphere. Colder, heavier air from the north and south poles tends to sink and move towards the equator, travelling close to the Earth's surface. Warm, light air from the equatorial belt moves towards the poles, travelling high in the atmosphere. The day–night warming and cooling cycles, plus the rotation of the Earth and the shifting of seasons across the year, add to the unpredictable behaviour of weather systems.

Storms

After a hot, sticky day, warm, humid air rises and swiftly accumulates into cumulus clouds. When these clouds become very tall, the differential between the higher- and lower-altitude regions creates tremendous imbalances in temperature, humidity and electrical charge, at which point, a thunder cloud rapidly forms. Its upper regions become positively charged because electrons are stripped away from water molecules in constant, energetic collision with each other, while lower regions of the cloud become negatively charged, as free-flying electrons accumulate there.

The tension is released in the form of sudden and immensely powerful flows of electrical current from one region to another – or between the cloud and the ground. The extremely rapid heating and expansion of air surrounding the electrical discharges (lightning) is responsible for the noise that thunderstorms make. Lightning can generate temperatures six times hotter than the surface of the Sun, while the accumulated energy within a large thunderstorm is greater than that of a nuclear bomb.

After the long, hot, sweltering summers that are so typical of equatorial regions, the tropical ocean waters are very warm. Water vapour rises quickly to form clouds. The vapour carries heat from the surface into the atmosphere, triggering a cycle of warm air updrafts that leave regions of very low pressure beneath them. As these weather systems drift across the ocean, they merge together and draw in yet more warm, moist air, gathering tremendous collective energy. The Coriolis effects generated by the Earth's rotation cause the unified system to spin in one massive, ever-tightening circle, which becomes a storm.

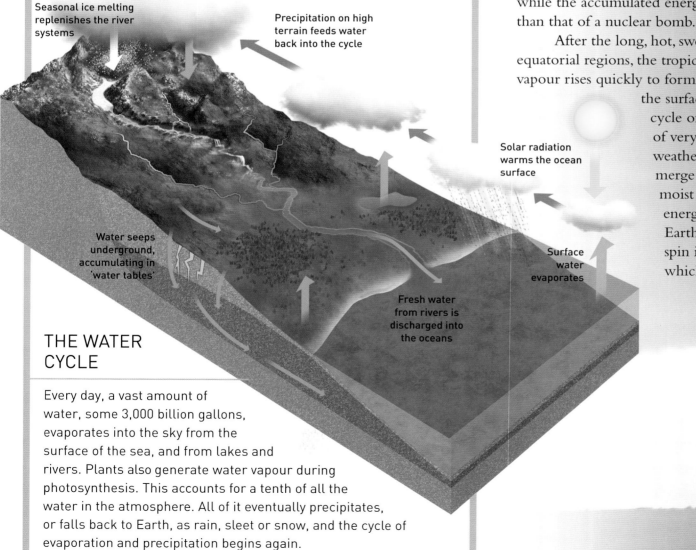

Seasonal ice melting replenishes the river systems

Precipitation on high terrain feeds water back into the cycle

Solar radiation warms the ocean surface

Water seeps underground, accumulating in 'water tables'

Surface water evaporates

Fresh water from rivers is discharged into the oceans

THE WATER CYCLE

Every day, a vast amount of water, some 3,000 billion gallons, evaporates into the sky from the surface of the sea, and from lakes and rivers. Plants also generate water vapour during photosynthesis. This accounts for a tenth of all the water in the atmosphere. All of it eventually precipitates, or falls back to Earth, as rain, sleet or snow, and the cycle of evaporation and precipitation begins again.

Hurricanes
▼ Extremely violent cyclones, typically originating near the equator and moving north. Hurricanes are usually accompanied by heavy rains.

Cyclones
◄ Violent storms with winds that twist clockwise in the southern hemisphere, and counterclockwise in the northern hemisphere.

Northeaster
▼ A low pressure system often affecting the east coast of the North American continent, typically bringing gale force winds and severe snowstorms.

Tornadoes
► Whirling funnel-shaped columns of air that come into direct contact with the Earth's surface. Tornadoes usually originate from powerful thunder-storms.

Supercell
A bolt of lightning in a supercell thunderstorm, a severe, long-lived storm within which the wind speed and direction changes with height. This produces a strong rotating updraft of warm air, known as a mesocyclone, and a separate downdraft of cold air.

SEE ALSO

■ **Weather Mapping** *page 43*

■ **Extreme Storms** *page 44*

■ **Atmospheric Currents** *page 47*

READING THE SKY

Water rises into the atmosphere as an imperceptible vapour. As currents of moist, warm
air ascend and cool down, the vapour condenses into microscopic droplets or crystals of ice,
which become visible to us because of the way that sunlight interacts with each speck.

Cirrus consists of thin clouds of ice crystals
forming at heights between 3 and 9 miles (5 and
15 km), where the air is very cold. The name comes
from the Latin word for 'curl of hair'. Cirrus clouds
result from warm air lifted over a wide area by colder
air working its way beneath. The streaky shapes are
often a sign that the weather is about to change.

Cirrostratus clouds are thin and hazy,
and are formed from very fine ice crystals.
Often the only visible sign of their presence is
a faint halo of light around the Sun, caused by
the refracting effect of the ice.

Altostratus clouds cover the entire
sky as a thin blue-grey haze through which
the Sun, or even the moon, can still be
seen. Altostratus coverage may precede
the arrival of poorer weather.

Cumulonimbus When these
clouds continue to grow vertically,
their tops may extend upwards to
more than 39,000 ft (12,000 m). Tall
cumulonimbus formations seed
powerful storms.

Stratocumulus clouds share some
of the qualities of stratus and cumulus.
Typically they appear as grey, lumpy
masses accumulated in bands or waves.

Stratus Named for the Latin word 'layer', these
grey, featureless sheets of cloud stretch monoto-
nously from horizon to horizon: the very definition
of 'dull weather', they are associated with rain and
drizzle. Stratus clouds sometimes settle at ground
or sea level, where they become known as fog.

Cumulus clouds, named after the Latin
word for 'heap', have the appearance of puffy
cotton wool. They form swiftly from warm,
rising currents of moist air. As they ascend
higher, they billow outwards, creating the
familiar shapes that we associate with
the word 'cloud'.

WEATHER MAPPING

The weather report on your local TV station may be specific to your country, or even your town, but the information used to make that report is derived from a globe-spanning collection of data.

REPORTS ON LOCALIZED WEATHER CONDITIONS – air temperature, pressure, wind speed and direction, visibility and other data – are collected at regular intervals, typically four times a day, at six-hour intervals, by more than 10,000 individual monitoring stations around the globe, and by hundreds of ships at sea, supported by a variety of weather-monitoring space satellites in orbit around the Earth. Individual countries may give weather reports based on their own, local styles of presentation, but the World Meteorological Organization (WMO) ensures that all weather stations conform to agreed standards of data collection, and that information is made freely available in a format agreed by more than 130 nations.

Weather maps often include contour lines denoting air pressure, with a wide variety of additional symbols for specific local conditions, such as snow or fog, sunshine or cloud. 'Satellite maps' derived from space-based radar systems show images of the densest cloud formations and areas of heavy rain, but no single representation can yield a complete picture of Earth's dynamic atmosphere.

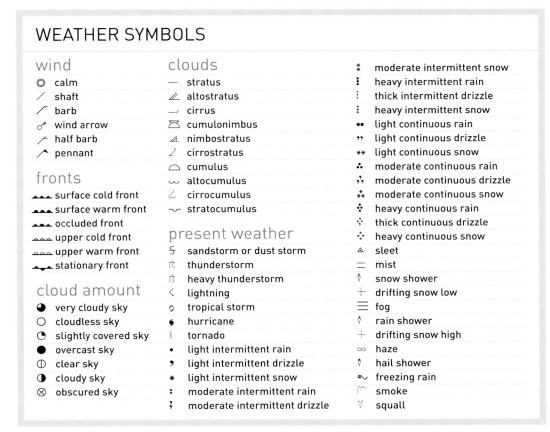

WEATHER SYMBOLS

wind
◎ calm
╱ shaft
╱ barb
♂ wind arrow
╱ half barb
╱ pennant

fronts
▲▲▲ surface cold front
▲▲▲ surface warm front
▲▲▲ occluded front
▲▲▲ upper cold front
▲▲▲ upper warm front
▲▲▲ stationary front

cloud amount
◕ very cloudy sky
○ cloudless sky
◔ slightly covered sky
● overcast sky
⦶ clear sky
◑ cloudy sky
⊗ obscured sky

clouds
— stratus
�-⌐ altostratus
⌐ cirrus
⊠ cumulonimbus
⊿ nimbostratus
↙ cirrostratus
◠ cumulus
◡ altocumulus
ε cirrocumulus
◡ stratocumulus

present weather
S sandstorm or dust storm
R thunderstorm
Iξ heavy thunderstorm
< lightning
⟨ tropical storm
| hurricane
| tornado
• light intermittent rain
, light intermittent drizzle
✻ light intermittent snow
: moderate intermittent rain
⁏ moderate intermittent drizzle

: moderate intermittent snow
⁝ heavy intermittent rain
⁞ thick intermittent drizzle
⁝ heavy intermittent snow
•• light continuous rain
,, light continuous drizzle
✻✻ light continuous snow
∴ moderate continuous rain
∴ moderate continuous drizzle
∴ moderate continuous snow
∴ heavy continuous rain
∴ thick continuous drizzle
∴ heavy continuous snow
△ sleet
= mist
⛇ snow shower
+ drifting snow low
≡ fog
⛆ rain shower
+ drifting snow high
∞ haze
⛆ hail shower
∿ freezing rain
⌐ smoke
∀ squall

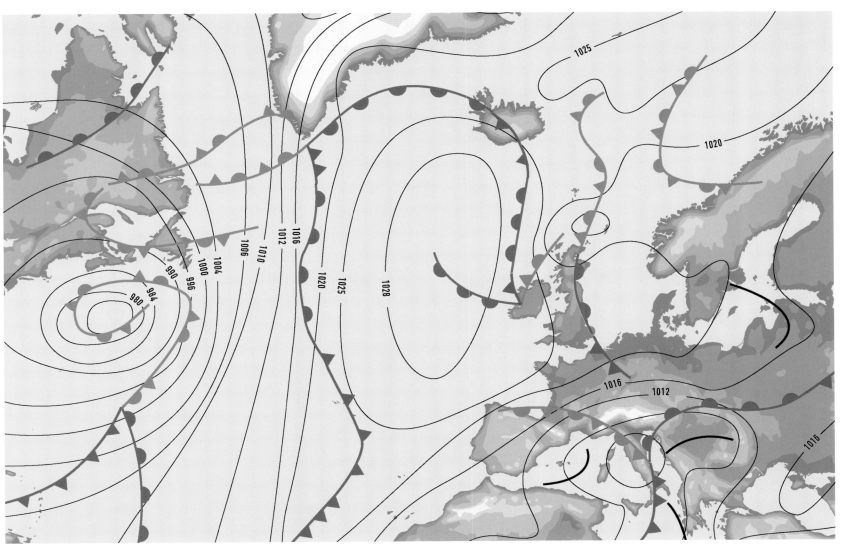

EXTREME STORMS

Wind and water in violent and unpredictable turmoil can create lethally dangerous conditions.
When major storms gather, our world of human constructions becomes very vulnerable.

A HURRICANE IS a vast, rotating storm centred around an area of very low pressure. Wind speeds can reach 150 mph (240 kilometres per hour). A hurricane travels along like a colossal and sinister spinning top, ranging over the earth's surface at speeds up to 20 mph (30 kilometres per hour).

Seemingly unconnected trigger mechanisms combine to start a hurricane. First, there has to be a source of very warm, humid air, rising from tropical ocean waters with surface temperatures greater than 25 degrees Celsius. In addition, a hurricane will only develop if the initial conditions occur in an approximately equatorial region where the rotation of the earth around its axis adds a significant twisting force to the accumulating air currents. As the warm sea surface heats the air just above it, a current of air rises up very fast, creating a region of low pressure immediately above the water surface into which fresh, cooler air must surge to fill the void.

Vast amounts of heat energy is carried aloft by the rising water vapour. As the saturated air climbs into cooler layers of the atmosphere, almost all the heat is rapidly released when the vapour condenses into droplets, and furious rain carries the heat downwards again towards the ocean, leaving cool air and low pressure above the

storm, into which warm air from below is eager to rise – and so on. The system becomes a self-feeding monster. It is the rotation of the Earth in particular that twists the storm into a cylindrical column whirling around an 'eye' of relatively calm, cloudless air.

When a hurricane moves over land it usually causes tremendous structural damage to vulnerable buildings. At the same time, friction between the storm's air currents and the rough terrain of dry land breaks up the pattern of air flow and eventually helps dissipate the storm.

Tornadoes, similarly terrifying phenomena, are whirling funnel-shaped columns of air that come into direct contact with the Earth's surface. They almost always originate from

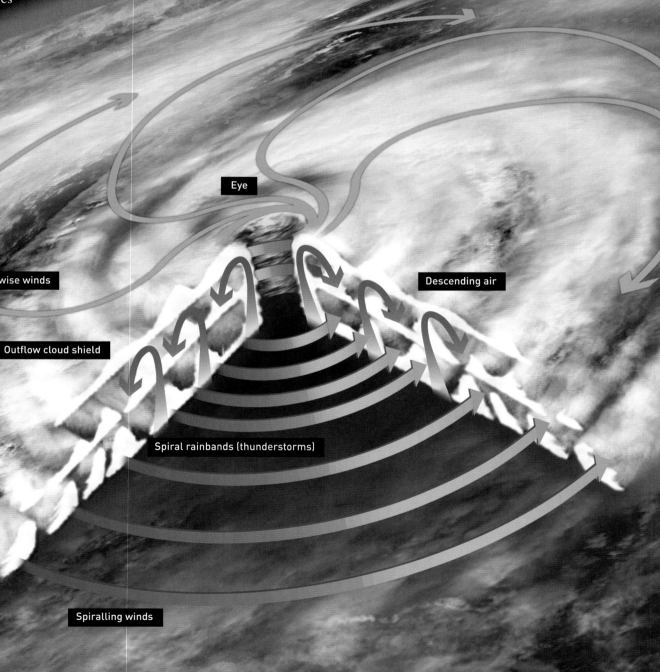

Eye

Clockwise winds

Descending air

Outflow cloud shield

Spiral rainbands (thunderstorms)

Spiralling winds

powerful thunderstorms. Cyclones are similarly violent storms with winds that twist clockwise in the southern hemisphere, and counterclockwise in the northern hemisphere. Hurricanes are essentially massive cyclones, typically originating near the equator and moving north. They are usually accompanied by torrential rains.

One of the strangest weather phenomena is a water spout. A funnel-shaped cloud forms at the base of a cumulus-type cloud and extends downward to the water surface, where it picks up spray in a thin-diameter vortex. An undulating column of water reaches all the way up into the clouds: a truly unsettling spectacle, and a warning for boats to get out of the area.

The teeth of the whirlwind A tornado is a violent rotating column of air, usually forming within powerful thunderstorms, whose lower extremity makes direct contact with the earth's surface. Tornados can destroy houses, hurl motor vehicles and boats into the air, and even tear trees right out of the ground. This one was photographed in Kansas in the summer of 2004.

Progress of hurricane

OCEAN CURRENTS

Ocean currents are driven primarily by three forces: the action of wind, the Earth's rotation, and temperature variations between the shallow sunlit surface and the frigid oceanic depths where sunlight never penetrates.

SURFACE OCEAN CURRENTS are deflected clockwise in the Northern hemisphere and counter-clockwise in the Southern hemisphere because of the 'Coriolis' effect: the frictional drag of the oceanic crust on the water above it. The currents also come into contact with the edges of continental land masses that deflect them, creating giant circles of current known as gyres.

Tidal cycles, rain, evaporation, the shape of the ocean floor and inflow of fresh water from rivers and salt water from adjacent seas also affect the patterns. Variation in the salt content (salinity) of ocean water is one of the most significant factors. Loss of water vapour in warm climates leaves the surface water saltier and denser than before. As it moves into cooler climes it sinks, forcing the less dense and less salty water underneath to be pushed aside.

Navigators have exploited familiar currents, and their associated winds, for generations. Beneath the surface, they are just as crucial to marine life, because they redistribute food and mineral nutrients across vast distances.

EL NIÑO

This amazing composite image, showing surface temperature (various colours) and cloud cover (white), was created by combining different kinds of data from space satellites. The height of the clouds has been exaggerated for clarity. The warm water current, seen as a red band at the centre, is part of a phenomenon known as El Niño. At intervals of roughly five years, the Pacific Ocean becomes markedly warmer in the equatorial belt. This affects the global climate for many months at a time.

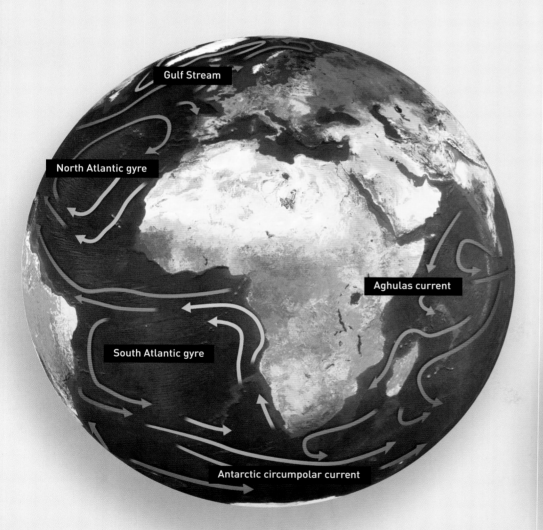

Major currents A simplified map of significant ocean current systems, with the directions of the warm currents highlighted in red, and the cooler currents shown in blue. The circular paths, or 'gyres,' are shaped by the coastlines of the continental land masses.

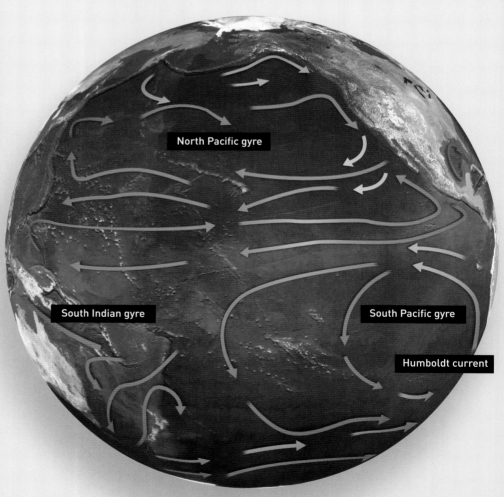

ATMOSPHERIC CURRENTS

The atmosphere's behaviour from day to day may be wildly variable,
but certain large-scale patterns of wind flow tend to persist over time.

The trade winds

The Earth's rotation around its axis creates distinct wind patterns around the world. In the mid-latitudes north and south of the equator, most of the winds attributable to this rotational 'Coriolis effect' blow from the west to the east. At the equator they blow mainly from the northeast in the northern hemisphere and from the southeast in the southern hemisphere. These air currents are known as 'trade winds' because of their long association with sailing ship trade routes.

Jet streams

First discovered in the 1940s, when high-altitude aircraft flights became common, jet streams are narrow and fast-flowing currents of air in the upper troposphere and lower stratosphere. They are formed by pressure differences between cold, dense polar air and warm, light tropical air. Jet airliners exploit the swift-moving currents as tail winds, thereby saving on fuel.

FAMILIAR WINDS

■ FRANCE: **the Mistral,** a cold, northwesterly wind blows along the Rhone valley.
■ WEST AFRICA: **the Harmattan** blows south from the Sahara, bringing dust storms.
■ MEDITERRANEAN: **the Levante,** an easterly wind bringing moist, warm air towards Spain and Africa.

■ NORTH AMERICA: **the Chinooks,** warm winds descending the eastern flanks of the Rocky Mountains.
■ SOUTH AMERICA: **the Pampero,** a chilly southwesterly wind blowing across the flat grasslands of Brazil, Argentina and Uruguay.

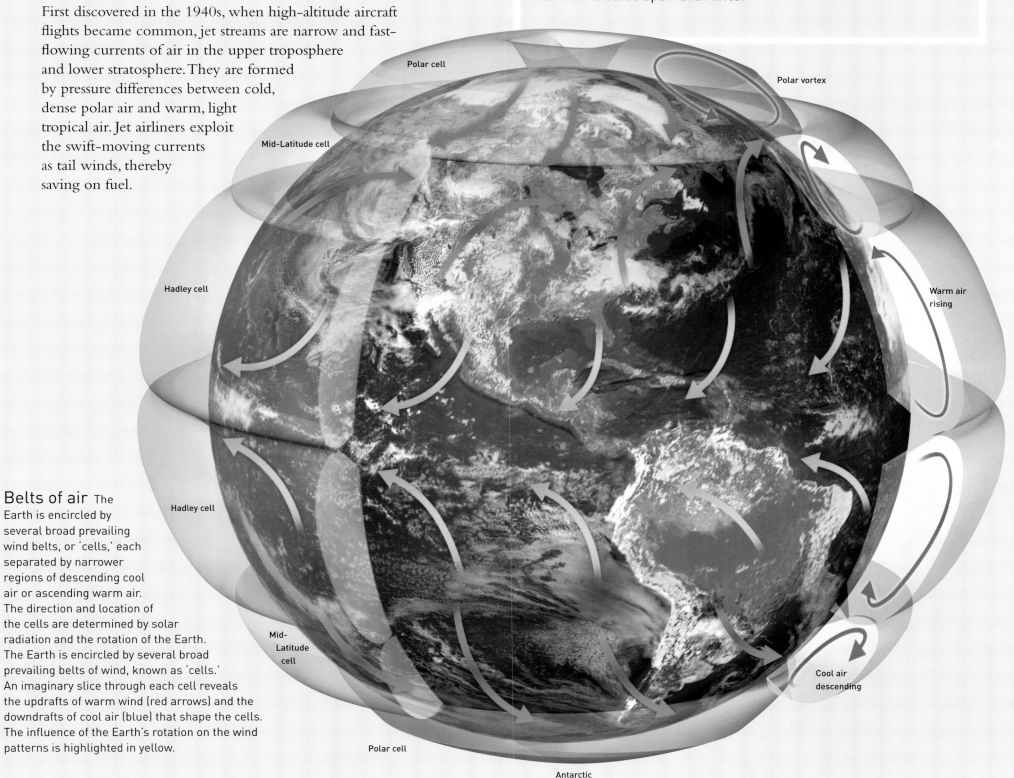

Belts of air The Earth is encircled by several broad prevailing wind belts, or 'cells,' each separated by narrower regions of descending cool air or ascending warm air. The direction and location of the cells are determined by solar radiation and the rotation of the Earth. The Earth is encircled by several broad prevailing belts of wind, known as 'cells.' An imaginary slice through each cell reveals the updrafts of warm wind (red arrows) and the downdrafts of cool air (blue) that shape the cells. The influence of the Earth's rotation on the wind patterns is highlighted in yellow.

Polar cell
Polar vortex
Mid-Latitude cell
Warm air rising
Hadley cell
Hadley cell
Mid-Latitude cell
Cool air descending
Polar cell
Antarctic

GLOBAL WARMING

The Earth has a dynamic, restless and changeable environment. On many previous occasions it has transformed suddenly from a world of sweltering heat to one of frigid cold. Why, then, is there so much alarm about 'global warming' and 'climate change'?

THE EARTH'S CLIMATE has been relatively benign for the last few thousand years. During that time, humans have spread far and wide across the globe, more or less assured that conditions will be survivable for them almost wherever they go. However, when the Earth's story is explored at time scales of 10,000 years or more, a much less comfortable picture of climatic change is revealed. In the 40,000 years that preceded this current era of stability, our ancient ancestors experienced extreme variations in global temperatures, including glacial ice ages that buried much of the Continental northern hemisphere under thick ice, even down to modern Spain and Portugal.

The first distinguishing feature about global warming is that it appears to be purely the product of a single species of life: human beings. The second distinguishing feature is that it has manifested itself extremely rapidly: not just over thousands, or tens of thousands of years, but in a matter of decades. Over the last century – an almost vanishingly short time in the 4.5 billion-year history of the Earth – the average temperature of the atmosphere just above the Earth's surface has risen by nearly 1 degree Celsius. This sounds inconsequential, yet it may be behind the conspicuous increase in violent storms, floods and forest fires that we have witnessed over the last decade. That increase of 1 degree Celsius makes the planet warmer, overall, than it has been for at least a thousand years.

The near to long-term outcomes of global warming are fiercely debated, but a majority of climate scientists fear that rising temperatures will eventually melt much of the ice currently held in the polar ice caps, thereby raising oceanic water levels sufficiently to endanger many coastal cities, towns and villages.

Melting of the North Pole

The South Pole's ice is on Antarctica, which is a land continent, but the North Pole's ice floats on the ocean. Charting the changes in ice coverage is complicated and dependent on seasonal as well as annual or decadal changes. However, it seems clear that the thinner sea ice on the fringes of the northern ice cap are all but vanishing during the summer months. Tensions are arising as various countries investigate fishing rights and energy exploitation in seas that used to be considered inaccessible because of ice.

▲ Arctic Sea 1979   Arctic Sea 2003 ▼

HOW GLOBAL WARMING WORKS

The principal cause of global warming appears to be the production and release into the atmosphere of carbon dioxide gas, generated by the burning of fossil fuels, such as oil, coal and natural gas. Almost all our technologies are driven by carbon-releasing energy sources, either in a direct way, such as in fuel-burning cars and aircraft, or indirectly, by electricity from oil or gas-fuelled power stations. More than 80 per cent of the world's energy is derived from fossil fuels whose combustion generates carbon dioxide gas. Although carbon dioxide accounts for only 0.4 per cent of the Earth's atmosphere, even the slightest increase of that small fraction has a dramatic effect.

Heat energy from the Sun reaches Earth in the form of infrared radiation. On balance, just as much of this radiation needs to be reflected back into space in order to keep the planet's temperature stable over time. Everything warm emits heat as infrared. Stones and boulders baked by the Sun during the day radiate their heat back into the sky at night. Likewise, the surface of the sea surrenders heat absorbed during the day.

Problems arise when that heat cannot escape all the way back into space. So-called 'greenhouse gases' mainly carbon dioxide, but also including methane and nitrous oxide, trap some of the infrared heat energy, retaining it in the atmosphere. The increasing warmth of the air leads to more evaporation of surface sea water, which in turn produces an increase in global cloud cover. Clouds also trap heat (this is why clear, cloud-free winter nights are so much colder than overcast nights).

RENEWABLE ENERGY SOURCES

Hydropower
Converts the potential energy of water behind a dam into mechanical energy to drive electricity-generating dynamos.

Bioenergy
Heat energy or chemical fuel reserves derived from the action of microorganisms on biomass, or from specially grown crops.

Wind farms
Giant propellers on tall towers convert wind energy into mechanical energy to drive dynamos.

Geothermal energy
Uses the temperature differential between the Earth's surface, where the rock is cool, and deeper regions where the rock is hot.

Solar power
Collects sunlight over a wide area and focuses it onto a much smaller area, then converts the concentrated heat into electricity.

SEE ALSO
■ **Extreme Storms**
page 44

Ice calving from a glacier

◄ When the vanguard edge of a glacier reaches the sea, the glacier is pushed out over the water. Eventually, the overhanging ice collapses under its own weight, and millions of tons fall into the sea to form new icebergs. This process is called calving.

Carbon Culprits

Destruction of rain forests to make way for grazing pasture threatens us in several ways. Those forests are a major source of atmospheric oxygen produced by plant photosynthesis. The forests are also 'carbon sinks' because they absorb carbon dioxide. The aviation industry is another obvious threat, along with digital technology which absorbs massive amounts of electrical energy derived from fossil fuels, while pumping out heat from countless computers and servers.

The initial warming caused by greenhouse gases generates the conditions for even more heat to become trapped in the atmosphere. Other feedback threats include the melting of Siberian and Alaskan tundra, where deep layers of compacted plant materials have remained frozen in the hard ground for many thousands of years. If the tundra thaws out over the coming century or so, then the plant matter will begin to decay, releasing large quantities of methane – a greenhouse gas – into the atmosphere. The melting of ice at the poles produces its own feedback effect. Ice reflects sunlight, keeping the Arctic regions cool, but the north pole in particular is reflecting less heat back into space than before – thus increasing the likelihood of further melting.

The total amount of ice fluctuates according to the seasons, but summer coverage of the Arctic has declined during the last three decades, by as much as ten per cent per year. Between 2005 and 2007, the Arctic lost ice equivalent in area to the state of Texas. Within the next two decades, the north pole may become free of ice altogether during the summer. Climate is one of the most complex and unpredictable phenomena to study. Although we are almost

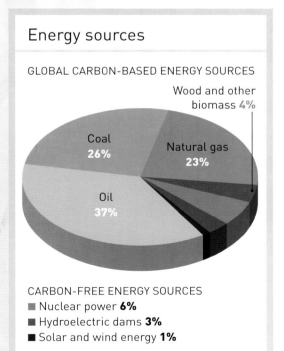

Energy sources

GLOBAL CARBON-BASED ENERGY SOURCES

- Wood and other biomass **4%**
- Coal **26%**
- Natural gas **23%**
- Oil **37%**

CARBON-FREE ENERGY SOURCES
- Nuclear power **6%**
- Hydroelectric dams **3%**
- Solar and wind energy **1%**

certain that the north pole is under threat, ice at the south pole seems, if anything, to be expanding by about half a per cent annually.

Consequences and choices

A further input to global warming arises from the deforestation of tropical rain forests and other areas where dense, tall vegetation is sacrificed in favour of flat, simple farmland. Forests contain countless very large plants and trees that absorb carbon dioxide and trap it into their physical structures. When this kind of massive but slow-growing vegetation is cut down, the capacity of that patch of land to absorb carbon dioxide is reduced. At the same time, since so many forest cuttings are subsequently burned, the trapped carbon is released back into the air.

Should we be alarmed by global warming? The long and variable history of our planet shows that dramatic shifts in climate tend to happen anyway, regardless of human technology. Many forms of life die out when their environment alters beyond what's good for them, but others survive, or even prosper, as competitors fade from the scene. Where human beings will fit into the future story of Earth's climate remains to be seen.

CHEM

ISTRY

CHEMISTRY

The word 'atom' comes from a 2,400-year-old Greek notion. The philosopher Democritus argued that matter must be made from indivisible, imperishable and unchanging particles, which he called *atomos*. It was a brilliant insight, based on good logical arguments, but Democritus did not choose to test any of his concepts experimentally. Like most of his contemporaries in the golden age of classical Greek thought, he believed that intellect alone should be sufficient to resolve the mysteries of nature. The business of grubbing around with experiments was manual work best done by servants, not thinkers.

For the next 2,200 years the atom made almost no further impact on human affairs. Craftspeople of the great ancient civilizations in China, Greece and Rome certainly knew how to smelt metals, make alloys and much else besides, but none had a theory to explain what was happening. It may have been the Egyptians who first began to tinker with substances purely for the sake of scholarship rather than craft. The ancient Greek name for Egypt was *Khemia*, but gradually this word took on a new meaning: 'transmutation'. After Egypt was occupied by Islamic Arabs in the 7th century, traders brought a convoluted mix of philosophy, superstition and the dawning of experimental science into the Christian kingdoms of Europe. It became known as *al-kimiya*, or 'alchemy'.

Old half-remembered traditions and craft instincts gave way to hard-edged practical analysis at the dawn of the industrial age. John Dalton was born in 1766 into a modest Quaker family in Cumbria, England, and earned his living for most of his life as a teacher, first at his local village school, where he began giving classes at the age of twelve, and then in the factory-dominated city of Manchester. Carefully weighing various substances before and after they reacted with each other, he worked out the ratios of different elements (substances that could not be broken down into anything other than themselves) that went into well-known compounds, and reanimated the atom as a practical idea rather than just a vague ancient Greek speculation.

Dalton concluded that all atoms of a given element are identical, and that compounds are formed by a combination of two or more different kinds of atom. In 1869 a brilliant Russian pioneer, Dmitri Mendeleev, produced a 'Periodic Table' in which elements are arranged according to their properties and reactivity. Wherever gaps existed in his Table, he predicted that new elements with the appropriate qualities would one day be found. He was right – but why?

Mendeleev and his contemporaries knew how to calculate the 'weight' of atoms in each element by comparing them with atoms of hydrogen, the lightest element. By the 1930s, the first nuclear physicists had revealed the structure of the atoms themselves, and how shells of electrons surrounding the nuclei formulate the bonds between them. Mendeleev's Periodic Table now had an explanation. In 1980 the nuclear chemist and Nobel laureate Glenn Seaborg changed a few thousand bismuth atoms into gold atoms by rearranging the protons and neutrons in their nuclei using a particle accelerator at the University of California, Berkeley. The alchemists' ancient dreams were not quite supplanted after all. Instead they were transmuted into modern chemistry.

ELEMENTS AND COMPOUNDS

There are many different kinds of matter: everything from copper and plastic to water and diamond. The differences between these substances, and the ways in which they react (or fail to react) with each other are determined by the nature of their atoms.

CHEMICAL ELEMENTS are the simplest substances in nature. They cannot be broken down into simpler substances. All the atoms within a sample of a particular element will be the same. The smallest amount of an element that we can usefully talk about is a single atom of that element.

Atoms consist of electrons surrounding a nucleus that contains protons and neutrons. Protons and electrons are electrically charged. Protons have a positive charge, while electrons have exactly the same charge as a proton, except that they are negative. The neutrons inside the nucleus have mass, but no electric charge. In a stable atom, the number of protons in the nucleus exactly balances out the negative charge in the same number of electrons. However, electrons can be gained or lost. A reliable way to identify an atomic element is to remain focused on its nucleus, which does not so easily gain or lose the particles within. The number of protons in an atom is called its atomic number.

Isotopes

Protons and electrons determine an atomic element's chemical characteristics. The neutrons are a different matter. They have no charge, but do have almost the same mass as a proton. Different isotopes of an atomic element contain different numbers of neutrons. The effect on chemical reactions is subtle, and its significance depends on the circumstances. 'Heavy' isotopes of carbon, with more neutrons in their nuclei, move more sluggishly in solution with water than light ones with fewer neutrons. Biological processes are biased towards lighter carbon isotopes.

Ions

Atoms are often not electrically balanced. The number of electrons surrounding the nucleus can vary. When an atom gains electrons it becomes a negatively charged ion because its electrons outnumber the positive protons in its nucleus. Alternatively, electrons can be lost, making the atom a positive ion.

Atomic bonds

Covalent bonds are made when atoms share pairs of electrons so that each atom's valence 'shell' becomes full. The bonds depend on the attractions between the positively charged nuclei and the negatively charged shared electrons. Ionic bonds occur between metallic and non-metallic elements. The metal donates at least one electron to the non-metal. This leaves the metal positively charged because it has lost an electron, while the non-metal becomes negatively charged as a consequence of gaining an electron. The attraction between the positive and the negative metal ions causes an ionic bond to be formed, which can be more easily sundered than a covalent bond.

Molecules and formulae

When more than one atom combine, a molecule is formed, making a chemical compound. Chemical formulae specify the ratio between atoms of different elements in a compound. For instance, water is a molecule written as H_2O, signifying two hydrogen atoms for every one of oxygen, while carbon dioxide, or CO_2, contains two atoms of oxygen for every one of carbon. Many elements will also combine with other atoms of the same element. The oxygen in the air, for instance, is in the form of O_2 molecules.

CHEMICAL BONDS

The simplest and most familiar example of a chemical bond between different elements occurs when two atoms of hydrogen combine with one of oxygen to make H_2O, otherwise known as a water molecule. Atoms combine with other atoms principally by sharing electrons. Chemical equations show the ratio of different elements in any given molecule: hence 'H_2O' or 'CO_2' (carbon dioxide made from one carbon and two oxygen atoms).

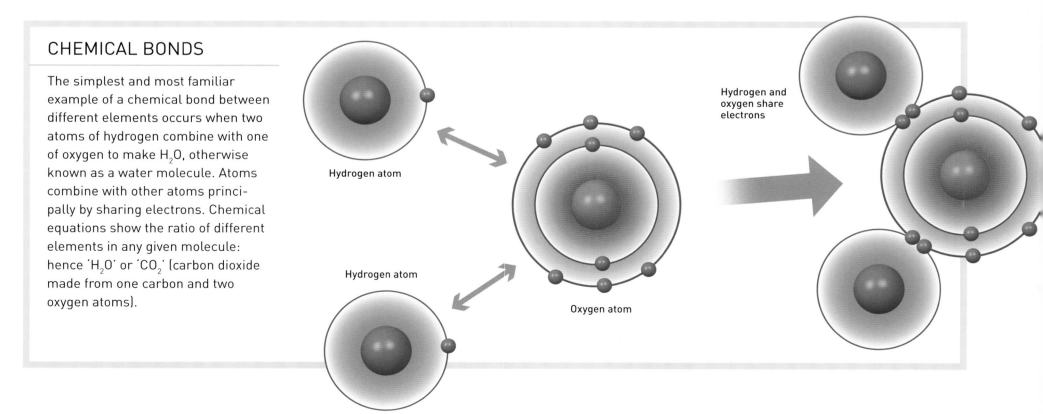

Hydrogen atom

Hydrogen atom

Oxygen atom

Hydrogen and oxygen share electrons

Electron shells

Electrons are arranged around an atom's nucleus at different energy levels, called shells. In many simple diagrams of atoms, we see electrons whizzing along neat circular paths like tiny satellites orbiting a planet. It is more realistic to think of electrons as clouds of electric charge surrounding the nucleus. Imagine if clouds in the Earth's atmosphere could only exist at certain discreet altitudes, and this gives some idea of how electrons are arranged around an atom.

Each shell can only contain a certain maximum number of electrons. For the innermost shell, the maximum number is two. The second shell can support eight. For atoms with three or more shells, the maximum number of electrons in each shell depends on the element in question. Hydrogen, the lightest element, has just one electron shell. The heaviest natural element, bismuth, has six. Electrons in higher shells have higher energy. They will tend to 'drop' down to the lowest and most stable energy levels, until all the available electron slots in each shell are filled.

The valence shell

The outermost electron shell, the 'valence shell', determines an atom's reactivity with other atoms. When that shell contains fewer electrons than the maximum allowable, there is room for electrons from other atoms to occupy those slots, thus filling vacancies in the valence shells of more than one atom at a time. The valence shell reaches stability when it contains either two or eight electrons. One of the reasons why hydrogen is so reactive is that it has just one electron, occupying one shell. In hydrogen's case, this single, low-energy inner shell is also the outer valance shell, and there is room for another electron in it. A free atom of hydrogen always seeks to fill that slot with an electron from another atom. Helium also only has one electron shell, but it supports two electrons, leaving no vacancies in that shell. Seemingly so close in character to hydrogen, helium can never bond with any other atoms. Similarly, argon has eight electrons in its outermost shell. Therefore, it has no tendency to combine with any other element.

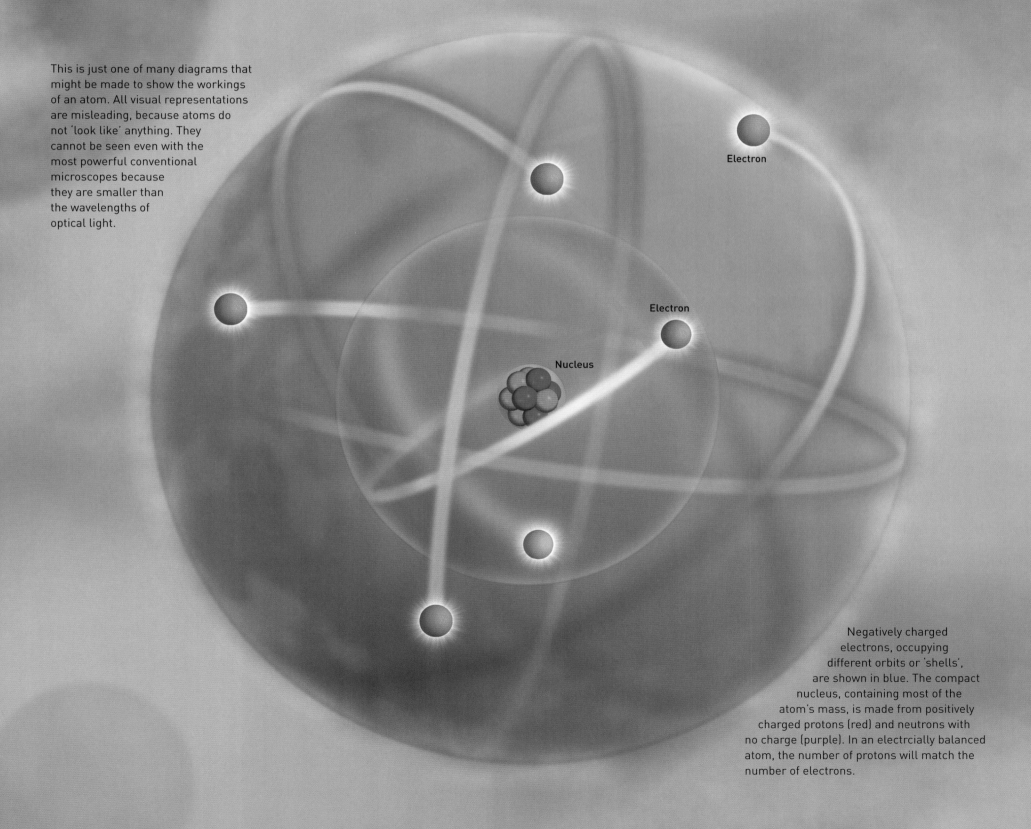

This is just one of many diagrams that might be made to show the workings of an atom. All visual representations are misleading, because atoms do not 'look like' anything. They cannot be seen even with the most powerful conventional microscopes because they are smaller than the wavelengths of optical light.

Electron

Electron

Nucleus

Negatively charged electrons, occupying different orbits or 'shells', are shown in blue. The compact nucleus, containing most of the atom's mass, is made from positively charged protons (red) and neutrons with no charge (purple). In an electrcially balanced atom, the number of protons will match the number of electrons.

THE PERIODIC TABLE

All known chemical elements have been charted on a grid known as the Periodic Table, where they are listed and arranged according to their relative masses and chemical tendencies. The underlying mechanism depends on how the atoms of each element are structured.

ELEMENTS in the Periodic Table are arranged left to right, and top to bottom, in order of increasing atomic number, as defined by the number of protons in the nucleus: the most reliable guide to identifying whichever element any given atom represents. The rows of the Table are called 'periods' and the columns are 'groups'. Periods relate to the number of electron shells that each atomic element possesses, while groups contain those elements whose valence shells have the same number of electrons, and, therefore, a tendency to react in similar ways during chemical reactions. The intersections of periods and groups reveal intimate links between the position of each atomic element in the Table and the structure of its electron shells, allowing for useful predictions about how elements will behave when exposed to other elements.

Modern iterations of the Table tend to be colour-coded to highlight 'families' of elements. For instance, transition metals can use two outermost electron shells, rather than just one outer valence shell, to bond with other elements, while inert ('noble') gases have full valence shells and therefore do not combine with other elements. Alkali metals and alkaline earth metals are highly reactive and therefore are not encountered naturally in combination with other elements. Semi-metals have both metallic and

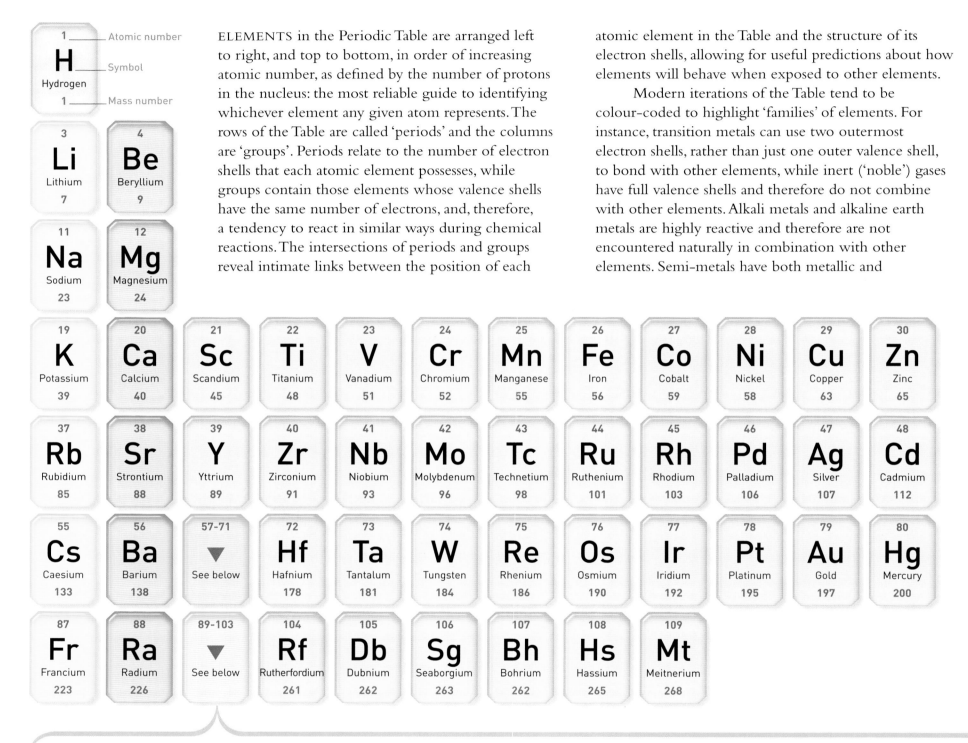

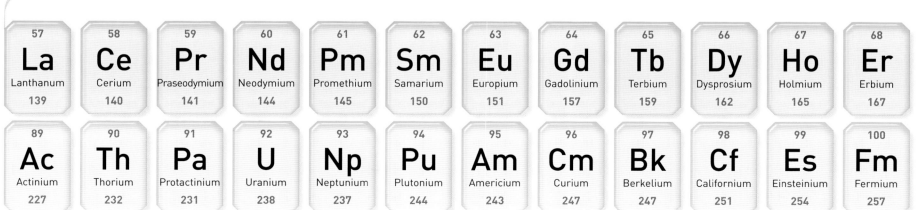

nonmetallic properties, being dull in appearance, like nonmetals, yet are capable of conducting electricity. Hydrogen forms a special family with just one member.

The separate block of two periods located below the main body of the Table show elements collectively known as rare earth metals. These share very similar characteristics, especially in the unusual behaviour of their electron shells, which do not conform to the simpler rules that apply throughout most of the rest of the Table. The actinides consist almost entirely of elements created artificially in nuclear experiments.

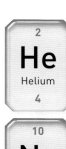

					2 **He** Helium 4
5 **B** Boron 11	6 **C** Carbon 12	7 **N** Nitrogen 14	8 **O** Oxygen 16	9 **F** Fluorine 19	10 **Ne** Neon 20
13 **Al** Aluminium 27	14 **Si** Silicon 28	15 **P** Phosphorus 31	16 **S** Sulphur 32	17 **Cl** Chlorine 35	18 **Ar** Argon 40
31 **Ga** Gallium 69	32 **Ge** Germanium 74	33 **As** Arsenic 75	34 **Se** Selenium 79	35 **Br** Bromine 80	36 **Kr** Krypton 84
49 **In** Indium 115	50 **Sn** Tin 118	51 **Sb** Antimony 121	52 **Te** Tellurium 127	53 **I** Iodine 127	54 **Xe** Xenon 131
81 **Ti** Thallium 205	82 **Pb** Lead 207	83 **Bi** Bismuth 209	84 **Po** Polonium 209	85 **At** Astatine 210	86 **Rn** Radon 222

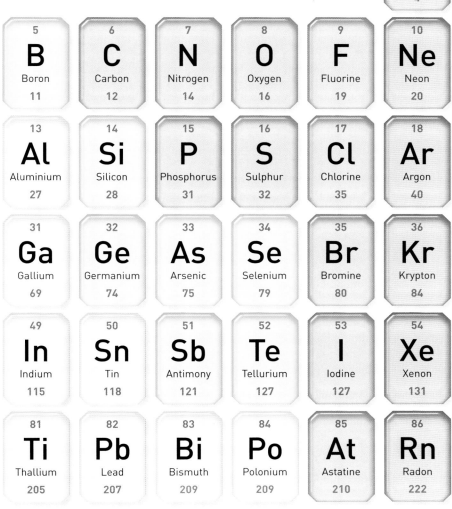

Alkali metals	Rare earths	Semi-metals
Noble gases	Alkaline-earth metals	Radioactive rare earths
Non-metals	Hydrogen	Transition metals
	Other metals	

69 **Tm** Thulium 169	70 **Yb** Ytterbium 173	71 **Lu** Lutetium 175
101 **Md** Mendelevium 258	102 **No** Nobelium 259	103 **Lr** Lawrencium 260

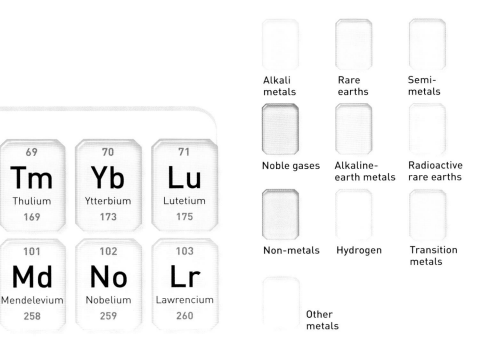

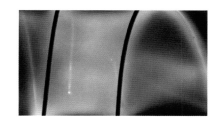

◼ Hydrogen *1* | **H**

More than nine-tenths of the universe consists of hydrogen. The bonds that it so easily makes with other elements can be broken almost as easily as they are made.

◼ Silicon *14* | **Si**

The second most abundant element in the Earth's crust after oxygen. Almost all window glass is derived from silica (silicon dioxide) found in ordinary beach sand.

◼ Iron *26* | **Fe**

One of the three elements that can be magnetized (the others are cobalt and nickel), iron is the major component of steel, a major construction material.

◼ Gold *79* | **Au**

Unreactive with other elements, gold is found in the natural world as pure nuggets, sometimes as large as a fist, though more usually the size of a speck of sand.

◼ Lead *82* | **Pb**

Lead was once used to make water pipes, until it was discovered to be poisonous. Today it is used in automobile batteries, roofing materials and radiation shielding.

◼ Sodium *11* | **Na**

A soft metal that tarnishes within minutes of being exposed to air, and which reacts vigorously with water. We flavour our food with sodium chloride, commonly known as 'salt'.

◼ Calcium *20* | **Ca**

The most abundant mineral in the body, essential for strong bones and teeth, and for the electrochemical reactions that power muscles and transmit nervous impulses.

◼ Copper *29* | **Cu**

An excellent conductor of electricity, and easily shaped into pipes or drawn into wires, copper is at the heart of almost all the electrical wiring in the world.

◼ Mercury *80* | **Hg**

This heavy, shiny metal is liquid at room temperature, and highly reactive. A difference of one atomic number separates mercury from gold, its inert neighbour.

◼ Uranium *92* | **U**

In nature, uranium is generally found as an oxide, such as in the olive-green mineral pitchblende. Its slow radioactive decay provides the main source of heat inside the earth.

CARBON

Carbon can make long chains by attaching molecular arrays to each other in endless different configurations. It makes possible the ten million different molecules needed for life. In the non-biological realm of technology and manufacturing, we are only just beginning to explore carbon's diverse potentials.

ALMOST EVERYTHING WE USE AS FUEL, whether in the form of food for us, coal for the fire or gasoline for automobiles, is based on one kind of carbon-based chain or another. These, in turn, are derived exclusively from living chemistry, either current or active in the distant past. In the nonliving world, carbon's value as an engineering material is due to the fact that it can bond in many different ways just with other carbon atoms. Graphite, the 'lead' in pencils, is a useful lubricant for machinery because its carbon atoms are loosely bonded in crystalline layers which easily slide over one another. By contrast the carbon atoms in a diamond are arranged with strong bonds in three dimensions, making it the toughest naturally occurring substance. A recently discovered artificial allotrope, 'white carbon', is as transparent as diamond but softer.

In the 1980s scientists discovered a ball-shaped molecule of 60 carbon atoms, named Buckminsterfullerene in honour of an architect renowned for his strong yet lightweight dome structures. Since then a wide array of artificial carbon allotropes have been investigated, and even exploited as high-strength yet super-lightweight materials, such as carbon fibres and 'nanotubes', microscopically fine, hollow filaments of carbon that possess extraordinary strength and excellent electrical conductivity.

Manufacturing – say, of a fine clockwork watch – usually involves taking large chunks of metal and whittling them down into the required cogwheels and springs. It is an inefficient procedure, because most of the metal ends up on the workshop floor as discarded shavings. In addition, huge amounts of energy are needed to extract pure metal from crude ores in the first place, and then to melt the metal into bars, plates or rods that can be yet more finely cut up and shaped by the watchmakers. Carbon-based 'nanotechnology' turns all this processing on its head, building upwards from the smallest scales by molecular accretion, with help from lasers and cobalt-nickel catalysts acting on a hot vapour of carbon ions. We are now entering an age when some of the distinctions between biology and engineering are starting to blur. We will grow our machines, rather than build them.

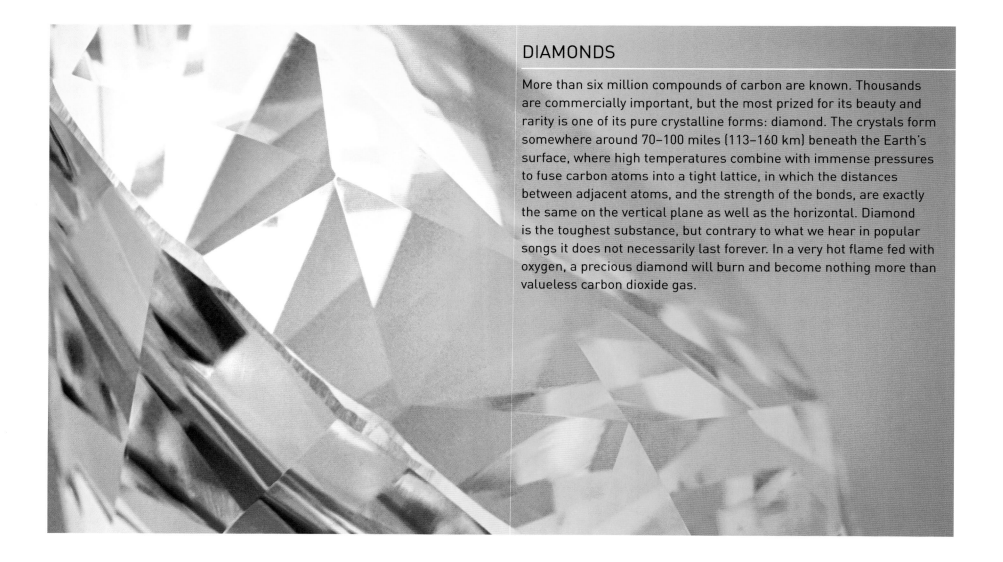

DIAMONDS

More than six million compounds of carbon are known. Thousands are commercially important, but the most prized for its beauty and rarity is one of its pure crystalline forms: diamond. The crystals form somewhere around 70–100 miles (113–160 km) beneath the Earth's surface, where high temperatures combine with immense pressures to fuse carbon atoms into a tight lattice, in which the distances between adjacent atoms, and the strength of the bonds, are exactly the same on the vertical plane as well as the horizontal. Diamond is the toughest substance, but contrary to what we hear in popular songs it does not necessarily last forever. In a very hot flame fed with oxygen, a precious diamond will burn and become nothing more than valueless carbon dioxide gas.

CARBON ATOMIC STRUCTURES

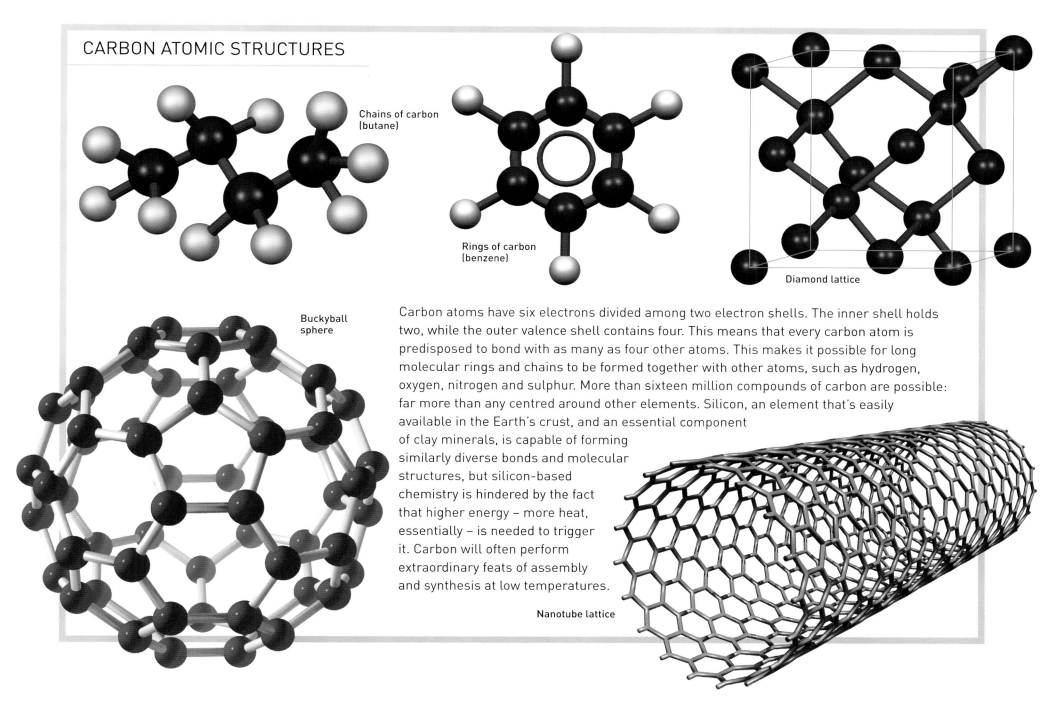

Chains of carbon
(butane)

Rings of carbon
(benzene)

Diamond lattice

Buckyball
sphere

Carbon atoms have six electrons divided among two electron shells. The inner shell holds two, while the outer valence shell contains four. This means that every carbon atom is predisposed to bond with as many as four other atoms. This makes it possible for long molecular rings and chains to be formed together with other atoms, such as hydrogen, oxygen, nitrogen and sulphur. More than sixteen million compounds of carbon are possible: far more than any centred around other elements. Silicon, an element that's easily available in the Earth's crust, and an essential component of clay minerals, is capable of forming similarly diverse bonds and molecular structures, but silicon-based chemistry is hindered by the fact that higher energy – more heat, essentially – is needed to trigger it. Carbon will often perform extraordinary feats of assembly and synthesis at low temperatures.

Nanotube lattice

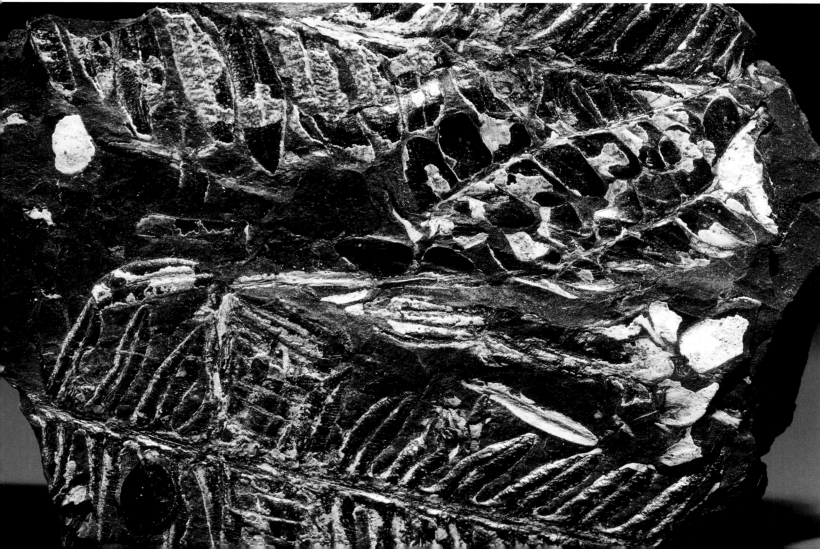

Black shale, a sedimentary carbon-bearing rock rich in plant fossils, especially ferns. This is typical of rocks associated with coal deposits.

OXYGEN AND COMBUSTION

It is all around us, but we can't see it, smell it or taste it. We couldn't live without it.
What we call 'burning' is the energetic reaction that occurs when oxygen reacts with other
chemicals under hot conditions to create oxides and yet more heat.

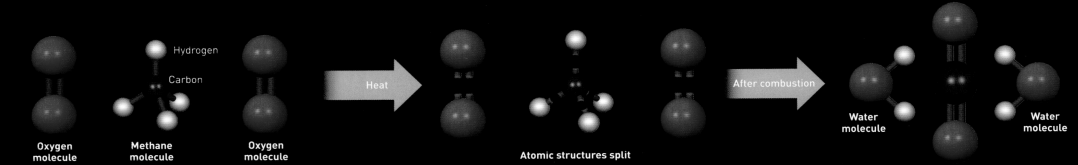

Oxygen molecule   Hydrogen   Carbon   **Methane molecule**   **Oxygen molecule**   Heat   **Atomic structures split**   After combustion   **Water molecule**   **Carbon dioxide molecule**   **Water molecule**

OXYGEN IS THE COLOURLESS, odourless gas that makes up
21 per cent of the atmosphere, amounting to more than a million
billion tonnes. It is essential for almost all forms of life, and in its
pure gaseous form is almost exclusively the product of photosynthetic organisms. It comprises over half the mass of a human being,
and is the most common element in the Earth's crust, where it
is most often found among silicon-based mineral compounds or
as calcium carbonate (limestone and marble), calcium sulphate
(gypsum), aluminium oxide (bauxite) and various iron oxides, the
primary sources of iron and steel. Oxygen also accounts for 90 per
cent of the mass of water. It doesn't just bind to hydrogen in that
familiar H_2O molecule. It also dissolves in water, thus providing a
source of breathing oxygen for fish and other aquatic creatures.

Oxygen can exist in a number of physical forms. The most
commonly found states are diatomic or triplet: molecules of two or
three oxygen atoms. Most atmospheric oxygen is in diatomic form,
while the triplet state is commonly called ozone. Found in very
sparse concentrations in the upper atmosphere, ozone plays a crucial
role in blocking harmful ultraviolet radiation from the sun.

Fire

Oxygen defines the process of combustion, more commonly known
as burning, and will combine with most elements in the presence
of heat. Combustion is an exothermic process, generating much
more heat than is initially fed in. Light energy may also be produced.
It is comparatively rare for us to burn pure elements. Instead we
burn fuels, such as coal or wood, that contain many different
chemicals. Oxygen breaks larger molecules apart into smaller and
simpler molecules, such as carbon dioxide and water vapour. The
net difference between the electron energy levels in the complicated molecules at the start of combustion and the simpler ones at
the end of it have to be accounted for. The excess energy is released
as photons of light and radiant heat. The flames of a fire are self-
perpetuating because the exothermic generation of heat brings yet
more fuel to ignition temperature. The spread of a fire will continue
so long as fuel and oxygen remain available.

Oxygen's reactivity is due to the structure of its two
electron shells. It has eight electrons, two in the inner shell and
six in the valence shell, which can hold as many as eight. Those
empty slots are easily filled by sharing electrons with other atoms.
In the typical combustion process above, two molecules of oxygen
(O_2) encounter one of methane (CH_4). A little heat enables the
atomic structures to split and recombine into simpler forms: one
molecule of carbon dioxide (CO_2) and two of water (H_2O). Heat and
light energy is also liberated.

Friction between the head of a match and an
abrasive 'strike' on the side of a matchbox creates
sufficient heat to activate a combustion process.

Corrosion and rusting

Leave most metal structures exposed for sufficient time to air and water and they will change spontaneously. The results are seldom desirable. What exactly is happening at the chemical level?

Slice through a piece of sodium to reveal its shiny pure texture, and the cut surface will become dull almost immediately if exposed to the air. The sodium atoms on the exterior of the cut surface react with oxygen to form a dull coating of sodium oxide. This is just one of the faster and more extreme examples of corrosion, a process that afflicts a wide range of metals and other materials. The special case of corrosion in iron or steel (an alloy of iron and carbon) is called rusting. Given that these are among the world's most common construction materials, rust is an expensive and sometimes dangerous nuisance.

Iron is seldom found in nature in its pure state (except in certain types of meteorite). Typically it is mined from deposits rich in various iron oxides. When processed and turned into purer forms, iron will readily recombine with oxygen, especially in the additional presence of water. Many other metals corrode only on the surfaces immediately exposed to corrosive environments. This can have the effect of creating an insulating layer, sealing the inside of those metals from further damage. Iron is different in that rust can

Dry air or pure water alone would not have affected the hull of this ship. Mildy acidic water and oxygen are both required for rusting.

penetrate its entire structure, speeding up the corrosion rather than slowing it down.

Iron and steel may seem solid, but water molecules easily penetrate microscopic pits and cracks in the metal. In very pure water, iron is reasonably safe — but water is seldom pure. Weak solutions of carbonic acid, formed by the dissolving of carbon dioxide in water, are common in nature. Acids react with many metals, including iron. If sodium is present, as is the case with salty sea water, corrosion will occur even faster. The net result is that iron atoms in water lose electrons easily and become unstable positive ions, which in turn attract negative ions from outside the metal, encouraging further reactions with water molecules and oxygen.

A common solution is to coat the iron or steel with an airtight and waterproof physical barrier, such as paint or a plastic coating. The shipping world, with its reliance on gigantic steel hulls, uses a more subtle technique: sacrificial protection. The iron-rich hulls are studded with bars of an even more reactive metal, such as magnesium or zinc. The hulls remain intact while the sacrificial metals corrode. This method works because the more reactive metal yields electrons to the hulls, making it more difficult for the iron atoms to lose electrons. Failure to replace the sacrificial bars in a timely manner can lead to unfortunate consequences.

SEE ALSO
■ **Earth's Atmosphere**
page 38

INDUSTRIAL METALS

We like to think that we live in a cool, weightless, post-industrial world of information and abstract digital constructs. Nothing could be further from the truth. Massive furnaces and molten metals underpin the modern age.

ONLY A FEW METALS are found uncombined in the ground. The natural form of most metals is within oxides and other compounds, known as 'ores'. Haematite, for instance, is a commonly available oxide of iron, while bauxite is mainly aluminium oxide and malachite is copper carbonate. The sequence in which various metals were discovered and harnessed gives a clue as to their reactivity. Gold and silver have been exploited for many thousands of years because they are unreactive, and therefore can be dug up in nuggets of more or less pure form. The Bronze Age was characterized by the ability of our ancestors to break down ores of copper and tin and mix them together to make an alloy stronger than either of its constituents: bronze. Despite their skills, they would have had little idea what causes this hardening effect. Alloys contain atoms of different sizes. The regular crystalline arrangements of the constituent metals are disrupted, making it harder for the molecular layers to slide over each other or peel apart. The Iron Age came later, because of the much higher temperatures needed to release iron from its ores and combine it with carbon, to make the alloy steel. Aluminium, magnesium and sodium are modern materials, purified only with the help of electricity.

Metal oxides that cannot be split apart just by heating alone are usually broken down by heating in the presence of carbon. Iron, for instance, is extracted from its ore in this way using a blast furnace. The raw materials are iron ore, limestone and coke (lumps of almost pure carbon derived from burned coal). Hot air is blown into the bottom of the furnace. The carbon in the coke burns in the air to produce carbon dioxide, which reacts in the extreme heat with yet more carbon, producing carbon monoxide gas. This reacts with the iron oxides in the ore, drawing out the oxygen to make further carbon dioxide, at last releasing the metal in pure form.

Aluminium is extracted from its bauxite ores by electrolysis, an expensive process requiring a large input of electricity. Molten aluminium oxide contains positive ions. A voltage potential between two terminals causes these ions to accumulate on the negatively charged terminal (the cathode) while the oxygen accumulates at the positive terminal (the anode). Titanium, a strong yet lightweight metal much favoured by the aviation and space industries, cannot be extracted simply by using carbon to pull out the oxygen. The problem is that the titanium will react with the carbon, forming titanium carbide, which is very brittle. A fiendishly complex and costly process is used in which chlorine gas is passed over red-hot titanium ores in the presence of carbon, and later exposed to molten magnesium in an argon atmosphere.

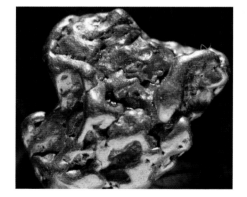

Lead ingot Lead is a heavy, soft, ductile metal with an atomic number of 82, used in roofing materials, batteries and bullets. It can be mixed with other metals to form alloys such as pewter and solder. Lead occurs naturally as galena (lead sulphide) and cerussite (lead carbonate). It forms several compounds poisonous to humans, and the metal itself is a cumulative toxin.

Gold nugget Gold (atomic number 79) needs only to be mechanically sourced from rivers or gold seams, rather than being chemically purified, although its comparative rarity makes it a challenge to find. It was once the basis of monetary systems. Many countries adopted a 'gold standard' by which to gauge the value of their units of currency.

ALUMINIUM SMELTING

A simplified diagram of aluminium production from bauxite. This is crushed, then treated with sodium hydroxide (caustic soda). A conveyor belt deposits the resulting mass into a crucible containing molten cryolite, a rare sodium–aluminium mineral whose main use is in the aluminium industry itself. Electrolysis draws out ions of pure metal (grey, lower right). The electrical energy required is enormous.

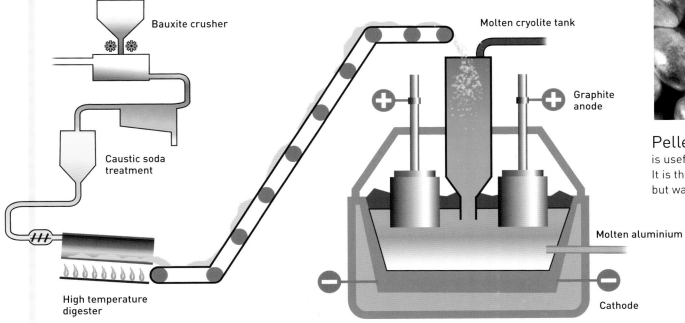

Bauxite crusher

Caustic soda treatment

High temperature digester

Molten cryolite tank

Graphite anode

Molten aluminium

Cathode

Steel containment cell

Pellets of aluminium a silvery metal which is useful because it is light and corrosion-resistant. It is the most abundant metal in the Earth's crust but was isolated only in 1825.

Furnaces and electrolysis tanks produce aluminium at a plant in eastern Europe. Pollution from the complicated processes creates health problems for workers and people living nearby.

FRACTIONATING TOWER

Similar in principle to the way that distillation works in the alcohol industry, this chemical-industrial technique separates the many different hydrocarbons in crude oil into vapour and then passes the vapour upwards through a cooling tower. The individual hydrocarbon compounds condense into liquid again at specific temperatures.

   A fractionating tower is kept hot at the bottom and cool at the top. The heaviest and most viscous molecules stay at the bottom end, while the lightest and most volatile rise to the top, only recondensing in the coolest regions of the tower. The separate products are drained away at different levels.

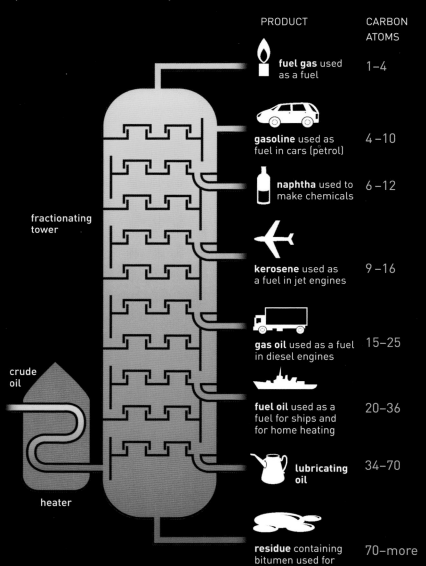

	PRODUCT	CARBON ATOMS
	fuel gas used as a fuel	1–4
	gasoline used as fuel in cars (petrol)	4–10
	naphtha used to make chemicals	6–12
	kerosene used as a fuel in jet engines	9–16
	gas oil used as a fuel in diesel engines	15–25
	fuel oil used as a fuel for ships and for home heating	20–36
	lubricating oil	34–70
	residue containing bitumen used for surfacing roads	70–more

fractionating tower

crude oil

heater

HYDROCARBONS

Crude oil, the viscous black-brown stuff that emerges from an oil drilling field, is
a complicated substance containing a mixture of thousands of different hydrocarbons:
molecules consisting of nothing but hydrogen and carbon atoms. These are the basis
for the world's energy supply and much of its industrial output.

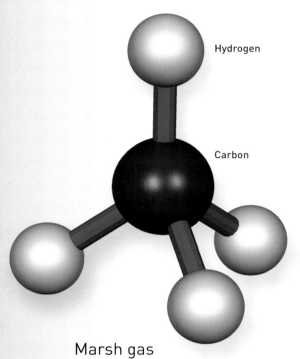

Hydrogen

Carbon

Marsh gas

Once known as marsh gas because
of its tendency to form among
rotting marshy vegetation, methane
(CH_4) is the principal constituent of
natural gas. It forms an explosive
mixture with air at a concentration
of less than five per cent.

A gas flare

burns off small amounts of natural
gas found in crude oil, where the
volume of gas is not sufficient to
justify its commercial extraction.
If this gas were allowed to build up
around the oil drilling equipment,
it could cause an explosion.

MOST OF THE MANY DIFFERENT KINDS of hydrocarbon in crude
oil or similar fossil fuel reserves are alkanes, a family of molecules that
shares the same general rule, where the number of hydrogen atoms is
double the number of carbon atoms, plus two. For example, methane
is CH_4 (one carbon atom, double the number of hydrogen atoms, and
then two more hydrogens) and ethane is C_2H_6. There are countless
products that can be derived from crude oil, but first, its hydrocarbons
have to be separated from each other so that they can be fed into
processes tailored specifically around their characteristics. Typically, this
is achieved in a 'fractionating tower'.

Crude oil is heated until most of it has evaporated and turned
into a mixture of gases. These are pumped into pipes spiralling upwards
through the tower. The further the pipes twist and wind upwards, the
cooler the gases inside them become, until they start to condense back
into liquids. The bottom of the tower, close to the crude oil heaters,
always remains the hottest area, while at the top the temperatures are
quite low.

The underlying principle of an oil industry fractionating tower
is that each family of hydrocarbons condenses at different temperatures
from the others. Valves placed at suitable intervals along the pipework
ensure that each type of hydrocarbon can be separated and drawn off
just at the moment when it has reached its condensation temperature.
Hydrocarbons drawn from the bottom of the fractionating tower have
the highest boiling points. They are dense and sticky, and made from
long molecules that are hard to burn. The very lightest hydrocarbon
fluids, drawn from the top of the tower, can turn back to vapour at
low temperatures and their small, simple molecules ignite very easily.

Hydrocarbon fuels certainly do burn easily when they react
with oxygen in the air, but the combustion has to happen efficiently
to get the best results. In a good burn, the hydrogen in the hydrocarbons is oxidized to create water (H_2O) while all the carbon is
oxidized into carbon dioxide. A poor burn, where the air flow is
restricted by clogged vents or dirty engine intakes, will still oxidize
hydrogen to water, but the carbon will oxidize with only a single
oxygen molecule, creating the toxic gas carbon monoxide. Heat in
the engine may also create equally unwelcome nitrogen dioxide from
nitrogen in the atmosphere. In a poor burn, unattached carbon atoms
are released into the air as black carbon soot.

Catalytic converters in automobile exhaust systems undo some
of the damage by changing carbon monoxide into carbon dioxide, or
stripping the nitrogen from nitrogen dioxide. The catalyst is usually
a combination of platinum and palladium metals coated
on a fine ceramic mesh to maximize the catalyst's surface
area within the small volume of the exhaust pipe. Even
when these combustion processes work at their cleanest,
the hydrocarbon industry still presents many other
challenges for the environment, but for this generation
at least, we continue to depend on it for fuel.

SEE ALSO

■ **Carbon**
page 60

PLASTICS

When we use the word 'plastic' we think of a substance that can easily be bent or moulded. The true definition of a plastic depends on its chemical basis: chain-like molecules made from many repeating units.

A POLYMER IS A VERY LONG MOLECULE in which one or two small units are repeated over and over again. (*Poly* is the Greek word for 'many', and *meros* means 'parts'.) The repeating units are known as monomers. Polymers exist widely in nature. Cellulose, for instance, is a polymer that can support the weight of plants without snapping at the slightest bend. This gives a clue to the valuable properties of polymers. They can create materials that are load-bearing, yet light and flexible. Natural polymers are also found in many resinous tree saps used as a source of latex and rubber.

Cellulose was once a source of a plastic called celluloid, used as the backing for early movie stock. This was extremely flammable, and in the early 20th century many cinemas caught fire when projector lamps ignited the films. A better product, cellophane, was common as a food wrapping. Today's plastics industry prefers artificial polymers built out of hydrocarbon monomers derived from crude oil. Plastics are used for manufacturing countless objects: anything from carrier bags and washing-up liquid bottles to clothes, drainpipes or the casings of computers and digital gadgets. Most plastic polymers contain carbon, oxygen, hydrogen and nitrogen, but the addition of other elements allows for a wide range of qualities. The chemical formulas vary but plastics all share one essential character-istic. Unlike metal or wood, they are very easy to form into whatever shape we please, and at conveniently low temperatures, too.

Most are thermoplastics, which start out life in a powder form and are then partially melted into soft sheets stretched over the mould for whatever product they are going into. A vacuum pulls the sheets against the walls of the mould, allowing for complex thin-walled structures to be manufactured (hence 'vacuum-formed' plastic). Once set into place, the polymers are easily separated from each other again with a little heating. Thermoplastics can be remelted and turned into new products.

Thermoset plastics are different in that they set hard and cannot be reformed or softened by heat, but will simply burn when the temperature gets too high. Their long-chain polymers are held in a rigid structure by cross-links between the molecules. There is also a third branch of the plastics family, the elastomers, rubbery materials that can be stretched and then return to their original shape when the stretching forces are halted.

Nylon is the general term for a wide range of synthetic fibres made by combining the amino group in one molecule with the acidic group of another to produce a long-chain polymer similar to a protein. The raw materials come from the petrochemical industry.

LIFE OF A BAG

Plastic bags are made from crude oil heated to release ethylene gas. This is converted to polyethylene, a gelatinous substance, which is then forced through holes to make stringy filaments, which are cut, heated and moulded into bags. The production process needs four times the energy required for making paper bags. Uncountable billions of plastic bags are made every year. Recycling of plastic bags is difficult because different kinds of plastic cannot always be mixed. Sorting one type of unwanted bag type from another is too costly and labour-intensive. A high proportion end up in the natural environment as litter, or in delib-erately created landfill rubbish dumps. Most of these plastics are non-biodegradable. They do not rot, but survive for years or even decades. This presents a serious hazard to wildlife.

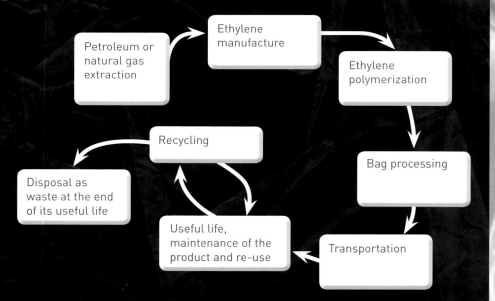

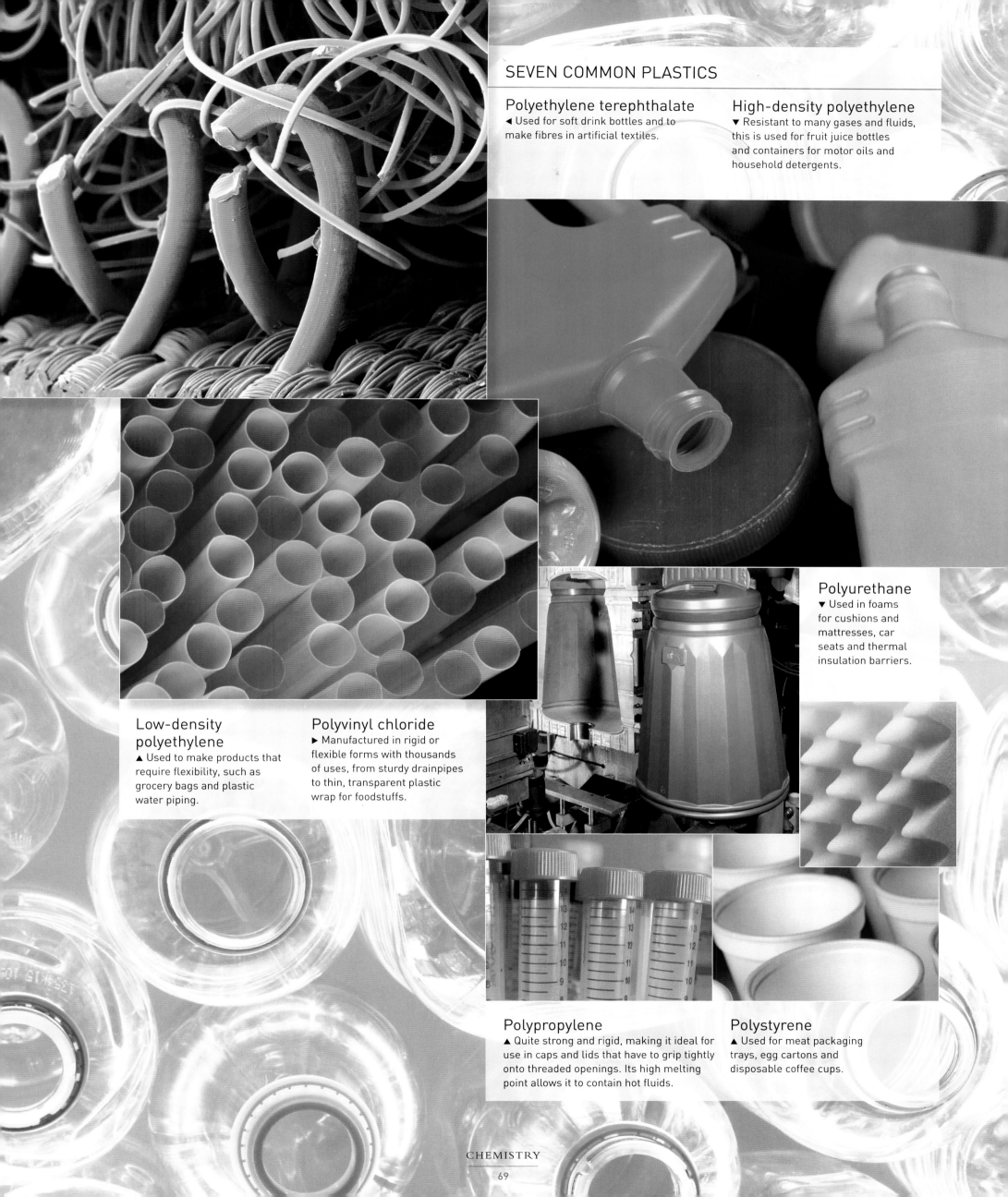

SEVEN COMMON PLASTICS

Polyethylene terephthalate
◄ Used for soft drink bottles and to make fibres in artificial textiles.

High-density polyethylene
▼ Resistant to many gases and fluids, this is used for fruit juice bottles and containers for motor oils and household detergents.

Polyurethane
▼ Used in foams for cushions and mattresses, car seats and thermal insulation barriers.

Low-density polyethylene
▲ Used to make products that require flexibility, such as grocery bags and plastic water piping.

Polyvinyl chloride
► Manufactured in rigid or flexible forms with thousands of uses, from sturdy drainpipes to thin, transparent plastic wrap for foodstuffs.

Polypropylene
▲ Quite strong and rigid, making it ideal for use in caps and lids that have to grip tightly onto threaded openings. Its high melting point allows it to contain hot fluids.

Polystyrene
▲ Used for meat packaging trays, egg cartons and disposable coffee cups.

ACIDS AND ALKALIS, SALTS AND METALS

The word 'acid' is derived from the Latin for 'sour'. What does or does not constitute an acid, or its chemical opposite, an alkali, is best discovered by seeing how each reacts with the other – and with metals.

ACIDS ARE COMPOUNDS that dissolve in water in such a way that positively charged hydrogen ions are temporarily created by stripping away the electrons. A hydrogen atom has only one proton and one electron, so its positive ion is just a proton. This cannot exist independently for more than an instant. It must bond with a neutral water molecule. The electrons required for this bond can only come from the oxygen atom of the water molecule. The electrons from the oxygen are shared with the hydrogen ion to establish an uneasy bond. The resulting acid will easily react with proton-accepting 'bases' containing negative ions. Acid–base reactions create salts. When bases are soluble in water, they are classed as alkalis.

The chemistry of acids and alkalis is complex at the atomic level: so much so that not all chemists use the same classifications or explanations. The easiest way of identifying acids and alkalis at a practical level is to see how they react with a sensitized ribbon of paper, called a litmus strip. Coloured dyes extracted from lichens turn from yellow and orange to deep red in the presence of acids, and green to dark blue when exposed to alkalis. The pH scale gives a specific number for acidity or alkalinity, ranging from zero at the most acidic end (battery acid, for instance) to 14 at the most alkaline end (caustic soda). Pure water is neutral, and has a pH of 7. Each litmus colour reveals the specific pH number of the substance in question. The pH acronym stands for 'potential hydrogen'.

ACID

THE pH SCALE

Our kitchens contain juices, foodtstuffs and cleaning agents ranging across a broad spectrum of the pH scale.

Human acids
The digestive acids in our stomachs occupy the pH 1–3 range.

pH1

In the fruitbowl
Grapes, oranges and apples have pH values from about 3 to 5.

pH3

Daily bread
White sliced bread is found between pH 5 and pH 6 on the scale.

pH5

pH0

Sulphuric acid
Pure H_2SO_4 is one of the most corrosive acids, and is so dangerous that it is seldom made available to the public unless much diluted in water, or safely sealed inside the casing of the lead–acid battery in a car.

pH2

pH6

Vinegar
Harmless microorganisms turn the sugars in fruits (grapes or apples, for instance) into acetic acid. Yeasts change natural sugars to alcohol. Then a group of bacteria (called 'acetobacter') converts the alcohol portion to the acetic acid that gives vinegar its sharpness.

pH4

Butter
Occupies pH 6 on the chart, so long as it is unsalted.

Tomato juice
Tomatoes contain small traces of citric and oxalic acids, but the overall effect on the body is to help maintain a healthy alkaline balance.

SULPHURIC ACID CP
QTY: 250ml

Corrosive

Metals

Typically a metal will be a shiny (lustrous) and ductile (bendable) element, good at conducting heat and electric currents. Not all metals fit neatly into that description. Mercury is certainly lustrous, but is a liquid at room temperature and therefore can hardly be described as ductile. Lead bends well but is an extremely poor conductor. Gold, copper and iron are among the most obvious and familiar metals, but more than 75 per cent of elements in the Periodic Table are metals, too. Most will react with oxygen, forming a metal oxide. Think how easily iron rusts if left untended for too long. On the other hand, pure gold never loses its lustre. No single neat set of rules defines how all metals must behave. Metals like magnesium and zinc or iron, which do not react vigorously with ordinary cold water, will certainly do so with hydrochloric acid, producing hydrogen gas and a metal-specific salt. Copper is sensitive to some acids with the exception of the hydrochloric variety. 'Alkali metals' such as lithium, sodium and potassium are in Group 1 of the Periodic Table because they have a single electron in their valence shells, making them very reactive. They form oxides and hydroxides that dissolve in water, making alkaline solutions.

Printing of illustrations on paper has long relied on the corrosive action of acids on polished metal plates, and especially copper. A waxy 'resist' layer is scratched by an artist, or – in these modern times – chemically imprinted with a photograph. Subsequent acid treatment 'bites' into the metal plate only where the resist layer is absent. The hollow pits created by the acid then hold ink, which is pressed onto paper.

Baking soda
pH8
Sodium bicarbonate combined with water and an acidic ingredient (such as lemon juice) produces carbon dioxide bubbles that expand in the oven, causing baked goods to rise.

Milk of magnesia
pH10
Magnesium hydroxide ($Mg(OH)_2$) is a milky white alkaline medicine that reduces excess stomach acid.

Bug killer
pH12
Toilets are disinfected with sodium hypochlorite bleach which destroys the membranes of potentially infectious bacteria.

Caustic soda
pH14
Sodium hydroxide, a highly corrosive alkali typically found in drain- cleaning and paint- stripping fluids.

ALKALI

Milk
pH7
It might seem surprising, but fresh milk is mildly acidic because of its lactic acid content.

Toothpaste
pH9
Very fine, chalky calcium carbonate grains give toothpaste its abrasive cleaning power, while putting it in the alkaline zone of the pH scale.

toothpaste

Ammonia
pH11
NH_3, used as a weak solution in water in general-purpose cleaning products.

Ammonia (conc)

Oven cleaners
pH13
Solvents such as ethanolamine and ethylene glycol, in conjunction with sodium hydroxide, break down grease and carbon deposits and lift them away from oven surfaces.

SODIUM HYDROXIDE

ACID RAIN?

It might seem strange to think of rain as acid, but it is. Sulphur dioxide, nitrogen oxides and other gases from industrial activity react with water in the atmosphere to create mild acids. Although these are not as fierce as to burn our skin, they affect the metabolisms of many living things, including plants. Large areas of forests have been adversely affected by 'acid rain', because it dissolves nutrients in the soil.

SEE ALSO
Periodic Table
page 58

ORGANIC CHEMISTRY

Whenever a chemical compound includes carbon, it is classed as 'organic'.
That's not to say that it must be associated with organisms, or living things,
yet nothing that lives can exist without organic compounds.

THERE COMES A POINT where carbon compounds verge on the biological without actually constituting anything that can be even remotely thought of as alive. Amino acids, the fundamental building blocks for life, have existed for vastly longer than any of the organisms that exploit them. Scans of deep space reveal that interstellar nebulae, the clouds of dust and gas drifting between the stars (and themselves the product of previous stars) contain hundreds of different chemicals, including amino acids and simple sugars manufactured by ultraviolet radiation from stars acting on molecules within the clouds.

Sugars are among numerous types of carbohydrate. Not to be confused with hydrocarbons made purely from hydrogen and carbon, carbohydrates contain one additional element: oxygen. Amino acids are a little more complex, invariably containing carbon, oxygen, hydrogen and nitrogen, and some also have sulphur as well. Amino acids always consist of a basic amino group (NH_2) and an acidic carboxyl group (COOH), with a third 'R' group that can vary widely in molecular structure. Carbon atoms are the essential links between all the groups. Upwards of 400 different amino acids have been identified, of which twenty in particular make up the assembly units for all proteins: the first level

Amino acids have a common core structure of hydrogen (H), carbon (C), oxygen (O) and nitrogen (N), to which is attached a variable 'R group'. Amino acids are the simplest building blocks of life. They assemble in long chains to make proteins.

of organic molecules that are directly associated with living things. Proteins are very long chains of different amino acids, with the ordering of the amino groups determining the shape, identity and functioning of each protein. The human body contains at least two million different proteins. Other animals and plants between them make use of at least ten million others. This is where the simplicities of non-living organic chemistry are left far behind, and the complexities of life begin.

SUGAR REFINERY PROCESS

Household and cooking sugar is derived from the pith of tropical sugar cane and temperate-region beet plants. Bleaching agents such as lime (calcium hydroxide) and carbon dioxide are added. The chalky clumps, as they form, collect unwanted fats, moulds and other impurities from the viscous syrup. Next, the chalk is filtered out, taking with it the non-sugar impurities. The syrup is then diluted with water and further refined by being filtered through beef bone char, similar to charcoal but made by burning animal bones at high temperatures. The final stage is to pour the syrup solution into vacuum pans, large tanks where the air pressure is lowered so that the water swiftly evaporates. As it does so, the increasingly high concentrations of sugar remaining in the pan become solid dry crystals. These are ground into fine powder for packaging of the final product: almost pure sucrose.

Valine   Leucine   Tyrosine

Single amino acids with different side chains...

Amino acids
A peptide bond is formed when the carboxyl group of one molecule reacts with the amino group of another molecule, releasing a molecule of water. The bonding of two amino acids creates a dipeptide. Three amino acids make a tripeptide. If more than 10 amino acids form a chain, they are called polypeptides. Any chain with more than 50 amino acids is classed as a protein.

can bond to form...

a strand of amino acids, part of a protein.

▾ Volcanic creativity
Volcanic eruptions release hydrogen and methane into the atmosphere. Collisions between ash and ice particles in the higher, colder regions of the atmosphere generate electric charge. Lightning bolts hitting wet ground can stimulate many kinds of chemistry. Organic precursor molecules for life may have been produced in tidal pools around volcanic islands. As the water in the pools evaporated, amino acids and other increasingly complex molecules may have become concentrated.

SEE ALSO

Our Origins
page 14

BIOL

.OGY

BIOLOGY

Nothing fascinates us more than the quality in nature that we call 'aliveness'. How is it that mere physical structures of flesh, blood and bone, made of nothing but water, simple gases and common minerals, can move of their own volition? What magic ingredient creates the distinction between the inanimate world and the endless dynamism of biology? This was a question at once thrilling and disturbing for Mary Shelley, who had the idea to write *Frankenstein, or the Modern Prometheus* when she and the superstar poets Percy Shelley and Lord Byron were holidaying near Lake Geneva in the summer of 1816 and sheltering in their villa while a storm raged outside.

Shelley wondered if it might be possible for human ingenuity to conjure up the secret of life, and perhaps even reanimate the dead. In an 1831 edition of her famous novel, she described a dream in which 'I saw the pale student of unhallowed arts kneeling beside the thing he had put together. I saw the hideous phantasm of a man stretched out, and then, on the working of some powerful engine, show signs of life, and stir with an uneasy, half vital motion.'

Fascinated by the science of her time, Shelley was familiar with the work of the Italian experimenter Luigi Galvani in the 1780s, during which he found that the muscles of dead frogs twitched in a lifelike manner when given an electric shock. In some experiments he inserted copper hooks into frogs' spines and wired these grim specimens to the iron railings of his balcony garden, exploiting the static charge from thunderstorms. 'Perhaps a corpse could be reanimated,' Shelley speculated. 'Perhaps the component parts of a creature might be manufactured, brought together, and embued with vital warmth.'

Four years earlier, the Scottish botanist Robert Brown thought he had discovered that same 'vital warmth'. He was examining pollen grains under a simple microscope, and had suspended fine grains in water. He noted how they seemed to move about, tracing random zigzag paths across his microscope's field of view. At first, he concluded that the movement of each grain 'arose neither from currents in the fluid, nor from its gradual evaporation, but belonged to the particle itself'. Other observers enthusiastically concluded that Brown had witnessed a fundamental 'life force' animating the tiniest pieces of biological matter. His initial findings caused great excitement.

Brown was a conscientious scientist. Even as he prepared to publish his results, he revised his text to warn that he had seen a similar motion among pollen grains that he had preserved in alcohol many months before, so that surely they had been rendered lifeless by the time he put them under the microscope. If there was some kind of a life force at work, it almost certainly wasn't being exerted by the grains themselves. It had to be something in the water. Seventy years later, when Albert Einstein happened upon Brown's publications, that 'something' would become the province of atomic scientists – and they, in their turn, would provide the 'life force' that drives biology.

Of course, modern biologists no longer talk in terms of a force. Instead they see an array of processes driven by myriad chemical reactions and the electrical charges of atomic ions. These are not so far removed, after all, from Shelley's and Galvani's shared suspicion that electricity and life must have some connection. With the structure of DNA now not merely understood but made artifically transmutable in the laboratory, we also verge on Shelley's eerie world in which 'component parts of a creature' can be spliced together at the genetic level and 'embued with vital warmth'. Above all, we understand – perhaps just in time – that biology happens not just within individual plants and animals, but on a planetary scale. We do not merely dissect the processes of life. We are a dynamic part of them.

DNA

Deoxyribonucleic acid (DNA) has often been described as the blueprint for life. In fact it is more like an extremely detailed recipe in the form of a biochemical computer program. The key to DNA's power as an information system lies in its structure.

AN ARCHITECT'S PLAN yields significant information about what a finished building should look like, while a recipe ensures that if certain actions are carried out in a specific order, using a particular set of ingredients, then the required meal will happen even if it cannot be visualized in advance. In this sense, DNA is more a recipe than a plan. The 'computer' aspect of its function comes from the fact that, although it is an extremely long and complex set of instructions, all of them are coded using just four very simple information units. Furthermore, DNA doesn't merely specify what should happen when an organism grows. It also controls the growth process itself.

DNA's most important quality is that the two long and densely intertwined spirals can split completely apart, right down the middle of all the base pairs, and then each half can generate a copy of its missing opposite half, reconfiguring the complete DNA as a distinct and exact copy of the original. Each split strand retains the pattern needed for duplicating the full sequence of base pairs, because an exposed C, for example, can only link with a G, and A must always connect with T. When cells divide in order to grow new tissues, each new cell carries with it a copy of the DNA from the original parent cell.

The ordering of base pairs in very long sequences defines the information required for growing and maintaining an organism, and for passing its characteristics down to the next generation during cell division. Specific sequences of base pairs along the DNA's length comprise genes, the instructions that define particular physical and behavioural characteristics or 'traits' of an organism. Human DNA has three billion base pairs encoding approximately 25,000 genes. An individual molecule (or strand) of our DNA is one-tenth of one- billionth of a centimetre wide, but would stretch across nearly three metres if uncoiled into a straight line.

DNA is packed tightly around histones, bundles of protein whose task is to fold and compress the DNA into even tighter

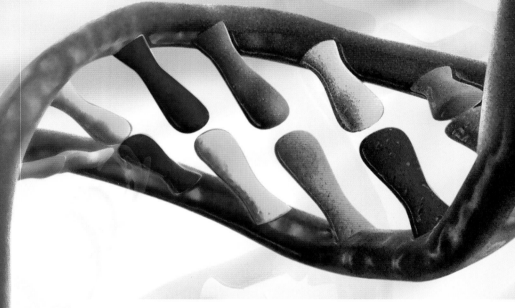

DNA is constructed like an elegant but somewhat surreal spiral staircase with its handrails twisting around each other in opposite directions.

DOMINANT AND RECESSIVE GENES

Alleles of particular genes are 'dominant' or 'recessive'. In this illustration, the allele that codes for brown eyes is B (dominant) and the allele that produces blue eyes is b (recessive). A person can inherit BB, Bb or bb. Only an inheritance of the allele for blue eyes from both parents gives that person blue eyes.

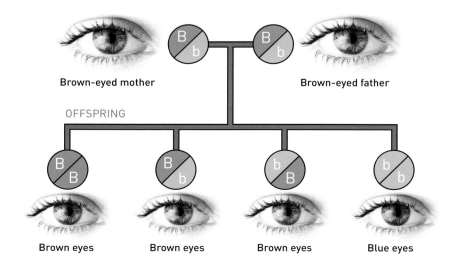

Brown-eyed mother   Brown-eyed father

OFFSPRING

Brown eyes   Brown eyes   Brown eyes   Blue eyes

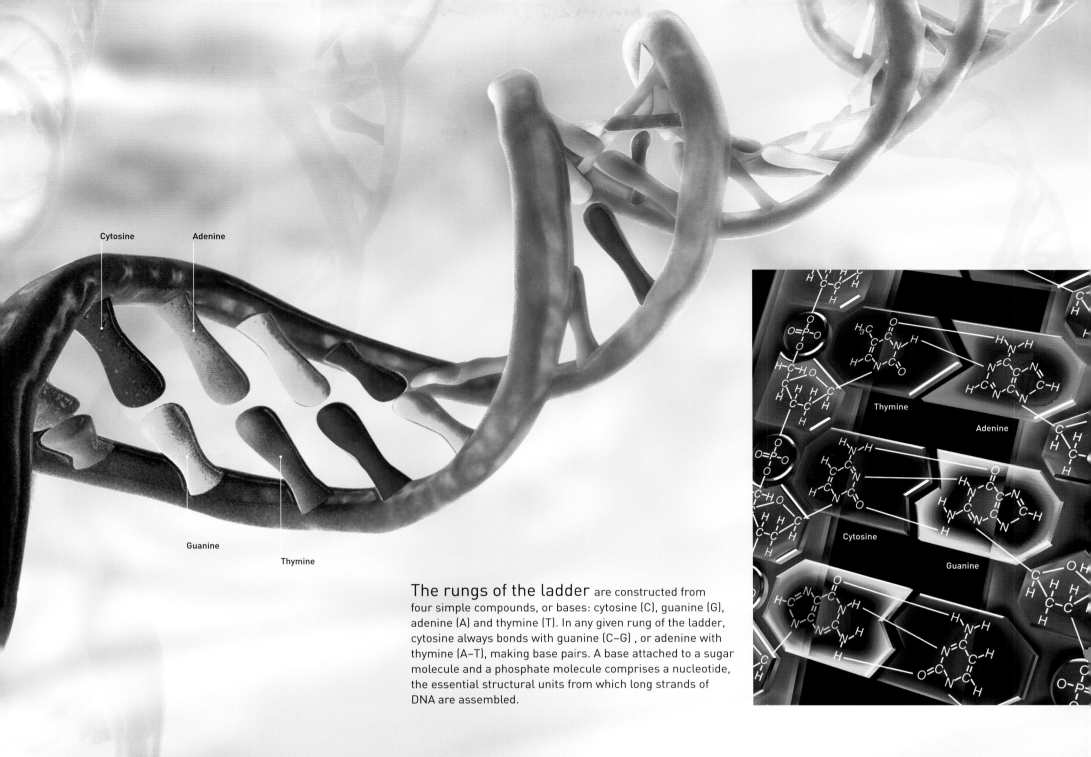

Cytosine
Adenine

Guanine

Thymine

Thymine

Adenine

Cytosine

Guanine

The rungs of the ladder are constructed from four simple compounds, or bases: cytosine (C), guanine (G), adenine (A) and thymine (T). In any given rung of the ladder, cytosine always bonds with guanine (C–G) , or adenine with thymine (A–T), making base pairs. A base attached to a sugar molecule and a phosphate molecule comprises a nucleotide, the essential structural units from which long strands of DNA are assembled.

rod-shaped packages, called chromosomes. The 'genome', the total DNA information content for any particular organism, is divided up among a specific number of chromosomes. Some ant species pack all their DNA into one chromosome, while human DNA is divided among 23 'homologous pairs' of chromosomes, amounting to 46 chromosomes in all. One chromosome from each pair is derived from the mother, and the other comes from the father.

Assembly instructions

Each gene holds the information, or 'codes for', one protein. Within the genes, each set of three base pairs (three rungs of the ladder) defines one amino acid. The assembly of new proteins happens inside an organism's cells, every one of which (apart from in the reproductive system) carries a complete copy of that organism's DNA. The gene sequence defining a protein is meticulously copied from the DNA into a new strand of a closely related type of molecule, messenger ribonucleic acid (mRNA). The mRNA then emerges from the cell nucleus and enters the cytoplasm, where it interacts with organelles called ribosomes. The mRNA directs the assembly of amino acids that link together and then fold into a completed protein molecule. Individual cells respond to gene instructions very selectively. A heart muscle cell, for instance, will have no need to manufacture proteins that are specifically associated

with brain cells. Some genes enable cells to make proteins needed for regular 'housekeeping' functions. Other genes play a role in the initial development of an embryo and are then shut down for ever.

Alleles

Genes in each homologous pair are matched on either side of the male–female contribution, but there are usually minor variations between genes, called alleles. For instance, the genes that code for eye colour are all extremely similar, but the allele for blue eyes codes slightly differently from the one for green. A dominant gene is one that actually puts into action (expresses) its coding no matter what its partner allele in the homologous pair happens to be. A recessive gene will express what it codes for only if it is matched by an exact duplicate in the homologous pairing. Brown eyes are, in fact, coded by a dominant gene, while blue eyes are a recessive trait. Both parents would need to contribute matching genes for blue eyes in order for their offspring to have blue eyes. If one parent contributes the gene for brown and the other for blue, the offspring will have brown eyes no matter what. The recessive allele of the eye colour gene will not express itself. Occasionally, human parents unwittingly both pass on recessive genes for unfortunate traits, such as a tendency to develop breast cancer or cystic fibrosis.

ANIMAL CELL

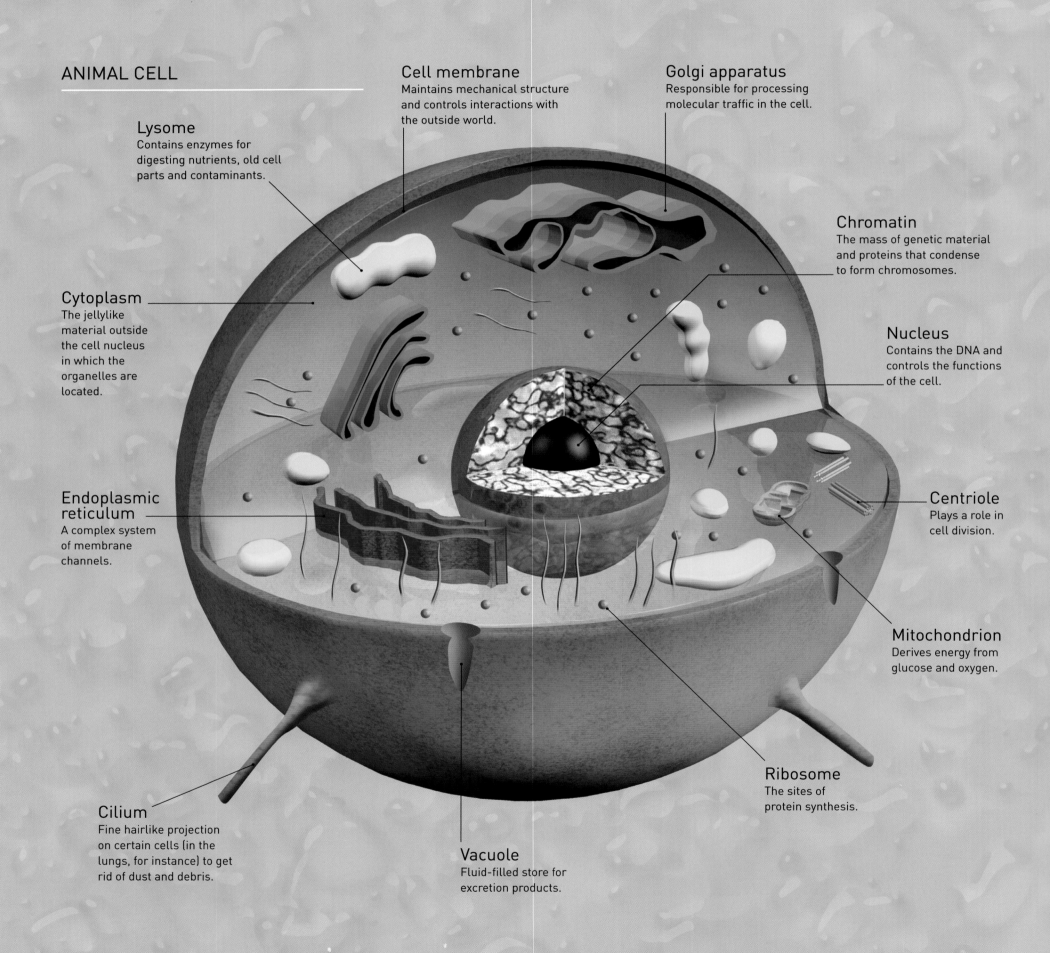

Cell membrane
Maintains mechanical structure and controls interactions with the outside world.

Golgi apparatus
Responsible for processing molecular traffic in the cell.

Lysome
Contains enzymes for digesting nutrients, old cell parts and contaminants.

Chromatin
The mass of genetic material and proteins that condense to form chromosomes.

Cytoplasm
The jellylike material outside the cell nucleus in which the organelles are located.

Nucleus
Contains the DNA and controls the functions of the cell.

Endoplasmic reticulum
A complex system of membrane channels.

Centriole
Plays a role in cell division.

Mitochondrion
Derives energy from glucose and oxygen.

Cilium
Fine hairlike projection on certain cells (in the lungs, for instance) to get rid of dust and debris.

Vacuole
Fluid-filled store for excretion products.

Ribosome
The sites of protein synthesis.

THE CELL

What is nature's fundamental building block? DNA is the essential basis for all living things, but it is an information carrier, not a structure. For tangible physical systems in biology such as leaves and branches, bones and muscles, the underlying construction unit is the cell.

ALL CELLS HAVE CERTAIN CHARACTERISTICS in common. The first and most obvious is that they have a physical boundary, a membrane, that defines the division between themselves and the outside world, or other, adjacent cells. While holding a cell's internal components together, the bag-like membrane is also a chemically sophisticated gatekeeper, finely controlling what comes in or what goes out.

The biggest internal structure of a cell is the nucleus. It controls all the cell's activities and stores its genetic information in the form of DNA. Smaller specks of material, mitochondria, exploit glucose and oxygen to produce energy for the cell's functioning. The mitochondria and other 'organelles' (the miniature cell equivalent of specialized 'organs') drift within the cytoplasm, a jelly-like soup of enzymes that facilitate chemical reactions inside the cell.

All organisms are built from cells. The differences between animal and plant cells are attributable to just three 'extras' that only plant cells possess. The first is a tough external wall made from long, straight molecules of cellulose bundled into stringy fibres (micro-fibrils) that lend structural support. The second is the prominence, in plant cells, of an interior fluid-filled chamber, called the vacuole, whose internal pressure pushes against the sides of the cell to provide additional rigidity. The third and final distinction between animal and plant cells are chloroplasts, the grains that perform photosynthesis.

Molecules of water, oxygen and carbon dioxide can pass through tiny gaps in a cell membrane's molecules (phospholipids) without necessarily requiring any input of energy. Larger molecules, such as glucose, are helped through the membrane by carrier molecules that absorb the 'passengers', then change shape and orientation so that the collected molecular package can pass through the membrane. When a cell needs to push or 'pump' substances across its membrane from a region of low concentration to a region of higher concentration, it must provide energy for the transaction. This comes from a special molecule, adenosine triphosphate (ATP). Animals obtain their bulk energy by oxidizing foods, while plants obtain theirs by trapping sunlight using chlorophyll, but before any of this energy can be exploited, it must first be transformed into a molecular form that individual cells can handle easily. ATP is the rechargable energy provider for almost any process that happens in or around cells – and by extension, within organisms as a whole.

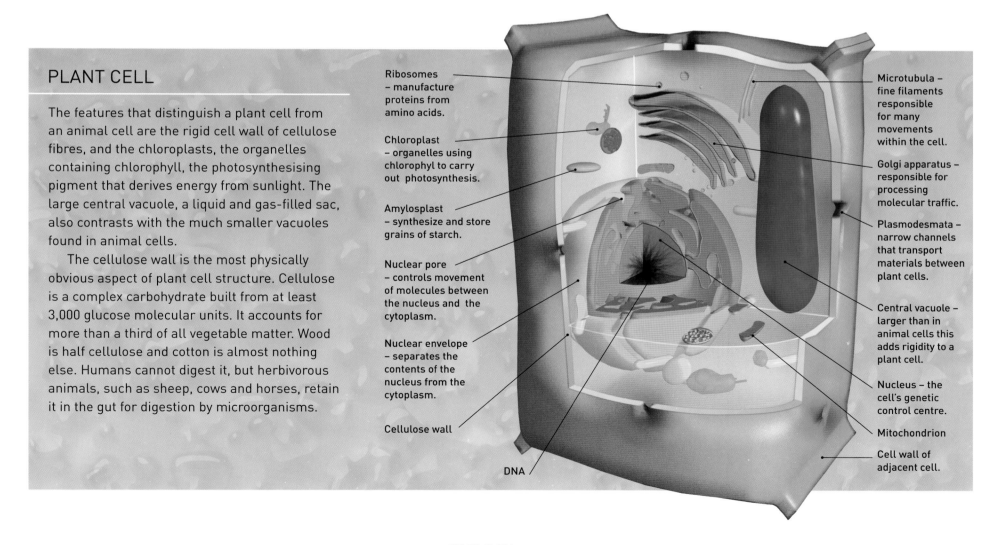

PLANT CELL

The features that distinguish a plant cell from an animal cell are the rigid cell wall of cellulose fibres, and the chloroplasts, the organelles containing chlorophyll, the photosynthesising pigment that derives energy from sunlight. The large central vacuole, a liquid and gas-filled sac, also contrasts with the much smaller vacuoles found in animal cells.

The cellulose wall is the most physically obvious aspect of plant cell structure. Cellulose is a complex carbohydrate built from at least 3,000 glucose molecular units. It accounts for more than a third of all vegetable matter. Wood is half cellulose and cotton is almost nothing else. Humans cannot digest it, but herbivorous animals, such as sheep, cows and horses, retain it in the gut for digestion by microorganisms.

Ribosomes – manufacture proteins from amino acids.

Chloroplast – organelles using chlorophyl to carry out photosynthesis.

Amylosplast – synthesize and store grains of starch.

Nuclear pore – controls movement of molecules between the nucleus and the cytoplasm.

Nuclear envelope – separates the contents of the nucleus from the cytoplasm.

Cellulose wall

DNA

Microtubula – fine filaments responsible for many movements within the cell.

Golgi apparatus – responsible for processing molecular traffic.

Plasmodesmata – narrow channels that transport materials between plant cells.

Central vacuole – larger than in animal cells this adds rigidity to a plant cell.

Nucleus – the cell's genetic control centre.

Mitochondrion

Cell wall of adjacent cell.

CELL DIVISION

The growth and repair of an organism's bodily tissues is based on single cells that divide to make 'daughter' cells. A precise choreography of events ensures that the DNA in the original nucleus is accurately copied and transferred into the new cell.

Interphase – the cell grows and its DNA is replicated.

Early prophase – the DNA is coiled inside chromosomes with two identical joined parts (chromatids).

Late prophase – the cell nucleus fragments, and microtubules attach to the chromatids.

Metaphase – chromatids align along the centre of the cell.

IN A PROCESS KNOWN AS MITOSIS, the DNA in a cell copies itself, then the cell divides once. First, all the chromosomes are replicated, and each is linked to its replica by a chemical bridge, called the centromere. This paired assembly is called a chromatid. All the centromeres then become aligned more or less across the middle of the cell. Then the centromeres split in unison, and the two identical sets of chromosomes derived from each of the chromatids are pulled by molecular 'conveyor belt' structures inside the cell, known as microtubules, to opposite ends of the cell. A nucleus forms around each set. When the membrane splits and makes a final, physical separation between the new daughter cells, each one contains its own nucleus with a full set of chromosomes.

Gametes

Mitosis grows and repairs almost all bodily tissues. A related process, known as meiosis, is specifically for sexual reproduction. It occurs only in specialized cells in the testes and ovaries. During meiosis, cells divide to produce 'gametes', male sperm or female eggs. The DNA replicates as in any cell division, but this time the chromosome pairs separate and are divided among two daughter cells. These cells split again, and the result is four daughter cells, gametes, that contain only half the original set of chromosomes. Deliberately discarding half the DNA destined for the next generation might seem quite literally counterproductive, but if all organisms were born with exactly the same DNA as their parents, the slightest adversity affecting one of them would doom all of them. Gene 'shuffling' is a better strategy. Sexual reproduction combines male and female gametes to make embryo cells with a complete but new set of DNA based on contributions from both parents, yet not exactly the same as either parent's DNA. This is how genetic diversity is assured.

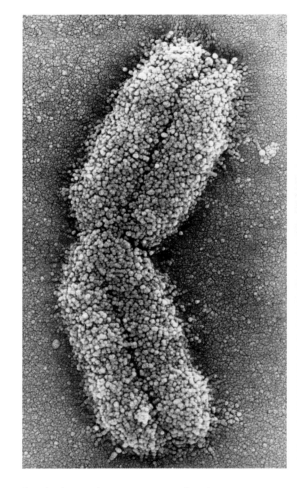

An electron microscope scan of a chromosome about to split from its duplicate at the narrow join at the centre called the centromere.

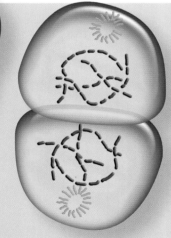

Anaphase – the chromatids are pulled apart to form new chromosomes.

MITOSIS

Most of our body's cells undergo mitosis several times throughout our lifetime. Some short-lived cells, such as those in tissues lining the body, can replicate many thousands of times, whereas other long-lived cells such as in brain tissue or nerves do not replicate at all once adulthood is reached.

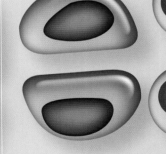

Telophase – the chromosomes group at each end of the cell, forming two new nuclei.

Cytokinesis – a duplicate daughter cell splits away from the parent cell.

The process repeats for successive cell generations.

Degradation of genetic information over successive generations affects mitosis. This is the cause of ageing.

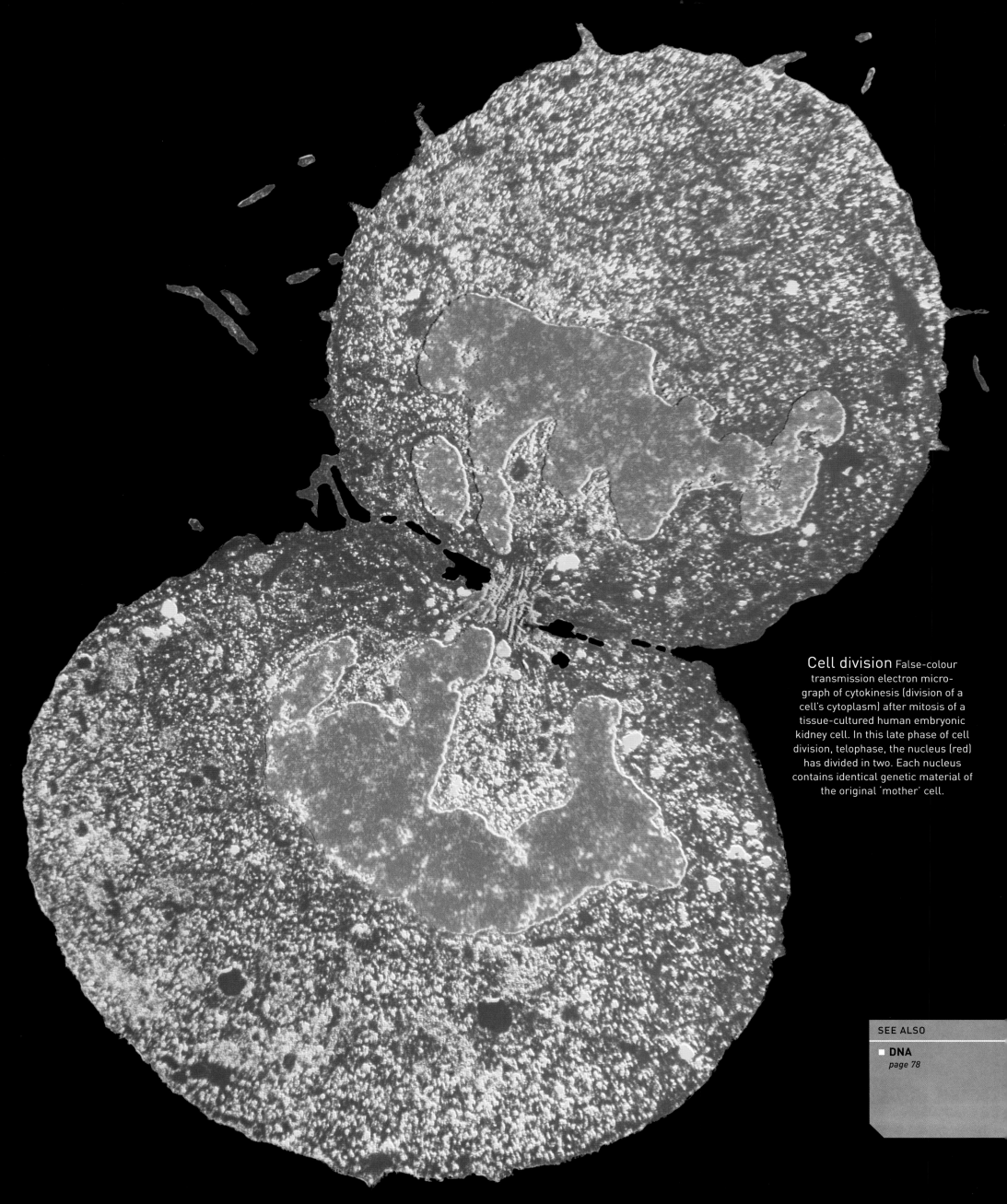

Cell division False-colour transmission electron micrograph of cytokinesis (division of a cell's cytoplasm) after mitosis of a tissue-cultured human embryonic kidney cell. In this late phase of cell division, telophase, the nucleus (red) has divided in two. Each nucleus contains identical genetic material of the original 'mother' cell.

SEE ALSO
■ **DNA**
page 78

GENETIC MODIFICATION

Just a few decades ago, we barely understood how DNA actually functions. We were still deciphering its basic molecular shape. Today we can manipulate it to create entirely new organisms.

THE GENETIC CODE for all living things uses the same code of nucleotides and bases, no matter what any particular organism happens to be. It is merely the sequences of the chemical 'words' that change from one animal or plant to another, not the 'language' itself. A gene that codes (for instance) for a certain protein to be made in one organism will code for the same protein in another.

Scientists are now discovering how to 'rewrite' sequences of DNA in order to produce new variations of existing species, or to make transgenic organisms that are neither quite one species nor another. Transgenic organisms carry in all their cells at least one gene from a completely different organism that has been artificially inserted in the laboratory. The process of transferring genes between species is called genetic modification, and the products of this new branch of research are called genetically modified organisms (GMOs).

Why would anyone want to rearrange the natural order of existence in such a way? The simple answer is that as we gain ever more understanding of biological processes, we wish to harness them as a technology for our own ends, just as we make use of any other resource. One typical example is the transfer of factor IX, a blood clotting agent, from healthy humans into sheep. It is then produced in the sheep's milk, and thereby becomes easily available for making a medicine to treat haemophiliacs, human patients so lacking in

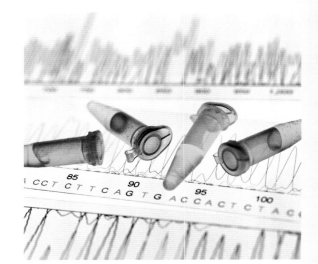

that particular factor that they are in constant danger of bleeding to death from the slightest injury, and most especially, internal bruising.

Insulin, another important life-saving substance, is produced by exploiting host cells such as baker's yeast or a non-harmful strain of *Escherichia coli* bacteria. First the native DNA is removed from the host cell, and then the human gene that codes for the production of insulin is inserted. Now the cell has a gene telling it to produce insulin. The cell is then allowed to reproduce, and the quantities of insulin increase as the cells multiply. Special detergents and other chemicals are then used to open the bacterial cells and extract the insulin materials. Few people would complain that such simple entities as bacteria 'suffer' as a result. GMOs of this kind seem straightforwardly beneficial.

A more contentious application is the use of a gene, derived from bacteria, that exhibits resistance to herbicides. When that gene is inserted into crop plants, fields can be sprayed with herbicides to kill off weeds without affecting the modified crops. Here is where the possibilities of science intersect directly with the desires of society. Some proponents of GMOs in the human food chain argue that poor communities around the world must surely benefit from (for instance) pest- and disease-resistant food crops, while others say that introducing modified plants into the natural environment without fully understanding the long-term effects is reckless.

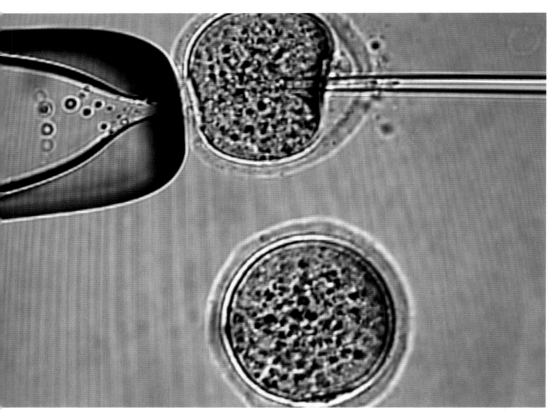

Stem cell research

◄ Seen through a microscope, a mouse egg (upper centre) is held in place by a glass pipette (upper left) during insertion of genetic material for cloning. The egg's own DNA has been removed and now an adult nucleus from a different cell is being injected in its place with a very fine needle (upper right). The resulting embryo will consist of embryonic stem cells, the cell precursors from which all the body's specialized cells develop. Stem cells made from the cell nuclei of human patients could be used for therapeutic cloning, the creation of personalized tissues to replace diseased or damaged body parts.

Human genome research

▶ Hand holding one of the 60 trays which contain the entire human genome as 23,040 different fragments of cloned DNA. DNA (deoxyribonucleic acid) is the substance which controls every characteristic of an organism. It is made up of two chains linked by bases. Specific sequences of bases are called genes, each of which performs a specific task within the living organism. The human genome project aims to find the base sequence of all the genes in human DNA, allowing for improved drug design and a greater understanding of genetic diseases.

CLONING

Dolly the sheep was a clone created by a team at the Roslin Institute in Scotland. She became a worldwide sensation when her birth was announced in 1997. Genetically, she was the product of an adult cell extracted from a six-year-old ewe. Dolly was an exact duplicate of that ewe. However, since the DNA in the first ewe was already six years old, it had naturally already accumulated the flaws and copying errors that are a normal part of the ageing process. Dolly developed arthritis quite young, and died sooner than expected in 2003.

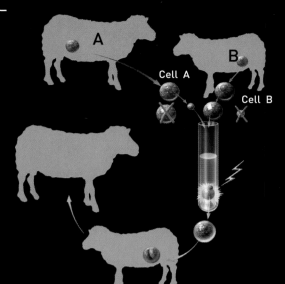

How to clone a sheep

Just a single adult cell was taken from ewe A and the nucleus containing the genetic code (DNA) was preserved. An ovule (egg cell) was taken from ewe B and the cell structure, apart from its nucleus, was preserved. In a test tube, using an electrical discharge, the nucleus from the A cell was fused with the cytoplasm from the B cell, which then divided. When it was a few days old, the resulting embryo was implanted into the uterus of a surrogate mother. After a few months, a baby ewe (Dolly) was born, identical to ewe A who supplied her with her genetic code.

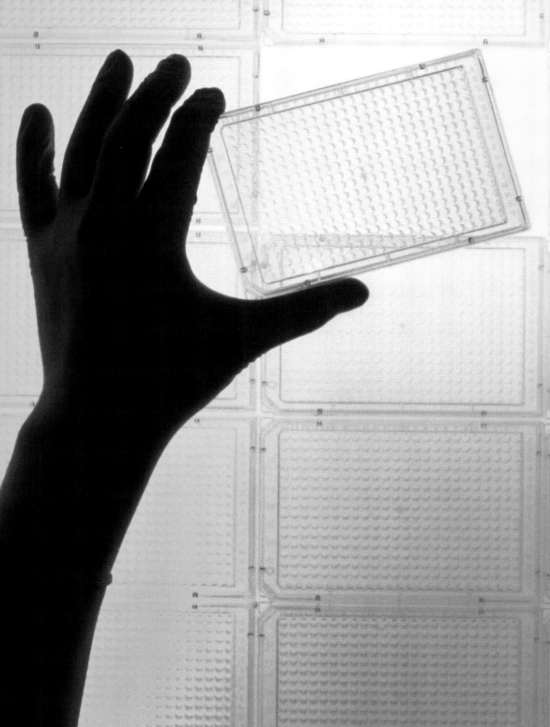

Cloning is the process of reproducing parent organisms exactly. Every specific of that particular organism is preserved and replicated. Human cloning is unlikely to be authorized. However, the mass production of particular cell types may allow damaged organs to be replaced in human patients, especially if the new organs are based on that patient's own cells. Current research relies largely on embryos.

All animal embryos start out as tiny bundles of cells, many of which have not yet differentiated into the cells for different organs, such as the heart and liver, or for structures like sinew and bone. These 'stem cells' have the potential to be 'programmed' to grow as new tissues for transplanting into desperately needy patients. Many lives could be saved. On the other hand, we are uneasy about exploiting the as-yet unborn, even at the earliest microscopic stages of cellular development, to benefit those already living.

ARTIFICIAL LIFE?

During the early summer of 2010 researchers announced that they had inserted artificially arranged sequences of DNA into a host mycoplasma mycoides bacterium. As the bug began to divide and replicate, the coding in the transplanted genetic material took over, and the replication cycle gave rise to a new organism whose genome has never before existed in nature. This was not quite a purely man-made life form, because the cell membrane and cytoplasm were all derived from existing natural biological systems, but there is no doubting our ability to shape the characteristics of microorganisms at will. In the future, synthetic organisms may help solve a wide variety of challenges, ranging from biofuels and pollution control to the replacement of damaged human tissues. Unexpected consequences need to be tracked. The team inserted 'watermark' coding into the artificial DNA so that the descendants of this new organism can always be identified.

THE HUMAN GENOME PROJECT

As the result of a major global effort, our quest to understand human DNA has achieved its first great milestone: a complete printout of all the chemical data that defines it.

THE HUMAN GENOME PROJECT (HGP) was formally initiated in 1990 with support from the US Department of Energy and the National Institutes of Health, and was soon joined by scientists from around the world. The project was expected to take up to two decades to complete, but technological advances in DNA sequencing allowed the first 'draft' description of the genome to be published in 2003, with a more refined version announced three years later. The aim was to identify the full sequence of all the bases in the genome, and then map the genes that they encode. A genome is the entire set of DNA contained in all the chromosomes of an organism. Every living thing has its own unique version. The smallest known example, in a particular bacterium, contains about 600,000

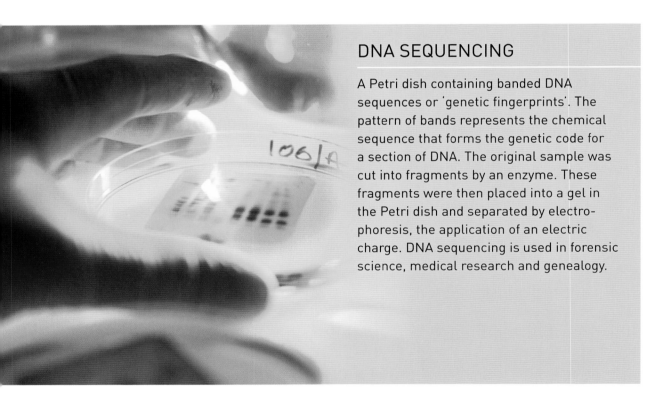

DNA SEQUENCING

A Petri dish containing banded DNA sequences or 'genetic fingerprints'. The pattern of bands represents the chemical sequence that forms the genetic code for a section of DNA. The original sample was cut into fragments by an enzyme. These fragments were then placed into a gel in the Petri dish and separated by electrophoresis, the application of an electric charge. DNA sequencing is used in forensic science, medical research and genealogy.

DNA base pairs, while mammalian genomes, including those of human beings, comprise some 3 billion base pairs. Strictly speaking, a human genome should relate to just one person in particular. In fact the HGP worked from DNA samples derived from several anonymous volunteers. The resulting data applies approximately to all of us because we all share the same basic set of genes.

When talk turns to DNA we hear a great deal about genes, yet they comprise only about two per cent of the human genome; the remainder consists of relatively vast non-coding regions of DNA, whose functions perhaps have to do with organizing its wider functioning. So-called 'junk DNA' may just be the remnants of our ancient evolutionary past: essential in the distant past but today of limited or even no immediate consequence. We cannot yet be sure. The HGP was just the first stage in answering such questions.

Already some of the answers yielded have been surprising – for instance, the fact that the human genome apparently contains as few as 25,000 functioning genes instead of the 100,000 or more that scientists had expected.

Analysing the genome

There are many different techniques for DNA sequencing, some of which were developed as a direct result of the scientific momentum generated by the HGP. A common first step is to insert strands of the relevant DNA into a 'plasmid', a loop of non-essential DNA in a suitable bacterium such as *Escherichia coli*. A complex process exploits the bacterium as a replicating machine to generate billions of copies of each strand. Given the fact that an individual nucleotide (the base and the fragment of DNA backbone to which it attaches) may consist of no more than 30–40 atoms, massive replication of the sheared DNA fragments is necessary in order to obtain samples large enough to analyse. Then the samples are divided into batches. By now the DNA double helixes have been split into single strands that are eager to rebond with their opposing strands. Each is treated with solutions of one of four artificially adapted nucleotides that rebuild the double helix up to a particular 'chain terminating' base, A, C, T or G. The result is that, after a further replication process, one finished batch of DNA will contain only fragments that end in T, another only pieces that end in A, and so on. Different fluorescent dyes are then added to each batch, so that the terminating bases, A, T, G or C, can be identified by colour coding.

Another step is electrophoresis, the sifting of DNA fragments according to molecular size, using an electric field. An inherent negative charge on all the nucleotides causes them to migrate in the same direction towards a positively charged terminal. The larger fragments tend to move more sluggishly than the smaller ones. A buffer material, typically a jelly-like transparent gel, slows down the process and prevents all the fragments from simply accumulating at the positive terminal. Instead they stretch through the gel like rubber bands. When fluorescent dyes are introduced, laser illumination reveals characteristic banded patterns in the gel. These are compared against existing libraries of patterns derived from base sequences that are already known.

Electrophoresis is founded on determining the different molecular sizes of DNA fragments. From this, with clever analysis, a great deal can be discovered, but an additional technique perfected by the US biologist and HGP entrepreneur Craig Venter is the

Circular genome map

A map showing shared genetic material between humans (outer ring) and (from inner ring outwards) chimpanzees, mice, rats, dogs, chickens and zebrafish. Each ring is based on the colour-coded representation of one chromosome. Similar colour patterns within each ring reveal 'hot spots' of shared genetic material. The more fragmented patterns indicate greater evolutionary divergence from humans.

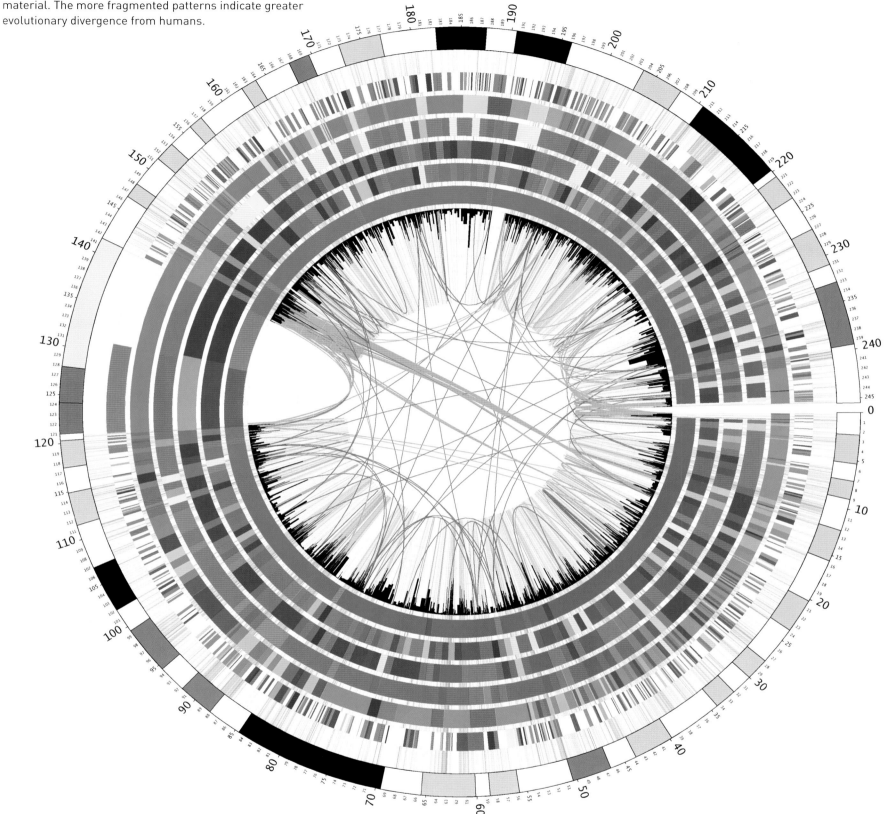

so-called 'shotgun' approach. Powerful jets of water surging through fine tubes and mechanical filters are used to shear DNA into very small fragments: so small, in fact, that Venter's critics wondered, at first, if they could possibly be worth studying. But shotgun sequencing does not concern itself with the overall details of any particular fragment. Instead, computers search for precisely matching sequence overlaps, just a few bases long, between one fragment and the next. The rest of the data are ignored. Any given 'read' delivers so little information, it seems barely worth the effort. However, the ever-expanding jigsaw of minuscule comparisons builds up to reveal

the sequences of bases in the DNA, and gradually all the sequences in the entire genome.

In the future, the HGP may lead to the development of cancer treatments and other drug regimes tailored specifically for our individual genomes. We might one day be able to eliminate inheritable diseases such as cystic fibrosis or sickle cell anaemia. There will be many arguments, moral, ethical and legal, about the implications of manipulating the genome as opposed to merely studying it.

SEE ALSO

DNA
page 78

BACTERIA AND VIRUSES

What is the smallest organism that can exist and still be called 'alive'? Where lies the boundary between living and non-living bundles of chemistry? These are not easy questions to settle.

BACTERIA ARE RECOGNIZABLY BIOLOGICAL CELLS that have walls and internal structures. They feed, excrete and reproduce. Under a microscope, or swarming on the surface of nutrients in a laboratory dish, they are tangibly 'there' as living entities. Viruses, on the other hand, are little more than strands of DNA molecules (or closely related RNA) covered by a protein coating. They are a thousand times smaller than bacteria. While bacteria can reproduce independently, viruses can only do so by hijacking cells. The protein shell protecting a virus's DNA is covered with spiked protrusions that identify suitable host cells to invade. Then the virus's DNA takes control and forces the cell to use up all of its resources to manufacture more viruses. The weakened cell eventually bursts like a balloon and is destroyed. The freshly manufactured viruses then attach themselves to new, unaffected host cells, and the cycle of infection continues.

Are viruses alive? Living things usually do more than just reproduce. Above all, they eat to gain energy. Bacteria have evolved an incredible variety of lifestyles, from ingesting each other or

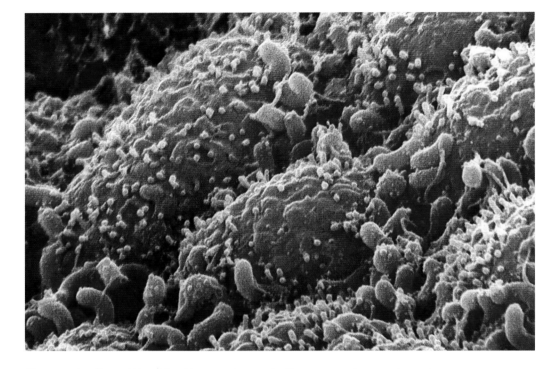

Bacteria (healthy) in the gut
▲ Coloured scanning electron micrograph (SEM) of bacteria (red) on the surface of the duodenum, the first part of the small intestine that receives food from the stomach. A healthy human intestine has a large population of bacteria, most of which are harmless and some of which aid digestion. The white, hair-like structures on the duodenum tissues are microvilli, which absorb nutrients from food.

Influenza virus structure
▶ The core of the virus is its genetic material, here shown as ribbons of single-stranded RNA (ribonucleic acid). Surrounding these is a protein coat, the capsid. The exterior spherical structure is a membrane consisting of fatty lipid molecules. The stud-like structures on the surface are proteins that help the virus identify and then attach to the cell that it will exploit to generate more copies of itself.

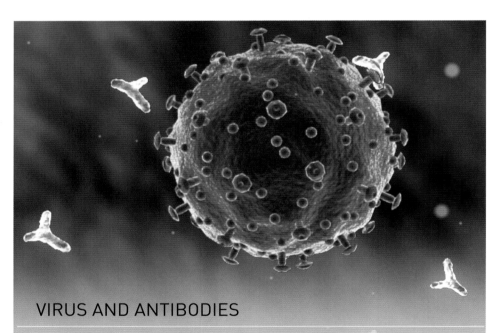

VIRUS AND ANTIBODIES

This computer simulation shows a virus particle (purple) surrounded by antibodies, protein assemblies that enable the immune system to identify and neutralise invasive objects (pathogens) such as bacteria or viruses. They can either neutralise pathogens directly by binding to an active region or 'tag' them for subsequent destruction by white blood cells. Viruses have killed many millions of people over the course of history. The list of threats is staggering. It includes chickenpox, conjunctivitis, Creutzfeldt–Jakob disease (CJD), encephalitis, glandular fever, hepatitis, herpes, influenza, kuru, lassa fever, measles, mumps, polio, rabies, rubella (German measles), shingles, smallpox, warts and yellow fever. Some viral infections can be limited with immunization. Others, such as AIDS and the common cold, are elusive because the viruses mutate so swiftly.

invading larger organisms (sometimes beneficially), to processing minerals and gases in the Earth's crust. They are undoubtedly alive. Viruses, on the other hand, have no internal metabolism and no need for food. They are just chemical replicating machines. Viruses may or may not be alive, but they are very much a part of all other life on Earth, and of the human experience, from chickenpox and measles to mumps and polio. They infect animals, plants and even bacteria. We are in a constant war with the Ebola virus, the West Nile virus, AIDS and influenza, the 'common cold' in its deadliest form. A particularly lethal type of influenza virus killed more than 21 million people around the world in 1918, in the space of just a few months. We are learning to harness the invasive skills of viruses for inserting beneficial genetic material into human cells to cure diseases and inherited ailments. Genetically engineered viruses may one day save as many lives as they destroy. But we still have no clear answer as to whether or not they are alive.

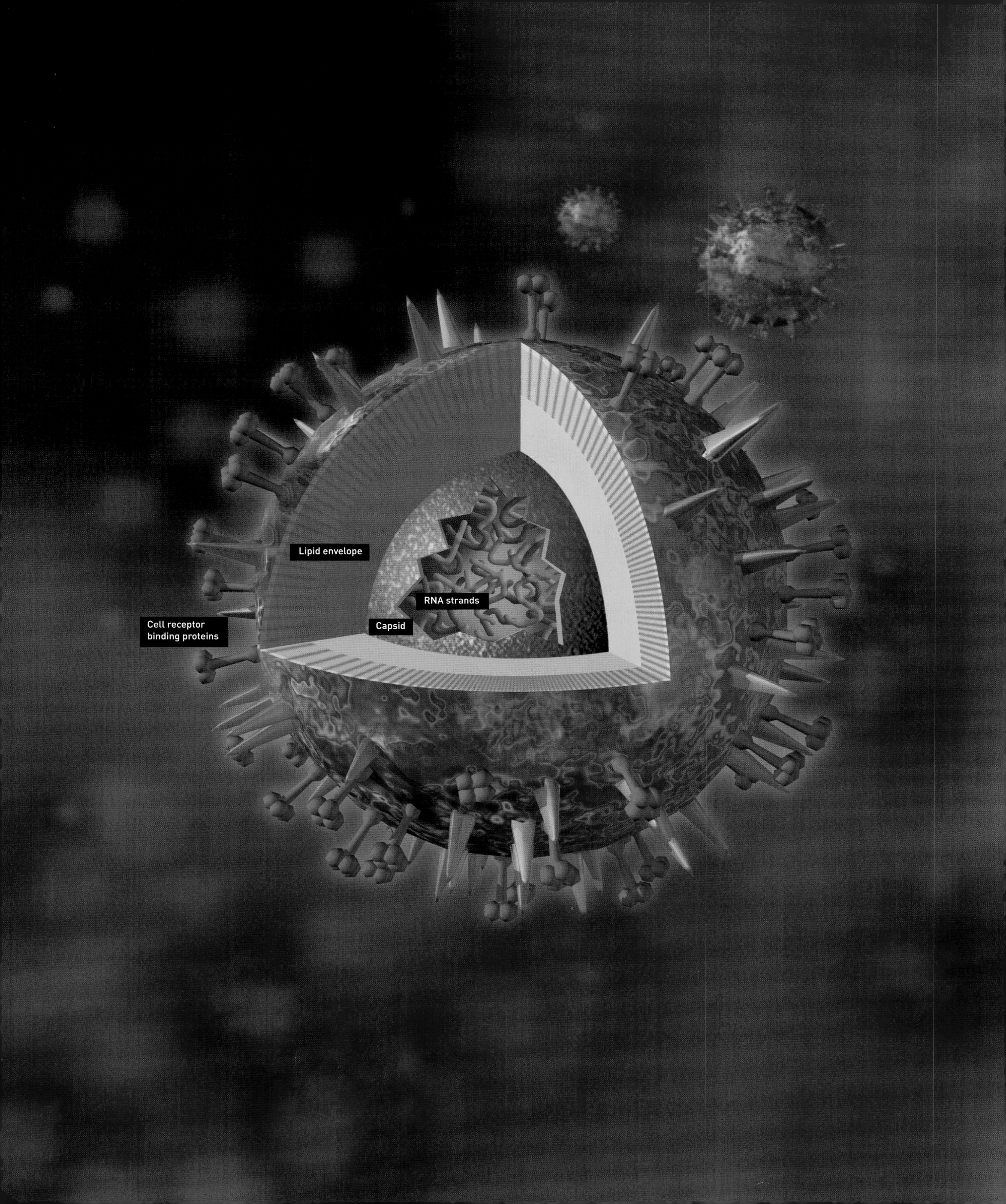

Cell receptor
binding proteins

Lipid envelope

RNA strands

Capsid

LIFE ON EARTH

The longest time division geologists use is an eon. These are divided into shorter times called eras, and these in turn are split into even shorter times: periods, epochs and ages.

Precambrian era
4.6 billion–550 million years ago

This is the immense gulf of time encompassing the formation of the Earth and the emergence of the first primitive single-celled life forms, and drawing to a close with the first multicellular plants and animals.

ARCHAEAN ('ANCIENT') PERIOD
■ 3,800–2,500 million years ago

In an atmosphere of methane, ammonia and other gases that would poison most life on the planet today, the first forms of life emerged and thrived. These simple organisms, mainly photosynthetic blue-green algae, had the Earth to themselves for a billion years and more.

4 billion years ago

3 billion years ago

Blue-green algae in the Precambrian era were prokaryotic cyanobacteria lacking a distinct nucleus and using chlorophyll to harness energy from sunlight.

EARLIEST FOSSILS

Light shining through a wafer-thin slice of flint rock from Ontario, Canada, shows the distinct microscopic fossil traces of early life forms, dating from at least two billion years ago. The filaments and spherical shapes resemble modern algae. Rocks in Iceland dating from more than three billion years ago reveal faint chemical traces of even simpler organisms.

HADEAN ('HELLISH') PERIOD
■ 4,600–3,800 million years ago

An object about the size of Mars collided with the Earth around 4.6 billion years ago, soon after they both formed. The impact was side-on, rather than a direct hit. Material from the outer layers of both bodies was thrown into orbit around the Earth, forming a ring. This then coalesced to form the Moon.

Cells with a nucleus

Stromatolite structures found at Shark Bay, Western Australia. Ancient secretions of calcium carbonate reveal the traces of numerous cyanobacteria (blue-green algae) which once existed in dense mats. Stromatolites are among the oldest organic remains yet discovered. Some specimens are three billion years old. In coastal waters such as Shark Bay, stromatolite formation still continues.

1 billion years ago

2 billion years ago

PROTEROZOIC ('EARLY LIFE') ERA

■ 2,500–544 million years ago

Biological diversity increased, based on eukaryotic cells with membranes containing specialized structures known as organelles, controlled by a central nucleus. Sexual reproduction increased genetic diversity and enhanced the ability to adapt to environmental changes. The first worm-like multicellular creatures emerged somewhere around 700 million years ago. By this time the Earth's atmosphere had become oxygen-rich.

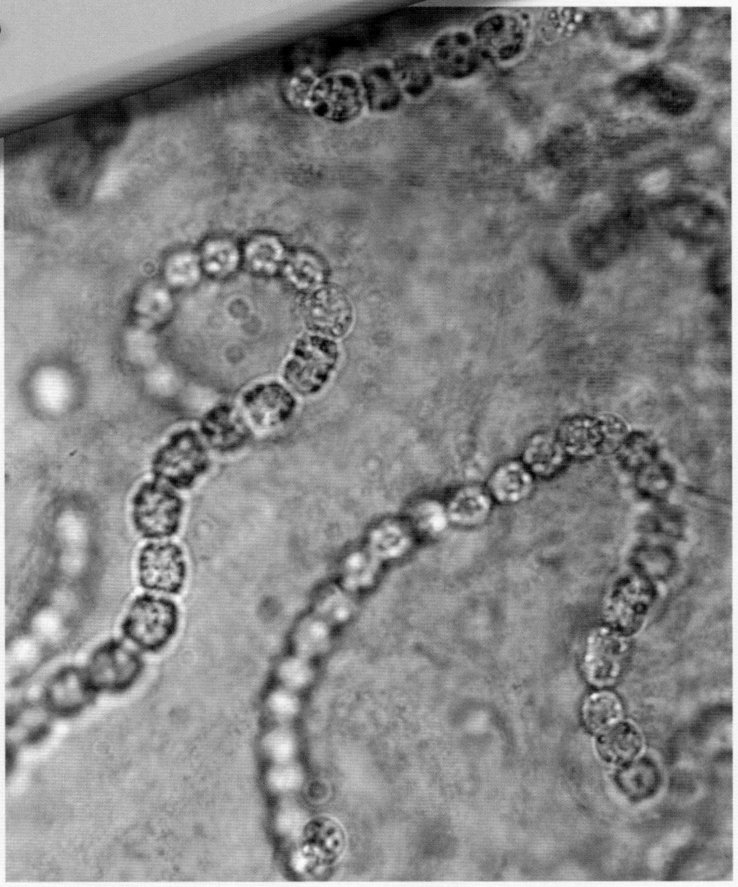

First multicellular organisms These are filaments of cyano-bacteria, made up of individual cells that clump together, but without becoming anything more than what they are: single-celled entities. Ancient species oxygenated the Earth's atmosphere.

First true animals

The first multicellular animals were soft-bodied bottom-dwelling marine creatures such as Dickinsonia (centre left), Tribrachidium (disc-shaped, yellow, centre right) and Spriggina (orange, lower centre), which lived between 635 and 540 million years ago.

SEE ALSO

■ **The Early Earth**
page 17

■ **The Early Environment**
page 18

Palaeozoic era
550–245 million years ago

This was a dramatic phase in the development of life. It encompassed the evolution of hard-shelled multicellular sea creatures, the invasion of land by plants and animals, and the emergence of fish, amphibians and early reptiles.

CAMBRIAN EXPLOSION
■ 544–505 million years ago

Cambrian sediments were first identified in Wales in the 19th century, but are now found widely around the world. Their fossil records show a dramatic increase in the variety and complexity of life forms, including sponges, corals and sea creatures with mineral skeletons. Trilobites dominated shallow water habitats. Increased competition for survival between predator and prey organisms speeded up evolutionary processes.

Jawless fish Birkenia elegans is one of the oldest known fish fossils. It dates from approximately 400 million years ago and represents an evolutionary stage before vertebrates had acquired jaws. This rare specimen was found in Scotland.

ORDOVICIAN PERIOD
■ 505–440 million years ago

Sedimentary rocks in the homelands of an ancient Welsh tribe explain the naming of this period, where ostracoderms, the first creatures with segmented backbones, evolved. They were jawless fish with external armour made from hardened minerals. The first fish with jaws and teeth, the acanthodians, appeared about 410 million years ago. Early, leafless land plants, called psilophytes, developed internal structures for transporting water from the ground into the plants.

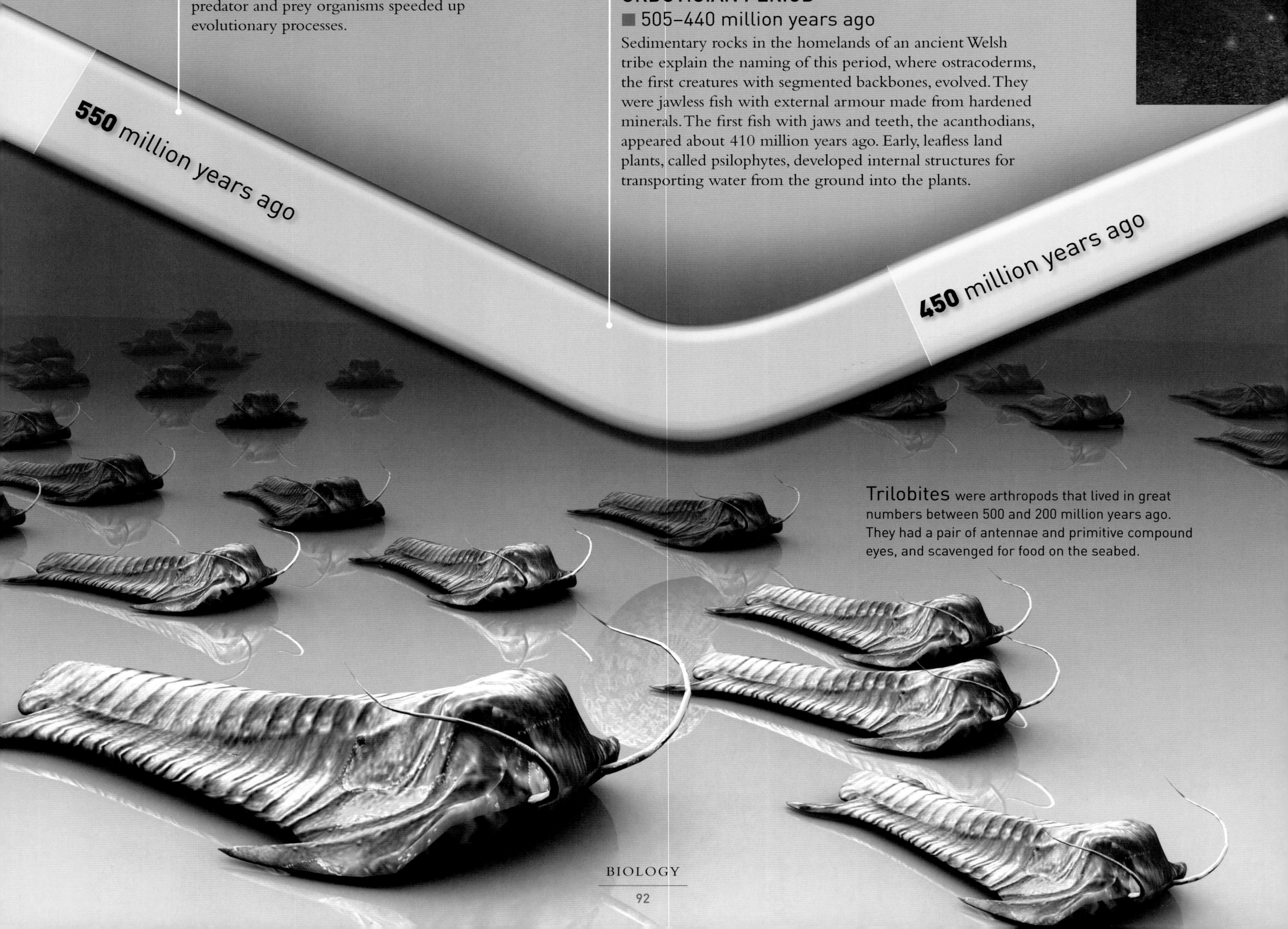

550 million years ago

450 million years ago

Trilobites were arthropods that lived in great numbers between 500 and 200 million years ago. They had a pair of antennae and primitive compound eyes, and scavenged for food on the seabed.

Tiktaalik lived in shallow waters during the Late Devonian period, 375 million years ago. A fossil specimen was found in the Canadian Arctic in 2004. Analysis of its skull showed it to be a transitional species between fish and tetrapods (four-limbed vertebrates). It had shoulders, lungs and ribs.

Fish in the Devonian period (from 408 to 360 million years ago) were acanthodians, the earliest known jawed fish. Their skeletons were made out of cartilage rather than bone, much like modern-day sharks and rays.

CARBONIFEROUS PERIOD
360–286 million years ago
The first reptiles, such as the small, lizard-like Hylonomus and Paleothyris, emerged from waterside habitats and onto dry land, aided by their ability to lay eggs protected by tough outer shells. Huge ferns, mosses and conifer trees were the dominant forms of plant life. The lush swampy forests of this period would eventually become compressed into layers of fossil fuel.

PERMIAN PERIOD
286–248 million years ago
Mammal-like reptiles, therapsids, first appeared about 285 million years ago, well before the first dinosaurs. Many different groups evolved. Unfortunately, at the end of this period, a change in the environment, possibly caused by toxic gases from massive volcanic activity, led to the first mass extinction, during which two-thirds of all species of life, both on land and in the sea, were wiped out.

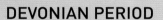

350 million years ago

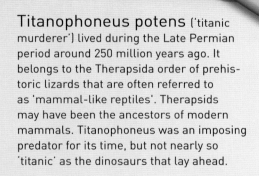

DEVONIAN PERIOD
410–360 million years ago
Named after Devonshire in England, where rocks from this period were first studied. Arthropods such as centipedes, scorpions and spiders colonized dry land, along with the first, wingless insects, and early four–footed vertebrates (tetrapods).

Titanophoneus potens ('titanic murderer') lived during the Late Permian period around 250 million years ago. It belongs to the Therapsida order of prehistoric lizards that are often referred to as 'mammal-like reptiles'. Therapsids may have been the ancestors of modern mammals. Titanophoneus was an imposing predator for its time, but not nearly so 'titanic' as the dinosaurs that lay ahead.

Carboniferous insects A dragonfly (Meganeura) in the forests of the Carboniferous period (354–290 million years ago). At this time, the land was dominated by insects and other invertebrates, some of which evolved to sizes much larger than found today. The millipede shown here was six feet (two metres) long, and the dragonfly had a wingspan as wide as a chair. Ferns and swamp plants dominated the land, eventually forming large beds of coal underground. The thick trunks are lepidodendrons, tree-like plants.

Mesozoic era
245–65 million years ago

During this era, divided into three periods, Triassic, Jurassic and Cretaceous, the dinosaurs consolidated their grip and prospered for 140 million years, until their dominion came to an end with violent abruptness.

Side view of a cayman's jaw (family Alligatoridae)

CROCODILIANS

Crocodiles and alligators are reptiles, and members of the Crocodilia order. The basic body structure has persisted more or less unchanged from its origins some 220 million years ago during the Triassic period, when the Crocodilia branched away from the archosaurs, the group from which dinosaurs also eventually emerged: but the crocodilians predated the dinosaurs by around 20 million years, and they survived after the dinosaurs' time came to an end.

250 million years ago

TRIASSIC PERIOD
■ 248–213 million years ago

Dinosaurs, 'terrible reptiles', became one of the most successful groups of animals that have ever lived. They evolved into many sizes and shapes, with equally various ways of life. In fact, dinosaurs were not simply large reptiles, but creatures with distinct bone structures and, in many cases, upright postures where the bulk of the body was supported just on the back legs. Many scientists now believe that dinosaurs were warm-blooded: capable of generating body heat internally. Reptiles are dependent on warmth from the Sun.

Dinosaurs

Dinosaurs were the dominant land animals for over 140 million years. More than 800 species have been identified from fossil remains. They ranged from agile predators smaller than chickens to placid 30-ton behemoths that lived on plants.

Dinosaurs were the land-dwelling descendants of archosaurs, egg-laying reptiles. They were distinct from other prehistoric creatures by virtue of certain anatomical details, of which the most obvious related to posture. Dinosaurs walked either bipedally on their hind legs, much like modern birds, or quadrupedally, on four feet. The sprawling and complicated dinosaur family is divided into two main groups, defined by the structure of their hip bones: the Saurischia, or 'lizard-hipped' dinosaurs, and the 'bird-hipped' Ornithischia. Annoyingly, some of the discoveries made by modern scientists have tended to muddle the classifications defined by earlier researchers. Contrary to what we might reasonably expect, all the bird species studied by today's ornithologists are descended from the bipedal Saurischia branch of the dinosaur family, while the Ornithischia dinosaurs walked mainly on all fours.

Saurischia contained two main groups: the therapods, carnivorous beasts with large hind legs and short, stunted forelegs – of which the ferocious tyrannosaurus and swift, clever velociraptors are probably the most familiar examples – and sauropods, long-necked, long-tailed and often absolutely enormous plant-eating dinosaurs like diplodocus, brachiosaurus and apatosaurus (the placid colossus previously known as brontosaurus because of analytic errors made in the 1870s). We can hardly be surprised at the difficulties faced by researchers working from fragile and often incomplete fossil remains. Ornithischia were mainly quadruped plant-eaters, and some were armour-plated beasts like the small-brained but heavily armoured stegosaurus and defensively horned triceratops. Ornithopods, a suborder of the Ornithischia group that thrived during the Cretaceous period, were bipedal herbivores with stiff tails for balance, like the iguanadon and edmontosaurus. Many had beak-like mouths. Hadrosaurs, or 'duck-billed' dinosaurs, were also common during the Cretaceous period. The two main dinosaur groups, Saurischia and Ornithischia, are part of a larger and diverse classification, Archosaurus, encompassing all dinosaur species, such as winged pterosaurs, and dinosaurs that took to the water. At least one subgroup continues to thrive today: Crocodilia.

Compsognathus, a bipedal dinosaur the size of a chicken, lived during the late Jurassic period, between 155 and 145 million years ago.

Archaeopteryx had many bird-like features, including feathers, but it had no breastbone 'keel' for its wing muscles and lacked the air pockets in the bones to make its skeleton lightweight. If archaeopteryx really was capable of flight, it would probably have been limited to short glides. The feathers may have been used more for warmth and display than flight.

JURASSIC PERIOD
■ 213–145 million years ago

Dinosaurs were the chief land animals; crocodiles, ichthyosaurs and plesiosaurs were the major sea predators; while the air was inhabited by pterosaurs, flying relatives of dinosaurs with large, skin-clad wings. Approximately 150 million years ago, a smaller, toothed flying creature roughly the size of a magpie exploited feathers as lightweight wing surfaces. Probably a descendant of a small dinosaur species that used feather-like cladding for warmth, archaeopteryx was the first creature we would recognize as a bird.

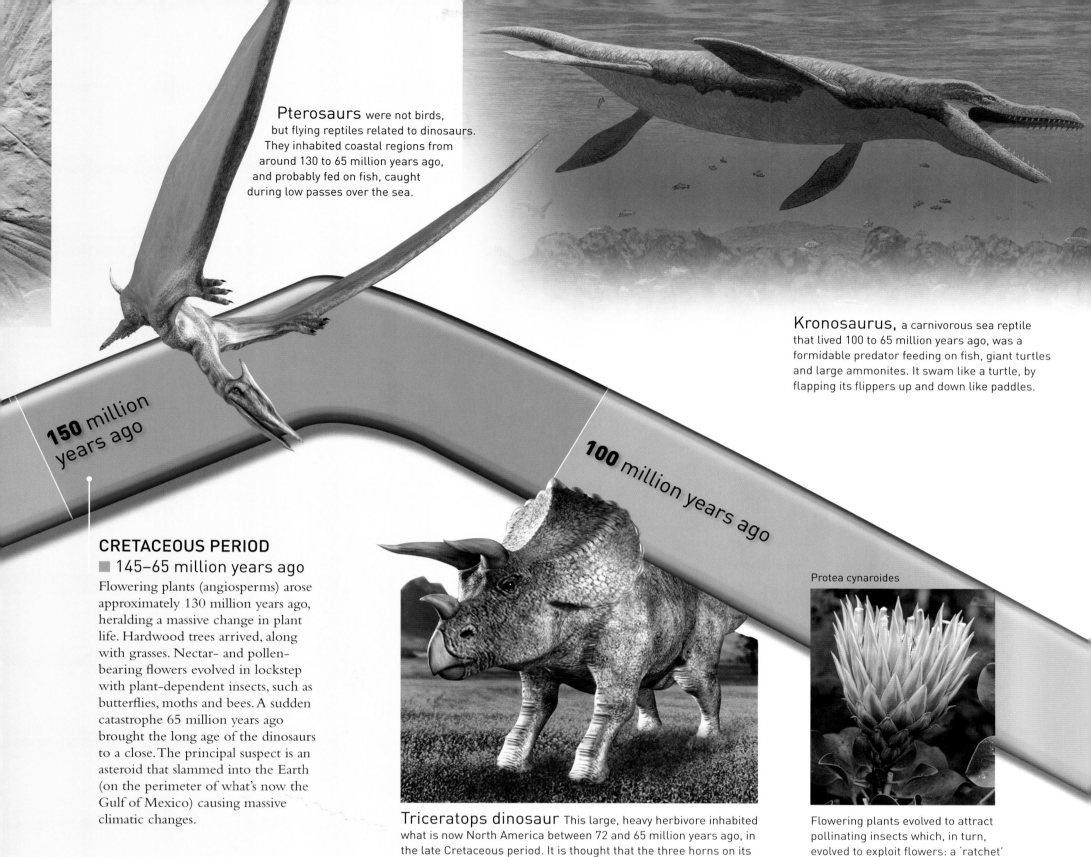

Pterosaurs were not birds, but flying reptiles related to dinosaurs. They inhabited coastal regions from around 130 to 65 million years ago, and probably fed on fish, caught during low passes over the sea.

Kronosaurus, a carnivorous sea reptile that lived 100 to 65 million years ago, was a formidable predator feeding on fish, giant turtles and large ammonites. It swam like a turtle, by flapping its flippers up and down like paddles.

150 million years ago

100 million years ago

CRETACEOUS PERIOD
▪ 145–65 million years ago

Flowering plants (angiosperms) arose approximately 130 million years ago, heralding a massive change in plant life. Hardwood trees arrived, along with grasses. Nectar- and pollen-bearing flowers evolved in lockstep with plant-dependent insects, such as butterflies, moths and bees. A sudden catastrophe 65 million years ago brought the long age of the dinosaurs to a close. The principal suspect is an asteroid that slammed into the Earth (on the perimeter of what's now the Gulf of Mexico) causing massive climatic changes.

Triceratops dinosaur This large, heavy herbivore inhabited what is now North America between 72 and 65 million years ago, in the late Cretaceous period. It is thought that the three horns on its head were a defence against predators. They may also have been used in fights between rival males or in mating displays.

Protea cynaroides

Flowering plants evolved to attract pollinating insects which, in turn, evolved to exploit flowers: a 'ratchet' process of evolutionary feedback.

PRESERVED IN ROCK

If an organism dies, and its body happens to be trapped in wet muddy sediment that stifles the oxygen supply and prevents rotting, some of its tissues may be preserved long enough to absorb minerals from the water in the surrounding sediments, and very gradually turn into three-dimensional mineral 'shadows' of the original tissues. These are called 'fossils'.

Water or mud are essential protective ingredients in the fossilization process, or else the fish's remains simply get consumed by other organisms.

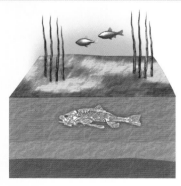

Sediments accumulate around the remains, blocking the air required for further bacterial decay. Minerals seep in, slowly transforming the tissues.

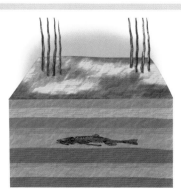

Additional layers of sediment accumulate, compacting the layers underneath into hard sedimentary rock, within which the fossil traces are preserved.

Geological changes push the fossil-bearing sedimentary rocks towards the surface, from where they can be recovered.

Cenozoic era

65 million years ago–present day

With the dinosaurs all but gone, the Cenozoic is sometimes known as the 'Age of Mammals', because the largest land animals during this era were indeed mammals – but flowering plants, insects, fish and birds also thrived.

The end of the dinosaurs

Circular concentrations of rock density in the Gulf of Mexico and a thin layer of soil found commonly around the world yield clues about one of the the most destructive disasters the Earth has ever faced.

Approximately 65.5 million years ago, a rogue asteroid 6 miles (10 km) across struck the Earth, in all likelihood bringing to an end the age of dinosaurs. The impact caused a huge explosion, gauging out a crater more than 100 miles (180 km) across. The shock waves alone, in both the atmosphere and the oceans, must have caused catastrophic damage across vast swathes of the Earth's surface. Dust hurled high into the atmosphere obscured the Sun for many months and possibly even years, before dissipating. Light and heat became scarce for a longer time than even the hardiest plants and animals could survive. The effect on food chains was appalling, and most especially for dinosaurs, the comparatively large and hungry creatures at the top of the chain.

Traces of the impact are hard to see because too much has happened to the Earth's surface across that huge area in the last 65 million years. The crater walls have long since been obscured by erosion. But the deepest layers of crust were compacted by the original impact as though by a hammer. Variations in rock density affect the local gravity field to this day. A colossal asteroid impact best explains the circular variations overlapping the Yucatan Peninsula and the Gulf of Mexico, a formation now known as the Chicxulub crater. Other evidence for a massive smash comes from the K–T Boundary, a thin, ashy layer of sediment found almost every-where around the world and dating from 65.5 million years ago. It contains iridium, often found in asteroids, but rarely available on Earth. Furthermore, quartz crystals in the K–T layer have been deformed by sudden high pressures and temperatures, as might be expected in a colossal impact event. The asteroid may also have triggered other global environmental upsets, such as volcanism that altered the mix of gases in the atmosphere. Whatever the exact circum-stances, there are thousands of different dinosaur fossils buried below the K–T boundary, while almost none have been discovered above it. This strongly suggests that, in geological terms at least, something swift and disastrous happened to the dinosaurs.

PALAEOCENE EPOCH
■ 65–56 million years ago

With the large dinosaurs gone, small mammals experienced tremendous evolutionary success, beginning with small, timid nocturnal rodents and insect eaters, and culminating in large, powerful predators – although exactly what they looked like remains in doubt. Fossil evidence from this epoch is scarce. Fossils of the earliest known primates, small squirrel-like creatures from which monkeys, apes and humans may be descended, date from 60 million years ago. Significant features include hands with opposable thumbs suitable for grasping tree branches, rotating shoulder joints and good stereoscopic vision, a large brain cavity and nails instead of claws.

75 million years ago

50 million years ago

Ground Zero Traces of the asteroid impact that wiped out the dinosaurs can still be detected in the remnants of the so-called Chicxulub crater on the Yucatan Peninsula, Mexico. The walls of the crater are not obvious to the naked eye, but investigation of the crustal rock reveals unusual mineral traces typical of asteroid impacts, along with distinctly circular density concentrations where bedrock was compacted by the colossal hammer blow from space.

Indricotherium was a large, tall, plant-eating mammal that lived during the late Oligocene and early Miocene epochs 20–30 million years ago. It belonged to the same group as the modern-day rhinoceros.

Ambulocetus ('walking whale') was a transitional stage in the evolution of whales from land-living into aquatic animals. Living around 50 million years ago, it had powerful limbs and webbed feet, and probably swam in an undulating style similar to modern otters and whales. Eyes and nostrils on the top of the skull allowed it to hunt by stealth in the water.

25 million years ago

5 million years ago

MIOCENE EPOCH
■ 24–5 million years ago
Mammals reached their essentially modern forms. Almost all the modern groups of whales were present, as well as seals and walruses. Many birds, such as herons, ducks, eagles and sparrows, were present. Higher primates underwent substantial evolution.

OLIGOCENE EPOCH
■ 34–24 million years ago
Tectonic plate movement caused Africa and Europe nearly to collide, creating the Mediterranean Sea. Mammals became the dominant vertebrate life form, including horses and carnivores, rhinoceroses and elephants.

EOCENE EPOCH
■ 56–34 million years ago
A mammalian group that had evolved on land gradually took to the waters again, becoming the ancestors of whales and dolphins. The flippers of modern examples still contain bones adapted from pre-Eocene limbs suited for walking on land.

Phoberomys pattersoni, a giant rodent, lived during the Miocene epoch, around 8 million years ago in what is now Venezuela. At that time, the area was covered in a vast river system with wetlands, grasslands and lagoons. The rodent may have been semi-aquatic, living in large herds on the wetlands, and feeding on grasses using its tough incisors.

Cenozoic era continued

EARLY TOOLS AND HUNTING

Most animals have to use their jaws and teeth to tear apart the food that they catch. This calls for a tremendous investment of energy for strong jaw muscles and large, sharp teeth. Early humans lost the need for powerful jaw muscles in favour of more energy and skull space for a larger brain. They shifted the task of cutting and sawing food to their tools: simple stones chipped roughly into shape – simple but stunningly effective.

A collection of Saharan neolithic tools from about 9,000 years ago, consisting of a flint scraper (left), a spear point (bottom right), an arrow head (top right) and a stemmed triangle arrow head (top centre).

Stone hand axes such as these were common over a period that lasted from 1.5 million to 200,000 years ago. They were used for a wide range of tasks, from butchering animals to carving wood. They were probably made by the early human species Homo erectus, and by early Homo sapiens. These examples were found in Tanzania, Africa.

Australopithecus afarensis This hominid lived between 3.9 and 2.9 million years ago, and may have been the ancestor of several lineages of early humans. Fossils have been found only in eastern Africa. Compared to modern humans, this hominid had a more protruding face and its skull held a smaller brain.

PLEISTOCENE EPOCH
■ 1.8 million–10,000 years ago

Ice sheets and glaciers predominated during a cold phase in Earth's history, covering up to a third of its surface. *Homo habilis*, the oldest-known species of human, evolved. Other mammals include the woolly mammoth and the sabre-toothed tiger.

Neanderthal man inhabited Europe and western Asia between 230,000 and 29,000 years ago, and was adapted for a cold climate. Its brain was slightly larger than that of modern humans.

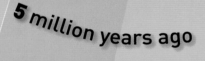

5 million years ago

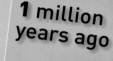

1 million years ago

PLIOCENE EPOCH
■ 5–1.8 million years ago

Camels and horses were abundant throughout North America. Primates continued to evolve, and the australopithecines, antecedents to *Homo sapiens*, developed in Africa.

Mammals of the Pleistocene epoch

Wildlife on the Spanish Peninsula during the Upper Pleistocene epoch (125,000 to 10,000 years ago), when the climate was glacial. Common spcies included horses, woolly mammoths and the woolly rhinoceros. In the foreground, cave lions are eating a reindeer.

Darwin's theory of evolution

Charles Darwin's theory of evolution generates heated argument because of its dependence on blind chance and its refusal to accept that life is the product of deliberate design. The fact remains that it is the best theory yet devised to explain why living things are so well adapted for the lives they lead.

As identified by Charles Darwin in his 1859 book *On the Origin of Species By Means of Natural Selection*, the mechanisms of evolution are stark and simple. All living things reproduce. In so doing, they transmit to the next generation certain physical and behavioural qualities (traits) that enable their offspring to survive in the environment where that species lives. If something in the environment changes – for instance, a warm, moist climate gradually turns cold and dry, or new and dangerous predators come on the scene – then the species must adapt to these changes or die out.

At first glance, all the offspring of a given plant or animal seem to look more or less like their parents, but they are never exact copies. Some may have slight but significant differences in body shape, external colouring or instinctive behaviour that can affect their ability to survive, for better or for worse. Beneficial differences continue to be passed down through the generations, but poor ones are eventually weeded out, because they do not aid survival, and the creatures or plants exhibiting them fail to thrive. These unfortunate losers in the evolutionary trials of life produce fewer offspring, and eventually become extinct.

Darwin showed that such differences, although subtle from one generation to the next, can become markedly pronounced over many generations, thereby creating new species – but he was uncertain exactly how this mechanism worked. Today we know that it happens at a molecular level, within the DNA that determines the growth and development of all organisms. External influences, such as radiation from the Sun, can mutate DNA itself. Occasionally this may nudge it in a potentially survivable direction, but on most occasions the damage is nothing but harmful. Sexual reproduction is a more valuable factor because it 'shuffles' the genes encoded within DNA as a matter of routine, so that no offspring organism ever has exactly the same DNA as either of its parents. Sometimes reshuffles can go dreadfully wrong. Inheritable illnesses are just as much a product of random gene rearrangements as 'beneficial' traits are.

Most of the time the new DNA created from parental contributions functions properly, and the offspring gets to try its chances in the lottery of life and reproduction. The emergence of distinct species usually relies on one more contributing factor: a physical separation between populations of animals that share common ancestry, yet which gradually diverge more and more  in their genetic make-up, so that if those populations do happen to bump into each other again, they can no longer interbreed. By far the biggest driver of evolution is the constant threat of death for individuals and extinction for species. The environment can change with spectacular suddenness. Organisms whose major genetic characteristics have survived unchallenged for tens of millions of years can be wiped out in a few generations. Of all the species that have existed since the first emergence of life, 99.9 per cent have become extinct, or else mutated into new forms.

Evolution in action

Natural selection usually operates over vast time spans, but sometimes we can witness it happening over just a few years. The peppered moth (Biston betularia) is typically a grey-white creature with small black spots on its wings. This colour scheme neatly disguises it as it sits on the bark of certain kinds of birch trees. In the mid-19th century, English naturalists noticed that the bright bark of the trees on which the moths rested had become dulled by industrial pollution. Birds were now spotting and eating more peppered moths than usual, but were missing the very occasional darker ones.

In 1850 there were twenty light-coloured peppered moths for each dark one. Just fifty years later, as the tree bark blackened under the remorseless onslaught of the industrial age, the population ratio was one light moth to twenty dark ones. A seemingly insignificant mutation in the colouring of the moth's wings, requiring just a minor adjustment in the moth's DNA, happened to make a fantastic difference to its chances for survival. Interestingly, the story continues. Since the 1950s the 'clean air' act has prevented factories from belching out filthy soot. The birch trees of Britain are not so dirty any more, and the darker peppered moths, for a while so successful, have been picked off, leaving lighter ones behind.

Darwin among the machines

In some areas of computing, 'genetic algorithms' are commanded to run through many thousands of cycles, or 'generations'. Results from each cycle that are close to what the programmers are trying to achieve are held over for the next cycle, while bad data are sifted out. This is a relatively new discipline, but in certain fields, such as calculating the perfect wing shape for an aircraft, many weeks or months of deliberate human design can be outperformed in a matter of hours. Whatever the arguments about how to interpret evolution's moral implications, it is basically a very straightforward idea with a powerful ability to explain how complicated things arise from simple ones.

SEE ALSO

■ DNA
page 78

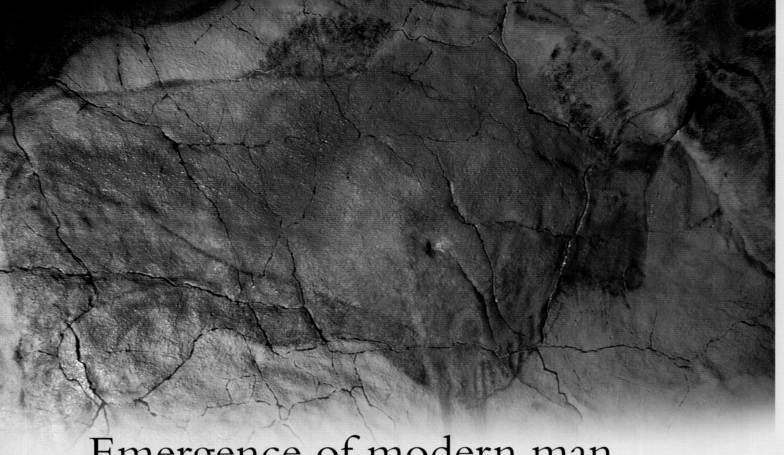

Cave painting of a bison in the Altamira cave, Spain. This cave contains several paintings of bisons, horses, deer and other animals that inhabited the area at the time, made using ochre, charcoal and haematite. The paintings were made in the Upper Palaeolithic (stone age) period, specifically in Solutrean (around 18,500 years ago) and Magdelenean (16,500–14,000 years ago) times. The cave was unoccupied by humans between these times. As well as the paintings, numerous artifacts from the two cultures were found. The cave was sealed by a rockfall some 13,000 years ago, and was rediscovered in the 1870s, after nearby quarry blasting disturbed the rocks.

Cro-Magnon
0.4–0.1 million years ago

Emergence of modern man

10,000 years ago–present day

Only very rarely do we find fossils of our ancient ancestors. The shape of the human family tree is still hotly debated. Different kinds of human sometimes co-existed on the Earth, until modern humans supplanted all others a few thousand years ago.

Homo sapiens
(modern humans) 0.5 million years ago–present day

Adapis
A lemur-like animal that lived around 50 million years ago

Our ancestors Seven skulls belonging to ancestors and relatives of modern humans.

Proconsul africanus
23 to 15 million years ago

Australopithecus africanus
3 to 1.8 million years ago

Homo erectus
1.6 to 0.3 million years ago

Homo habilis
2.1 to 1.6 million years ago

HOLOCENE EPOCH

■ 10,000 years ago–present day

Human civilization developed in its current guise and multiplicity. Agricultural and technological activities of mankind began to affect the climate on a global scale.

10 thousand years ago

Our lives today would be unrecognizable to our ancestors. Most of us gather in vast cities for which we are not particularly well-adapted in evolutionary terms. Technology shapes our behaviour more significantly than the raw, natural world, which many of us seldom experience.

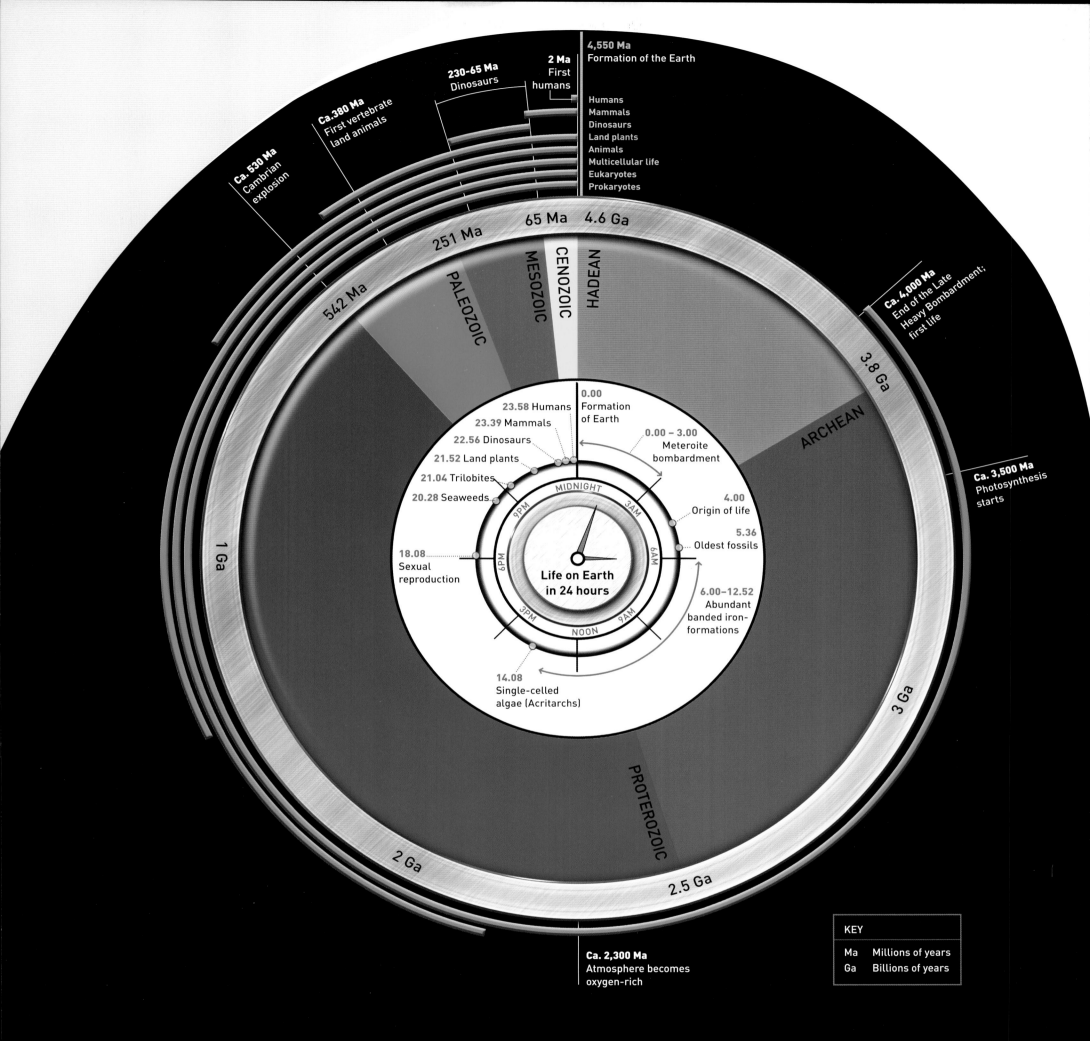

The clock of life

If the Earth's 4.6 billion-year history were compressed into a single 24-hour day, primitive-celled life emerges at 4am. By 8:30am, multicellular diversity takes hold. Dinosaurs arrive at 10:56pm and are gone by 11:39pm. Humans arise two minutes before midnight, with modern man emerging in the last 20 seconds. All our recorded history of technology, civilization and strife accounts for just the final one-tenth of a second.

THE TREE OF LIFE

The system of classifying living things may seem scientifically precise, yet it is in constant dispute as new information is discovered about the evolutionary and genetic relationships between organisms.

CLADISTICS IS JUST ONE among many commonly accepted ways of analysing the evolutionary relationships between organisms to construct a family 'tree', from the first single-celled origins of life to the many different plants and animals that exist today. Other classification systems are founded on feeding habits, genetic similarities or body structures. No single system tells the entire story. The branch-like structures in any diagrammatic representation of life's complexities are arguable interpretations at best. Classification is just a convenient tool by which scientists organize their data. However, some broad categories are more or less agreed. To date, five major biological 'kingdoms' have been identified. Monera, the simplest of organisms, are almost all microscopic. Each individual is just one prokaryotic cell, with no distinct nucleus. Recent discoveries reveal that some prokaryotes are so different from the rest that the Monera kingdom may have to be split to allow for a new kingdom dedicated just to archaeobacteria, primitive bacteria found only in extreme environments deep in the Earth's crust or at the bottom of the world's oceans.

The other four kingdoms are all eukaryotic: consisting of, or made from, cells containing a distinct nucleus. Protoctista comprises at least 100,000 species that are difficult to categorize, such as slime moulds, reef-building red algae, a huge range of microscopic parasites and even some very large organisms such as giant kelp, a seaweed that can grow up to 30 feet (10 metres) long. Fungi are also somewhat ambiguous. They are plant-like organisms that behave, in some ways, like animals. Unlike plants, they cannot photosynthesize but must absorb their food by excreting digestive enzymes onto the surfaces of tube-shaped filaments snaking under the soil or in the crevasses of damp wood. On the other hand, unlike animals, fungi are immobile, and reproduce by means of spores. The Fungi kingdom includes single-celled yeasts and multicellular moulds and mushrooms.

Then we reach the more obvious categories. Plantae are all the familar plants: grasses, flowers, trees and all those living things that do not move, that generate food via photosynthesis and that are multicellular and built from eukaryotic cells. Animalia are eukaryotic, multicellular and mobile organisms that obtain nutrients by consuming other organisms. The Animalia kingdom includes familiar creatures such as mammals, birds and reptiles, but also less obviously animalistic organisms such as corals and sea anemones.

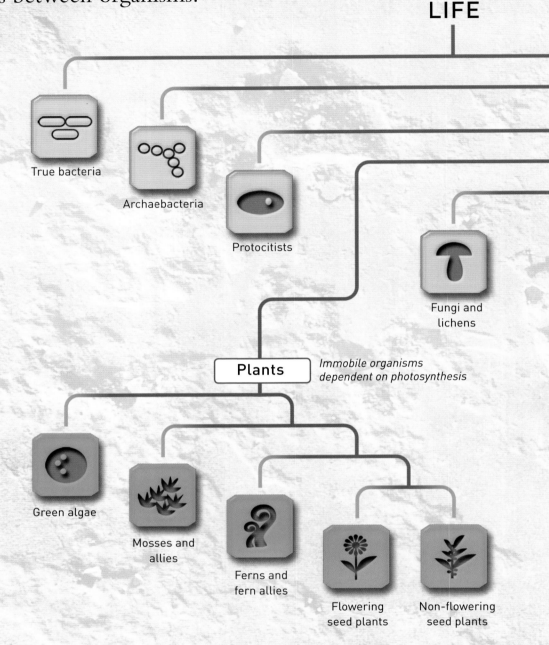

LIFE

True bacteria

Archaebacteria

Protocitists

Fungi and lichens

Plants — *Immobile organisms dependent on photosynthesis*

Green algae

Mosses and allies

Ferns and fern allies

Flowering seed plants

Non-flowering seed plants

TERMINOLOGY EXPLAINED

Archaeobacteria - closely related to the earliest life in Earth's history

Chelicerates - animals such as mites and spiders, defined by mouthparts

Cnidarians - the simplest organisms that exhibit differences between tissue types

Echinoderms - marine animals with radially symmetrical bodies such as starfish and sea urchins

Lophophorates - animals with distinct tentacle-like appendages for feeding

Myriapods - multi-segmented animals with many legs

Protoctists - simple organisms that are neither plants nor animals

Rotifers - microscopic animals commonly found in moist soil

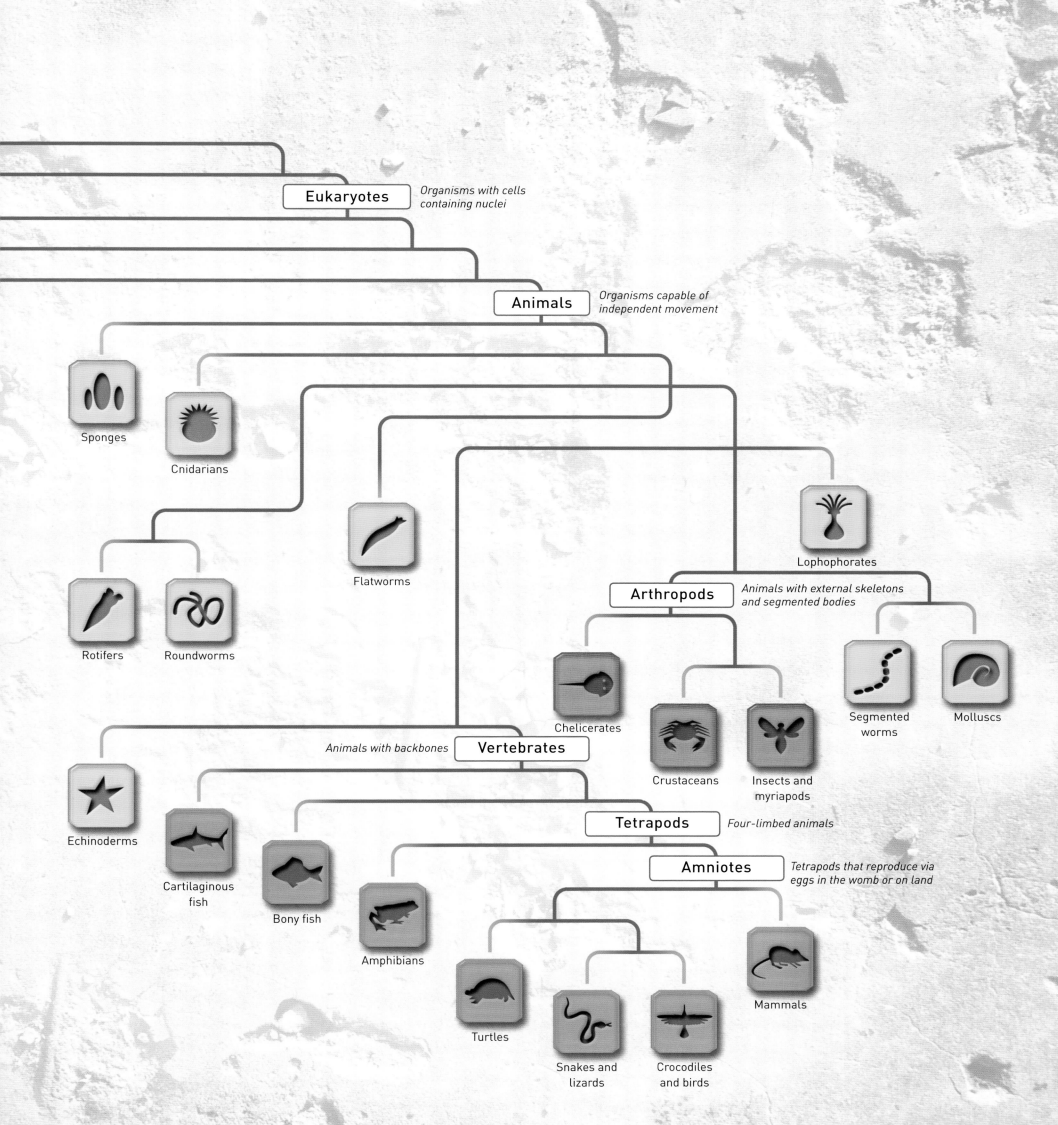

Eukaryotes — *Organisms with cells containing nuclei*

Animals — *Organisms capable of independent movement*

Sponges

Cnidarians

Rotifers

Roundworms

Flatworms

Lophophorates

Arthropods — *Animals with external skeletons and segmented bodies*

Chelicerates

Crustaceans

Insects and myriapods

Segmented worms

Molluscs

Vertebrates — *Animals with backbones*

Echinoderms

Cartilaginous fish

Bony fish

Amphibians

Tetrapods — *Four-limbed animals*

Amniotes — *Tetrapods that reproduce via eggs in the womb or on land*

Turtles

Snakes and lizards

Crocodiles and birds

Mammals

THE ANIMAL KINGDOM

Animals are more obviously 'alive' than plants. They experience sensations and have the power to move at their own volition. Most multicellular species have brains, ranging from the simplistic to the highly intelligent; and all have stomachs for storing the food that they harvest or catch.

Fish are legless egg-laying aquatic verterbrates (animals with backbones). They propel themselves through the water using fins and powerful flicks of their tails, and they have a characteristic way of breathing through gills on the sides of their heads, rather than through their mouths and nostrils.

The oxygen that fish breathe is not the oxygen bound up in the H_2O water molecules. Instead, fish breathe pure oxygen gas that is dissolved in the water. This is absorbed by the gills that fish have on the sides of the head. The gaseous oxygen content of water is less than a twentieth of the content in the atmosphere. Although

gills have a large surface area of thin membranes and filaments, it still takes vigorous pumping to circulate enough water so that oxygen can be extracted. Fish are cold-blooded. They do not generate internal body warmth, but must operate at the ambient temperature of the surrounding water. On the plus side, this reduces their oxygen requirements.

In much the same way that a submarine rises to the surface of the sea or sinks into the depths by adjusting the contents of its air-filled floatation tanks, most fish control their buoyancy using a 'swim bladder', a balloon-like internal organ filled with some of the oxygen extracted by the gills. By expanding or contracting the bladder, a fish controls its body's overall density, making it more buoyant or less, as required.

Amphibians

Amphibians are creatures who live something of a double life. They spend much of their time in water, typically mating and laying their soft, delicate eggs there rather than on dry land. Their young grow to maturity in water, then develop limbs and climb onto the land to hunt. Above all, they breathe the same air that we do, using their mouths and nostrils and a pair of lungs. Amphibians raise their nostrils above water at intervals to collect the air that they need. Frogs and toads are amphibians, as are salamanders and newts.

Development from egg to tadpole

Wood frog (Rana sylvatica) development from egg to tadpole with legs to froglet. Eleven weeks after the egg is laid and fertilized, a fully developed frog emerges from the water.

Frogs increase their chances of reproductive success by laying thousands of eggs at a time.

Frog eggs typically hatch less than three weeks after fertilization.

The tadpole eats the remains of its egg, then attaches itself to an under-water plant.

After about five weeks, the tadpole's tail shortens and it begins to grow limbs.

Safety in numbers A shoal of adult Big-eye trevally off the coast of Malaysia. The fish swim fast but keep close to each other to avoid predators. New hatchlings sometimes shelter among the tentacles of jellyfish to avoid being eaten.

Molluscs

Molluscs are soft-bodied creatures with bodies divided approximately into three parts: a head, a central mass containing the main digestive organs and a foot-like appendage for movement. Most molluscs live in water, but some live on land. Slugs are molluscs, but so are snails, mussels and oysters. A sticky excretion that hardens into an ever-expanding chalky shell is a typical feature. Sometimes the 'shell' is a strengthening agent inside a mollusc's body, as in cuttlefish or squid. Octopuses are also molluscs, distinquished by strong tentacles, sharp eyesight and startlingly intelligent behaviour.

A baby octopus from the Gulf of Mexico. Certain species that live in the Pacific can grow to more than 20 feet (7 m) in length. These surprisingly intelligent creatures only live for about three years.

Insects

There are at least 700,000 species, but many more probably have yet to be discovered. Insects all have bodies consiting of a head, a thorax of three segments, usually three pairs of legs and often one or two pairs of wings. Their heads have compound eyes and long antennae that are sensitive to touch and smell.

Ants comprise up to a tenth of the entire mass of animal life on the planet. Termites probably account for another ten per cent. There is hardly any corner of the dry-land world, apart from the coldest polar regions, where insects fail to thrive. They range in scale from parasitic 'fairy flies' the size of a pinhead to the appropriately named titan beetle, a South American monster as large as the palm of your hand. Perhaps we should be glad that we will never encounter anything any larger from the insect world. Every insect has a hard, crusty external shell, called an exoskeleton, that strengthens its body and allows its limbs to bear its weight. The soft internal organs are held in place by the inner walls of the exoskeleton, but there comes a point when gravity gains the upper hand, threatening to pull the organs away from the walls. Insects cannot grow beyond a certain size – at least, not on this world.

This is a lifesize photo of the Titan longhorn beetle, the largest insect in the world, a native of the the Amazonian rain forest. Its mandibles can snap a pencil in half, but adult Titan beetles, emerging from a long larval stage, do not feed. They simply fly around to find mates.

Arachnids

Spiders are certainly the most familiar arachnids, but they share this classification with scorpions, ticks and mites. Unlike insects, arachnids have two body sections: a prosoma (the head section) and an abdomen, from which eight legs sprout. All arachnids are predators. Typically they hunt other insects, or even creatures of their own kind. Many inject their prey with immobilizing poisons, followed by digestive enzymes, then suck them dry at leisure. The legs of the Goliath bird-eating spider would span a dinner plate. It does indeed occasionally catch and eat small birds.

A goliath bird-eater spider (*Theraphosa blondi*), belonging to the tarantula group.

BIOLOG

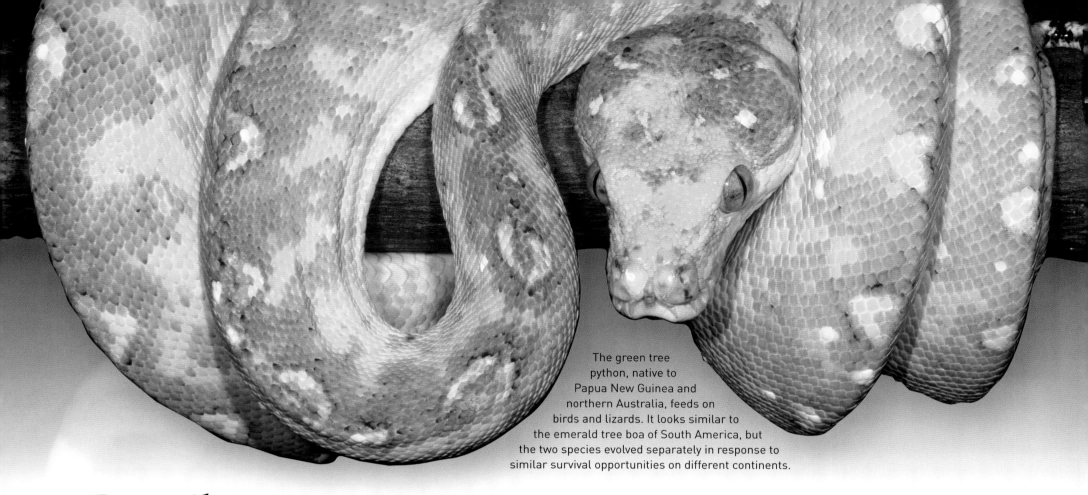

The green tree python, native to Papua New Guinea and northern Australia, feeds on birds and lizards. It looks similar to the emerald tree boa of South America, but the two species evolved separately in response to similar survival opportunities on different continents.

Reptiles

are the very essence of what we term 'cold-blooded' animals. They gain all their body warmth from the Sun, and therefore must conserve energy as best they can. They tend not to move unless they have to. Some of the larger snake species eat only at intervals of several weeks.

Reptiles have roamed the Earth for more than 300 million years. The dinosaurs were reptiles. They are four-footed creatures with tough, scaly skins – although the scales are actually small folds in a continuous skin, rather than the discrete scales we find on fish. Reptiles live on land and breathe with lungs. Modern species are divided mainly among three orders, Chelonia (tortoises and turtles), Crocodilia (crocodiles and alligators) and Squamata (lizards and snakes).

A fourth order, Rhynocephalia, is devoted purely to one very rare species, the tuatara, which lives only on certain off-shore islands in New Zealand. It has changed little since it first evolved some 225 million years ago. A tuatara can live for up to 100 years.

Unlike amphibians, reptiles lay hard-shelled eggs on land, from which fully formed young are born. Some snakes and lizards hatch eggs inside their bodies, giving birth to live young.

Corn snakes (*Elaphe guttata guttata*) beginning to hatch from eggs after slitting them with their egg teeth.

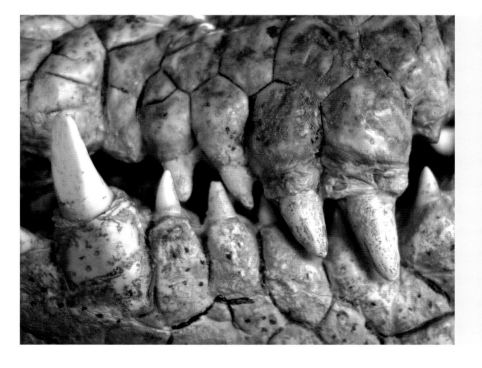

Crocodiles

and alligators are as close as we can come to experiencing what the more threatening dinosaurs might have been like. These monsters, which can grow to more than 23 feet (7 metres) in length, have spiny armour-plated skin, long, muscular tails, yellow eyes and powerful jaws equipped with large teeth. Crocodiles inhabit most tropical rivers and estuaries, while alligators are found mainly in the southern states of North America. They can stay under water for long periods, with just the tips of their nostrils protruding. This allows them to take prey animals by surprise. They adjust their buoyancy by swallowing stones.

SEE ALSO

Life on Earth
page 94

Mammals

Since the demise of the dinosaurs 65 million years ago, mammals have thrived. Now they are the dominant land vertebrates – and some have also taken to the sea. There are approximately 3,800 species.

ALL MAMMALS ARE WARM-BLOODED, maintaining a constant body temperature, at least while they are awake and active. Apart from some aquatic mammals such as whales and dolphins, all species have a hairy covering of fur on their skins, not feathers or scales. Even the 30,000 spines on a porcupine are specialized hairs stiffened for defence. Another defining characteristic is that mammals give birth to live young which are able to survive as individuals, although the mother invariably stays close at hand for warmth and protection. The young are nourished by suckling milk from teats on the mother's mammary glands: another feature possessed only by mammals. Marsupials, such as kangaroos, koalas and opossums, give birth to underdeveloped young that are nurtured in a pouch on the female that encloses the teats.

Mammals have large brains relative to their body sizes, as compared to other vertebrates. They rely on fewer instinctive 'knee-jerk' behaviour patterns than other vertebrate species and have a marked ability to learn from their day-to-day experiences. One of the drawbacks of a warm-blooded, energy-dependent lifestyle is the need to find food quickly and often. A clever brain helps. Other subtle qualities, such as different teeth for slicing and grinding, and arrangements between the palate, the tongue, the airways and nostrils that enable mammals to breathe through their noses while eating or suckling milk, are also typical – but the natural world seldom bothers itself with neat categorizations for tidy scientists. Anteaters have no teeth, and the spiny anteater of New Guinea and Australia, along with the duckbilled platypus of Australia and Tasmania, both lay eggs.

Human beings certainly do fit into a specific category. We are warm-blooded and covered in hairs. We breathe through our nostrils while eating or suckling. We have teeth for grinding (molars) and for slicing (canines). We exhibit adaptive intelligence by virtue of our relatively large brains, and our females provide milk for their young. We are mammals.

Marsupial
▼ A five-week-old American opossum nursing (obtaining milk from a teat) in its mother's pouch.

Humpback whales
▲ A mother and her calf. These vast creatures are found in deep water in most of the world's oceans.

Privileged young
▲ Large, fierce mammalian predators, such as bears, can devote their energies to intensively raising small numbers of young.

Strange animal
▶ The duck-billed platypus is an evolutionary oddity, a unique mammal that lays eggs rather than giving birth to live young.

Birds

Most dinosaurs are supposed to have been wiped out 65 million years ago, but perhaps not all of them. The modern skies are, perhaps, teeming with the descendants of small dinosaurs who had feathers instead of scales.

UNTIL RECENTLY, ARCHAEOPTERYX was regarded as the first known bird, dating from around 125 million years ago. Fossil discoveries in China just in the last few years show that scansori-opterygidae, or 'climbing wings', a flightless tree-living dinosaur roughly the size of a pigeon, existed at least 20 million years before archaeopteryx. Scansoriopterygidae had feathers for warmth or display in mating rituals, and possibly to enable brief gliding swoops between one tree branch and another. These were specialized scales. 'Climbing wings' probably wasn't an aerobatic master of the sky. Even so, its descendants' gradual adaptation and diversification into the huge variety of modern birds seems not so much a giant leap but a gentle progression.

Birds are different to most mammals in a number of obvious ways. They walk on two legs rather than four, and have two wings adapted from the forelegs. They have feathers instead of fur and a beak instead of jaws with teeth. They are warm blooded — in fact their body temperature tends to be slightly higher than mammals'. They have two eyes and also two ears, though these are seldom visible. Unlike mammals, most birds have little or no sense of smell; and of course, they lay eggs, with hard shells that can survive the attentions of small predators, at least, while the parents are away foraging for food.

Microraptor Fossils recently discovered in northeastern China reveal a bird-like animal called Microraptor gui, that lived around 125 million years ago, and could glide between one tree and another. It had feathers on its legs, and may have been an intermediate species between flightless bird-like dinosaurs and birds with a genuine ability to fly.

Bird flight calls for powerful muscles to flap the wings and overcome air resistance. These need to be firmly attached to the skeleton. Since flapping is a very different movement from walking or running, bird skeletons exhibit a number of distinctive features. In particular there is a flat keel-like breast plate, the carina, extending from the front of the rib cage, onto which the wing muscles are attached. Several vertebrae in the backbone, and especially those associated with the rib cage, have become fused for strength. A bird's skeleton is exceptionally light given the strength that it delivers. Many of the bones have an internal honeycomb structure with hollow air spaces and criss-crossing struts. Finally, the two-footed posture of birds on the ground is easily distinguishable from that of four-footed mammals and reptiles. In order to arrange its centre of balance as efficiently as possible, both for flight and for walking on the ground, a bird's legs up to the knee joint are held close to the flanks of its body. The backwards-facing 'knee' that we think we see as a bird hops along is its ankle joint.

SCIENCE OF BIRD MIGRATION

Bird migration tends to occur between the northern and southern hemispheres. Migratory birds escape the northern winters, but head back again in the spring to breed. There are many different migration patterns: inherited behaviours that enable birds to maximize their food-gathering and breeding opportunities according to the climate and time of year. How birds navigate during their sometimes globe-spanning journeys is still something of a mystery. They have sharper eyesight than humans, and a good memory for visual cues on the ground. While flying over featureless stretches of ocean, they appear to navigate using the Sun and even the stars. A small mass of cells between the eyes and brain of many migrating birds is a biological compass, sensitive to the Earth's magnetic field.

DINOSAURS AND BIRDS

Evidence linking the skeletal structures of modern birds to those of dinosaurs includes elongated arms and forelimbs, large 'orbits' (eye sockets in the skull), flexible wrist joints, hollow, thin-walled bones, an 'S'-shaped neck, and clavicles (the collarbone) fused to form a furcula (wishbone). However, not all biologists are agreed that birds must be descended from dinosaurs. There are many differences as well as similarities. It may be that birds and dinosaurs share a common ancestor, but that they diverged (branched along separate evolutionary paths).

SEE ALSO

□ **Life on Earth**
page 94

Animal reproduction

Having young is one of the defining characteristics of life. Nothing lives forever, and all organisms would become extinct very quickly without generating offspring. This seems obvious enough. The purposes of sex are more subtle.

ASEXUAL REPRODUCTION, where there is no requirement for separate 'male' and 'female' parents, is the most obvious way for an organism to reproduce itself. For instance, all bacteria and many protozoa (single-celled animals) reproduce by binary fission: separating into two distinct individuals approximately the same size, while freshwater sponges release groups of cells called gemmules that eventually grow into new individuals. This is not quite the same as mitosis, by which cells inside the body of a multicellular organism divide, but in asexual reproduction, each new individual does benefit from exactly the same DNA as the parent, along with the genes that have, quite obviously, suited that parent for survival.

Asexual reproduction can turn out numerous offspring with the minimum of fuss. This is ideal for many simple organisms whose environment is stable and benign. Animals of greater complexity, living in demanding environments, tend to have a reproductive strategy that is a great deal more elaborate, time-consuming and energy-intensive. It requires two parents, not one; and worse still, only half the genes in each parent's DNA are transmitted to the offspring. Yet, along with these drawbacks, sexual reproduction, in which a single male sex gamete, a sperm, unites during copulation with a single female gamete, the egg, conveys

many advantages. So long as an individual parent participates in co-creating more than one offspring, most if not all of that parent's genes will eventually emerge into the outside world, because the half-complete set of genes in a single gamete, either egg or sperm, will not be the same combination as in all the other gametes that a parent manufactures. Gene 'shuffling' takes place when gametes are produced. By combining different gene contributions from each parent to make brand-new DNA in an offspring, each individual gene's chances of survival are maximized. The greater the diversity, the greater the chances that some offspring will survive. An accelerating factor for the emergence of gene shuffling may have been the need for all complex organisms to keep one evolutionary step ahead of bacterial and viral infections.

Sexual selection

Female animals instinctively seek out clues about the fitness of prospective male partners. Many rituals have emerged during which males can 'court' females with elaborate dances and gifts of food, or by fighting other males in a show of strength and stamina. Among pack or clan animals such as wolves and primates, females may also want to see qualities other than strength alone, such as leadership and social adroitness. Sometimes this 'sexual selection' pressure seems to do nothing but answer its own requirements. The peacock is the most famous example. Females seek male birds that are strong and healthy. The males demonstrate this with a fine, heavy display of feathers that are not required for flying. The size of the display indicates the bird's strength, while the rich and elaborate colouring shows off its health and resistance against infections. From generation to generation, females prefer the biggest and finest tail feathers. Modern peacocks have grown tails so large and resplendent, they are in danger of hindering the bird's ability to get off the ground at all, let alone fly.

Half running, half hiding

Vulnerable animals often gather in large populations, so that predators easily become disoriented by too many targets all running at once. For many birds and fish, predator confusion is the main escape strategy. By flocking (or in the case of fish, 'schooling') in vast, seething swarms of fellow animals, they gamble on reducing the chances of being the one individual out of hundreds, or even thousands, that has to be unlucky that day. Swarms appear, at first glance, to twist and turn almost as though under intelligent leadership. Recent studies show that each animal needs only to respond instinctively to the movements of four or five animals near it in order for complex swarm behaviour to emerge.

Predator and prey

An evolutionary 'arms race' has operated for 500 million years between predator species and the creatures they hunt. The stakes are a matter of life and death, the survival strategies are many and various, but one thing remains ruthlessly inflexible: the amount of energy available for the struggle.

TO SEE HOW EVOLUTION shapes all species for survival in an eternally competitive world of hunter and hunted, there is no better example than the handsome, solitary creature renowned as the swiftest animal on dry land. The cheetah is a graceful athlete that can hurl itself across the flat grasslands of the African savannah at a stunning 60 miles (100 kilometres) per hour. Humans need a decent motor vehicle to go that fast. A predator who can outrun all potential prey animals might be expected to have an easy time, yet the cheetah sacrifices a great deal to reach that pinnacle of performance. As a consequence, it lives on the very edge of survivability.

The cheetah's brief and brilliant bursts of speed call for a wide range of biological trade-offs. For a start, it can only keep up its fastest pace for about sixty seconds, before its body overheats and its muscles strain from exhaustion. That's just the immediate energy budgeting. Longer-term debts also have to be paid throughout the animal's life. Like a specialist car designed for the smoothness of the race track but not the roughness of the streets, the cheetah's body is as lean and lightweight as physically possible, at the expense of day-to-day strength. Its fragility leads to a solitary and cautious existence. A cheetah scrupulously avoids fighting others of its kind for mates or territory, and never defends itself when hyenas or opportunistic lions steal its fresh 'kills'. There are not enough fats or other energy stores in its metabolism to allow for healing injuries while at the same time holding something in reserve for running. An injured cheetah is doomed to starve.

Even in a cheetah's childhood days, energy trade-offs shape its fate. Cheetah mothers may give birth to five or six cubs, but only one or two are likely to survive because, unlike many other cats, these animals aren't especially good at grasping cubs in their jaws and climbing up trees when threatened. The strong claws needed for such work have been pared down in the interests of running speed.

The cheetah's favourite prey animal is the Thomson gazelle, with a top speed of 40 miles (64 kilometres) an hour. This is significantly slower than a cheetah, but the Thomson has other tricks at its disposal apart from raw speed. When chased, it actually appears to 'waste' energy leaping into the air or randomly changing direction. This confuses the cheetah, who prefers a simple straight-line attack run. If the gazelle can survive the first thirty seconds of a chase, it will usually escape by virtue of its ability to endure over a longer distance than its pursuer. On the other hand, if a cheetah hides in long grass and sneaks close to its target, its unmatchable speed over short distances helps to ensure a 'kill'.

Keeping out of trouble

Insects with limited energy for evading predators often benefit from staying still, rather than actively trying to escape. A common technique is to be so well camouflaged against their surroundings that, more often than not, predators fail to spot them. The stick insect illustrated here looks uncannily like a part of the plant that it is resting on.

THE HUMAN BODY

The structure of skin, bones and internal organs that we live in doesn't merely contain us. It creates us. Our personalities are a product of a brain which, in turn, is influenced by being a part of the body that supports it. A human is the most complicated thing in the universe.

The integumentary system
The cutaneous membrane is the proper scientific term for the skin, the largest organ of the human body, accounting for nearly one sixth of our weight. It is waterproof, self-repairing, heat- and touch-sensitive, and the first line of defence between us and the outside world.

THE EPIDERMIS, the outer layer of skin that we can see, is in fact largely dead. Over the space of about five weeks, live skin cells migrate upwards from the bottom level of the epidermis, known as the basal layer. When the cells reach the surface they flatten out and harden to form the stratum corneum, or 'horny layer', a basic protection against physical damage. These cells are known as keratinocytes, because they are made largely from keratin, the tough protein also found in hair and nails. The stratum corneum varies greatly in thickness, depending on the daily wear and tear that any particular patch has to cope with. For instance, it is ten times thicker on the soles of the feet than on the eyelids. Eventually the keratinocytes die and fall off. Household dust (especially the tiny motes we see drifting in the air when we shake out a blanket) consists mainly of these shed skin cells.

Approximately ten per cent of cells in the basal layer are melanocytes, cells containing melanin, the pigment that gives us our skin colouring. On hot, sunny days, melanocytes respond to excessive levels of ultraviolet by generating more melanin, giving us a protective tan. Too little sunlight can be almost as harmful as too much, especially over the long term. Vitamin D compounds, molecules closely related to steroids, are essential for maintaining strong bones and teeth because they promote the body's absorption of calcium derived from foodtsuffs. Certain kinds of vitamin D are manufactured principally by the action of ultraviolet on epidermal skin cells. The epidermis also contains Langerhans cells that alert the immune system whenever the skin comes into contact with harmful bacteria or viruses.

The next layer down is the dermis, rich in substructures such as hair follicles, nerves, oil and sweat glands, and collagen fibres that give the skin overall its tear-proof yet flexible strength. Blood vessels in the dermis have a dual role. They deliver blood to the cells, just as they would for any other bodily tissues, but they also exchange heat with the outside world.

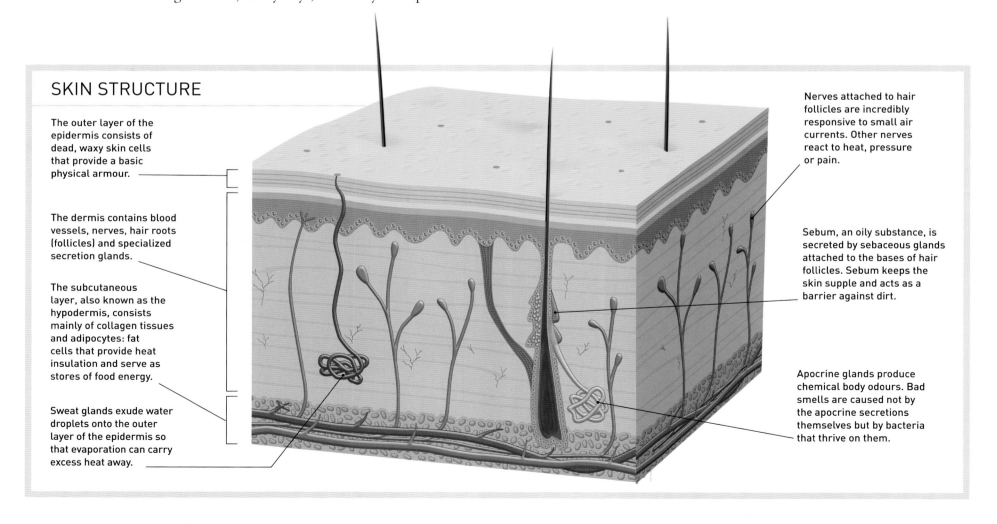

SKIN STRUCTURE

The outer layer of the epidermis consists of dead, waxy skin cells that provide a basic physical armour.

The dermis contains blood vessels, nerves, hair roots (follicles) and specialized secretion glands.

The subcutaneous layer, also known as the hypodermis, consists mainly of collagen tissues and adipocytes: fat cells that provide heat insulation and serve as stores of food energy.

Sweat glands exude water droplets onto the outer layer of the epidermis so that evaporation can carry excess heat away.

Nerves attached to hair follicles are incredibly responsive to small air currents. Other nerves react to heat, pressure or pain.

Sebum, an oily substance, is secreted by sebaceous glands attached to the bases of hair follicles. Sebum keeps the skin supple and acts as a barrier against dirt.

Apocrine glands produce chemical body odours. Bad smells are caused not by the apocrine secretions themselves but by bacteria that thrive on them.

The muscular system
The human body contains about 640 muscles, all of which convert chemical energy into physical movement. We can perform a dazzling array of physical actions, yet everything we 'do' is powered by just one kind of muscle action: contraction.

THERE ARE THREE DIFFERENT KINDS of muscle in the body: skeletal, cardiac and smooth. The skeletal muscles are the ones of which we are most conscious because they cause the body to move on command. Cardiac muscles are those in the heart, beating under unconscious (autonomic) control. Likewise the smooth muscles of the intestines squeeze food through the digestive system with no conscious thought on the part of their owner.

Whether or not the triggering nervous impulses are conscious or unconscious, all three muscle types function in the same way once activated. Muscle cells take the form of long, thin, cylindrical fibres about the thickness of a human hair. Bundles of fibres are arranged parallel to each other. Blood vessels, motor neurons (the nerves that trigger the fibres) and other nerves weave their way between the bundles. Each fibre contains hundreds of myofibrils, the organelles that actually cause the fibres to contract. Myofibrils contain two types of filament, thick and thin, all running along the axis of the surrounding fibre. The thick filaments are made primarily from myosin, a long protein polymer, while the thin filaments are composed of actin. During contraction, the myosin filaments extract energy from ATP molecules (the dominant conveyor of energy in cells) and extend molecular 'cross bridges' that latch on to the actin filaments lying alongside. The linked filaments then pull past each other, causing the fibre as a whole to contract.

The nerve signals for contraction are synchronized throughout a muscle so that all of the relevant fibres shorten simultaneously. In the case of skeletal muscles, the brain consciously analyses a load by a process of feedback, and sends signals only to a small proportion of fibres in order to lift, say, a feather or scratch a nose. At the other extreme, a heavy load will call for almost all fibres in a muscle to be contracted. At this point a noticeable rigidity or bulging of the muscle will become apparent.

Fast twitch – white muscle fibres are very strong and swiftly reactive, but tire out quickly.

Slow twitch – red muscle fibres work steadily over a long duration for excercises such as swimming or marathon running.

Tendons – transfer muscle contractions to the skeletal structure.

HOW MUSCLES WORK

Tendons, long and very tough connective tissues, link skeletal muscles with bones. All bodily movements are produced by muscles pulling on tendons and tendons pulling on bones. Skeletal muscles usually attach in opposing pairs: one muscle to pull the bone in one direction and another to pull it the other way. There is not one single muscle, nor any tendon, that can push instead of pulling. For instance, when you put your hands against a heavy parcel and shove against it with all your might to slide it across a rough wooden table, your upper arms are pulled together as the major chest muscles (pectorals) contract. At the same time the triceps, muscles on the rear of your upper arms, are contracted to pull the elbow joints straight. Your 'push' is in fact an interconnected set of pulls.

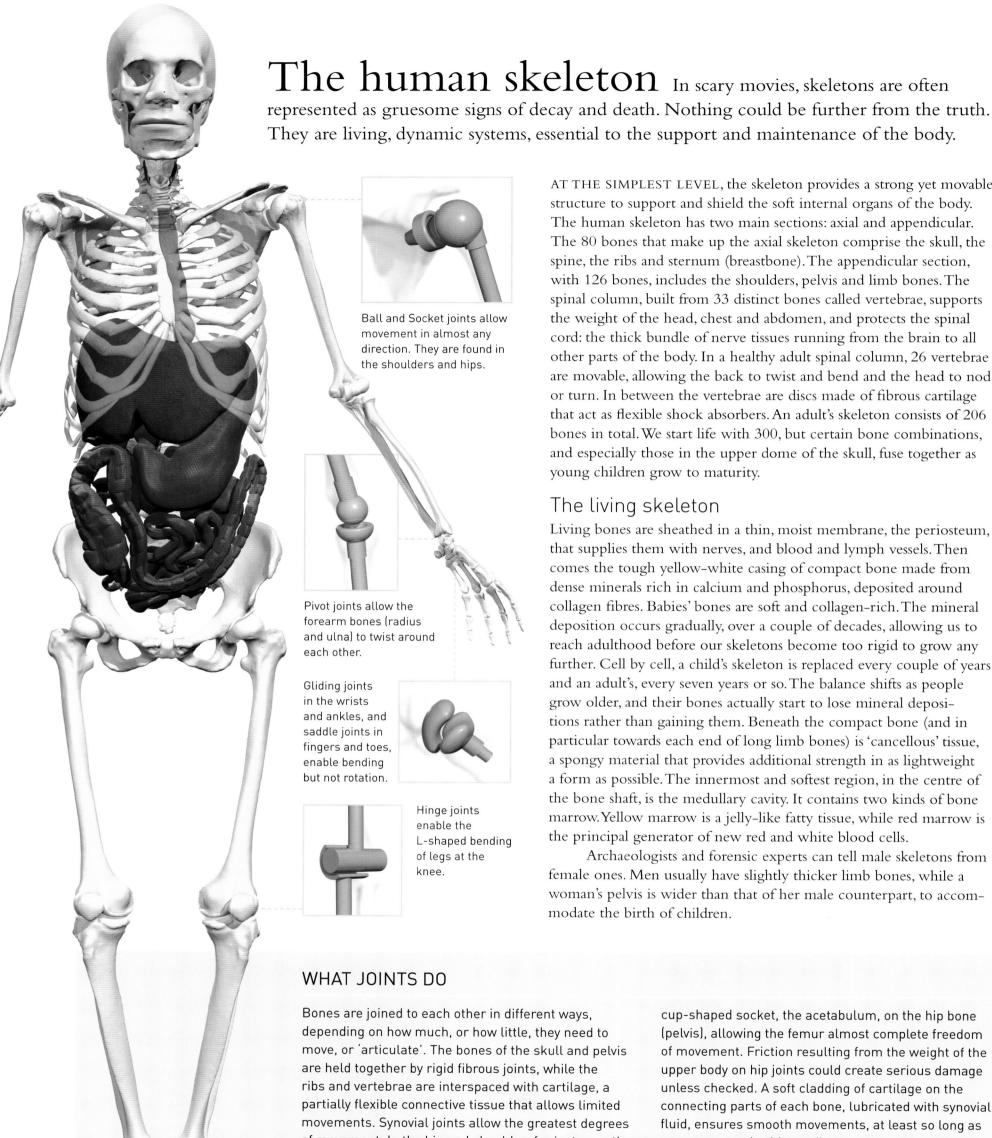

The human skeleton

In scary movies, skeletons are often represented as gruesome signs of decay and death. Nothing could be further from the truth. They are living, dynamic systems, essential to the support and maintenance of the body.

Ball and Socket joints allow movement in almost any direction. They are found in the shoulders and hips.

Pivot joints allow the forearm bones (radius and ulna) to twist around each other.

Gliding joints in the wrists and ankles, and saddle joints in fingers and toes, enable bending but not rotation.

Hinge joints enable the L-shaped bending of legs at the knee.

AT THE SIMPLEST LEVEL, the skeleton provides a strong yet movable structure to support and shield the soft internal organs of the body. The human skeleton has two main sections: axial and appendicular. The 80 bones that make up the axial skeleton comprise the skull, the spine, the ribs and sternum (breastbone). The appendicular section, with 126 bones, includes the shoulders, pelvis and limb bones. The spinal column, built from 33 distinct bones called vertebrae, supports the weight of the head, chest and abdomen, and protects the spinal cord: the thick bundle of nerve tissues running from the brain to all other parts of the body. In a healthy adult spinal column, 26 vertebrae are movable, allowing the back to twist and bend and the head to nod or turn. In between the vertebrae are discs made of fibrous cartilage that act as flexible shock absorbers. An adult's skeleton consists of 206 bones in total. We start life with 300, but certain bone combinations, and especially those in the upper dome of the skull, fuse together as young children grow to maturity.

The living skeleton

Living bones are sheathed in a thin, moist membrane, the periosteum, that supplies them with nerves, and blood and lymph vessels. Then comes the tough yellow-white casing of compact bone made from dense minerals rich in calcium and phosphorus, deposited around collagen fibres. Babies' bones are soft and collagen-rich. The mineral deposition occurs gradually, over a couple of decades, allowing us to reach adulthood before our skeletons become too rigid to grow any further. Cell by cell, a child's skeleton is replaced every couple of years, and an adult's, every seven years or so. The balance shifts as people grow older, and their bones actually start to lose mineral deposi-tions rather than gaining them. Beneath the compact bone (and in particular towards each end of long limb bones) is 'cancellous' tissue, a spongy material that provides additional strength in as lightweight a form as possible. The innermost and softest region, in the centre of the bone shaft, is the medullary cavity. It contains two kinds of bone marrow. Yellow marrow is a jelly-like fatty tissue, while red marrow is the principal generator of new red and white blood cells.

Archaeologists and forensic experts can tell male skeletons from female ones. Men usually have slightly thicker limb bones, while a woman's pelvis is wider than that of her male counterpart, to accom-modate the birth of children.

WHAT JOINTS DO

Bones are joined to each other in different ways, depending on how much, or how little, they need to move, or 'articulate'. The bones of the skull and pelvis are held together by rigid fibrous joints, while the ribs and vertebrae are interspaced with cartilage, a partially flexible connective tissue that allows limited movements. Synovial joints allow the greatest degrees of movement. In the hip and shoulder, for instance, the ball-shaped end of the femur (thigh bone) fits into a cup-shaped socket, the acetabulum, on the hip bone (pelvis), allowing the femur almost complete freedom of movement. Friction resulting from the weight of the upper body on hip joints could create serious damage unless checked. A soft cladding of cartilage on the connecting parts of each bone, lubricated with synovial fluid, ensures smooth movements, at least so long as we are young. As this cartilage wears out over time, synovial joints become stiff, causing arthritis.

The cardiovascular system

Blood is not merely a fluid. It is a complex traffic system, a carefully balanced energy economy and a river of relentless battle. It also transports oxygen inhaled by the lungs and returns unwanted carbon dioxide to be exhaled.

OXYGEN is absorbed into the bloodstream through the lungs. The left side of the heart then pumps oxygen-rich ('oxygenated') blood through a network of blood vessels – the arteries – to all other tissues in the body. When blood reaches these tissues it interacts with them through very fine thin-walled blood vessels called capillaries. Oxygen in the blood is absorbed by individual tissue cells to produce energy. In exchange, the cells release waste products, such as carbon dioxide and water, which are absorbed and carried away by the blood.

The 'deoxygenated' blood then travels along the veins and back towards the right side of the heart. Then it is pumped back into the lungs, from where the unwanted carbon dioxide and water vapour are expelled and fresh oxygen is absorbed. This reinvigorated blood is returned to the left side of the heart, and the entire cycle begins again. In a healthy adult, the heart beats approximately 70 times per minute, pumping the equivalent of nearly 5,000 gallons (23,000 litres) of blood around the body per day. Each side of the heart is divided into two chambers: the atrium, and a larger chamber beneath, the ventricle. Blood flows from each atrium to the ventricle below, through a one-way valve.

Blood pressure

Blood pressure is usually expressed as two numbers, such as '120 over 80'. The first 'systolic' number shows the maximum pressure of arteries when the heart is contracting to pump blood. The second 'diastolic' figure is the minimum pressure between heart beats. By tradition, blood pressure is measured according to the similar pressure that a certain height of mercury in a calibrated column would exert.

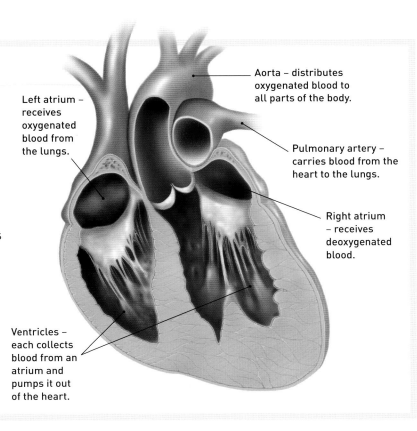

Carotid arteries – have several branches which supply oxygenated blood to the face, scalp, mouth and jaws.

Jugular veins – on each side of the neck return deoxygenated blood from the head and brain to the heart.

Abdominal aorta – the largest artery in the body, supplies oxygenated blood to the abdominal and pelvic organs and the legs.

Femoral artery – divides into smaller branches to provide blood to muscles and other tissues on the thigh.

BLOOD DISTRIBUTION

The circulatory system (main diagram), showing arteries in red and the veins in blue. Arteries are strong-walled vessels, built to withstand the pressure of blood from the heart. Blood flows in spurts, reflecting the heart's rhythmic pumping action. Arteries feed oxygenated blood into the system. Veins carry deoxygenated blood back to the heart. In veins the blood is not under such pressure, and flows more smoothly. Veins have internal valves along their length to prevent back flow of blood.

Left atrium – receives oxygenated blood from the lungs.

Aorta – distributes oxygenated blood to all parts of the body.

Pulmonary artery – carries blood from the heart to the lungs.

Right atrium – receives deoxygenated blood.

Ventricles – each collects blood from an atrium and pumps it out of the heart.

The respiratory system

Along with the beating of our hearts, breathing feels like the very essence of life. The lungs deliver oxygen into the blood during every intake of breath, and expel carbon dioxide as we exhale.

THE LUNGS are positioned on either side of the heart, in the chest cavity (thorax). They consist of sponge-like tissue with a very rich blood supply. The diaphragm, a sheet of muscle separating the chest from the abdominal cavity, alternately increases and decreases the internal volume of the chest cavity, causing the lungs to expand and contract.

Air is drawn in through the trachea (windpipe) and into each lung through two large airways, the bronchi. From here, air is routed into much smaller airways, called bronchioles, which repeatedly divide like a many-branched tree, ending in millions of thin-walled sacs, the alveoli. Each sac is tiny, but the collective surface area would amount to the size of a tennis court if only all the alveoli could be flattened and spread out. Here is where oxygen meets the blood directly. In an average day, 10,000 litres of air passes through the lungs.

HOW THE LUNGS WORK

A thin horizontal wall of muscle, the diaphragm, separates the interior of the thorax (essentially the upper torso containing the heart and lungs) from that of the abdomen in which the digestive system sits. When the diaphragm contracts and flattens out, it pulls at the lower side walls of the lungs, increasing their volume and lowering the air pressure inside them. Air from the outside rushes in through the airways to fill the partial vacuum. When the diaphragm relaxes, the lungs shrink again, expelling air.

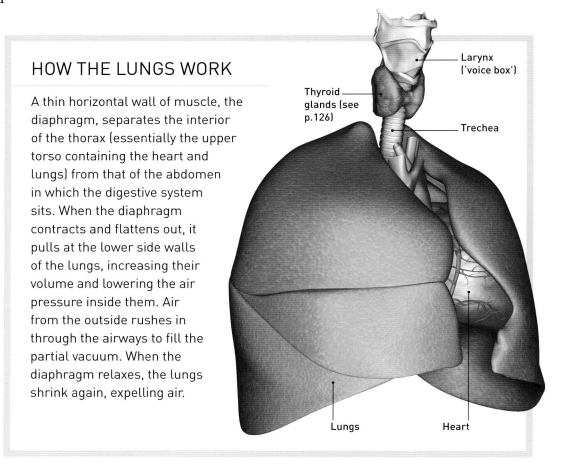

Larynx ('voice box')

Thyroid glands (see p.126)

Trechea

Lungs

Heart

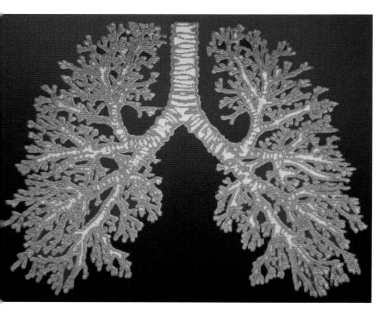

▲ Bronchial tree A network of airways inside the lungs carries air back and forth. The main trunk of the tree is the trachea (windpipe, top centre), which branches into the left and right bronchi. The branches become ever thinner. The finest are the bronchioles, terminating in alveoli (air sacs), where gaseous exchange with the blood takes place.

▶ Bronchiole and alveoli The alveoli are the final branchings of the respiratory tree. A healthy adult lung will have around 300 million alveoli. Their walls are just one cell layer thick. Oxygen diffuses into (and carbon dioxide diffuses out of) blood flowing through very fine capillaries, also with very thin walls.

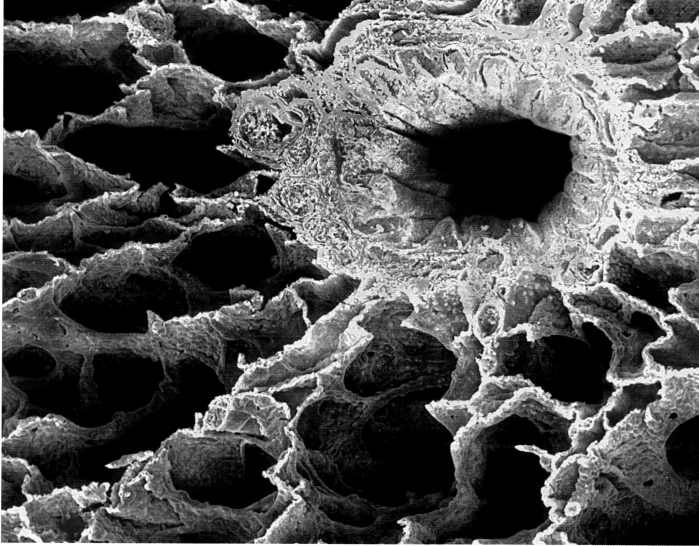

The digestive and hepatic systems

Whatever meal we eat, it is highly unlikely to be in a form that the body can use straight away as nourishment. Food and drink must be processed into specific molecules of nutrients. Then the unwanted remains need to be thrown away.

THE CORE of the digestive system is essentially one long hollow tube, called the digestive tract. It includes the mouth and oesophagus, the stomach, the small and large intestines, the rectum and the anus. Pulses of unconsciously-controlled muscle action in the outer walls of the tract, called peristaltic waves, push food through the system once it has been chewed and swallowed.

The hepatic system

The liver is supplied with blood by two vessels: the hepatic portal vein and the hepatic artery. The hepatic artery delivers oxygenated blood to the liver, where the oxygen is exploited for energy at the same time as the liver rids the blood of toxins. The hepatic portal vein carries deoxygenated, nutrient-rich blood from the small intestine to the liver, so that the nutrients can be further processed: the only instance of a vein directing blood from one organ into another, rather than directly to the heart. The liver then ensures that nutrient levels are not too high before the blood continues further along its journey. Too much glucose in the blood, derived perhaps from an unusually rich meal, would damage bodily tissues unless the liver readjusted the correct balance. Toxins are also filtered out of the blood and diverted for disposal. One of the liver's many functions is to store and then pass on the products of digestion to the rest of the body. It is unique in that it deals simultaneously with oxygenated and deoxygenated blood.

1. In the mouth, a digestive enzyme in saliva, called amylase, begins breaking down carbohydrates (starches and sugars) in food even before it is swallowed.

2. The oesophagus carries food from the mouth down to the stomach, using peristaltic waves. The proximity of its opening to that of the trachea (the airway into the lungs) presents a constant choking hazard: just one of many ways in which our evolution has been less than perfect.

3. The liver is the largest organ in the body. It makes and secretes bile, a fluid that aids digestion by breaking down fats. Bile is transferred to the gall bladder, where it is stored until required for digestion. The liver stores and releases glucose food energy into the bloodstream in answer to demands for energy from the muscles, brain and other tissues.

4. The stomach – stores food and mixes it with pepsin, rennin and other digestive enzymes that break it down with help from a weak solution of hydro-chloric acid. Carbohydrates from bread, pasta and potatoes are processed within an hour or so, while proteins and fats from meat may need to remain in the stomach for up to six hours.

5. Once food solids have begun to liquefy in the stomach, they move into the duodenum, where digestion continues.

6. The next phase occurs in the small intestine, where fully digested nutrients are absorbed into the body. The waste that is left behind is pushed through the large intestine, where water is drawn out of it.

7. At the end of its journey the solidified waste passes into the colon, and then down to the rectum, where it is temporarily stored before being expelled from the anus as faeces.

The urinary system

excretes wastes generated by the lungs, the intestines and even the skin, helping to maintain the correct balance of chemicals and water in the body.

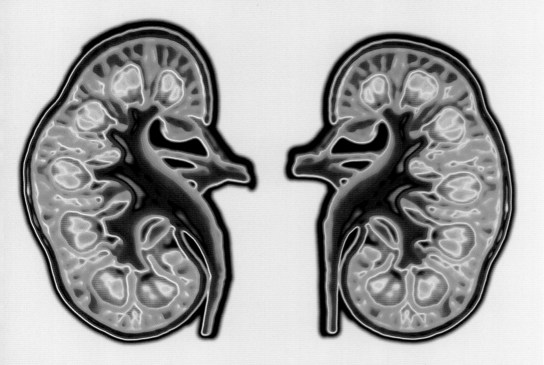

THE KIDNEYS are two fist-sized organs situated on the rear wall of the abdomen. Each kidney is comprised of approximately a million tubules, called nephrons. The outer regions filter the water content of blood, while the inner regions selectively reabsorb vital salts, making sure that nothing valuable is wasted. Leftover products accumulate in the fluid known as urine. This is sent to the bladder for temporary storage, before being expelled from the body through the urethra. We usually pay so little attention to urine, but it is in fact quite complicated. It contains some of the unwanted waste products of our metabolism, including uric acid (from which urine gets its name), ammonia and urea, a nitrogenous compound produced when foods containing protein are broken down in the body. Urea is brought to the kidneys in the bloodstream, and then filtered out by the nephrons for subsequent removal in the urine.

The kidneys ensure that fluctuations in the bloodstream's water, salt and glucose levels are smoothed out. Small, solid lumps called kidney stones may form when salts or minerals, normally taken away in the urine flow, become solid crystals inside the kidney. A constant flow of water helps prevent this. Adults should drink at least ten cups in the course of a day.

URINE

The bladder is a hollow sac shaped like a balloon. It sits in the pelvis and is held in place by ligaments attached to the pelvic bones. It stores urine until we are ready to expel it. A healthy bladder can hold two coffee cups' worth of urine for four or five hours, before nerve signals to the brain demand that it be emptied.

The immune system

The body is on constant alert against infectious viruses, bacteria, parasites and other potentially deadly threats. Defensive blood cells learn how to identify invaders. Then other cells destroy them.

CONSIDER WHAT HAPPENS to a human body when its owner dies, perhaps after encountering misfortune in a remote wilderness. Even if no large scavenging animals arrive to dismember the body, it will be comprehensively taken over by bacteria and small parasitic organisms in a matter of days, or even hours, because its immune system is no longer functioning to protect it. After a few weeks most of the body apart from the hard skeleton will have been destroyed. The living body is under just the same risk from enemies too small to see with the naked eye. Potential invaders swarm in every breath we take, and danger threatens from the slightest scratch, but our immune system fights back. If we are bitten by an insect or grazed by a little splinter of wood, the broken skin cells trigger an inflammation response that increases blood flow to the damaged area while drawing defensive blood cells to the wound in great numbers, in the certain expectation that pathogens will enter the body at this vulnerable point.

White blood cells (of which there are many varieties in a healthy body) are the most important components of the immune system. Known as leukocytes, they behave almost like independent living organisms, able to identify and then destroy harmful bacteria and other invasive agents, collectively known as pathogens. Leukocytes are produced in the thymus, spleen and bone marrow, and stored in lymph nodes distributed throughout the body. The leukocytes circulate via a network of lymphatic vessels and in the blood. The two principal types of leukocyte are lymphocytes, responsible for recognizing and marking out particular pathogens, and phagocytes, cells that engulf and destroy pathogens (bacteria in particular) once they have been identified. The most common phagocytes are neutrophils, and these in turn are the most common form of white blood cells overall. Bone marrow produces billions of these short-lived cells every day and releases them into the bloodstream.

AIDS Acquired immune deficiency syndrome, commonly known as AIDS, is a disease caused by the human immunodeficiency virus (HIV). This is a particularly problematic disease because it attacks the immune system itself, and in particular, the T-lymphocytes that would normally be the most aggressive line of defence against such pathogens. Sometimes the immune system frustrates medical interventions designed to save a patient from other threats, such as kidney failure or lung cancer. Transplanted organs are inappropriately identified as pathogens. Immune suppressant drugs have to be administered to transplant patients. The risk on such occasions is that genuine pathogens will take the opportunity to invade while the immune system is being artificially held in check.

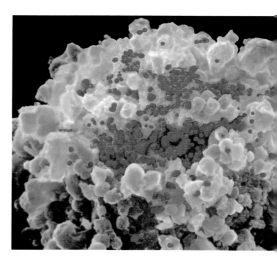

An electron microscope scan of a T-lymphocyte blood cell (green) infected with the Human Immunodeficiency Virus, or HIV, shown here in red.

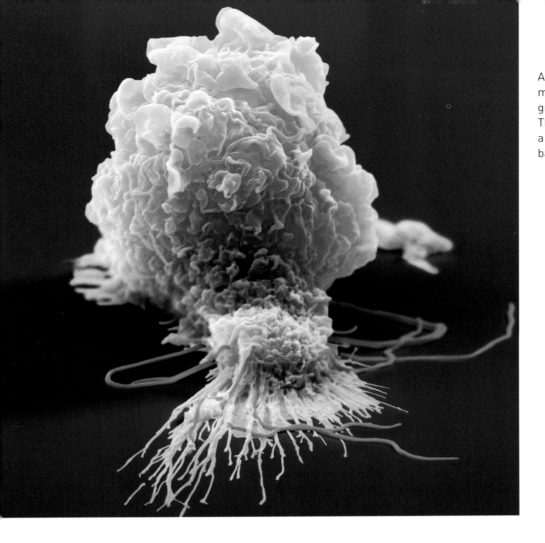

An electron microscope image of a macrophage white blood cell attacking a group of harmful bacteria (blue strings). The macrophage is engulfing the bacteria, a process known as phagocytosis. The bacteria will then be destroyed.

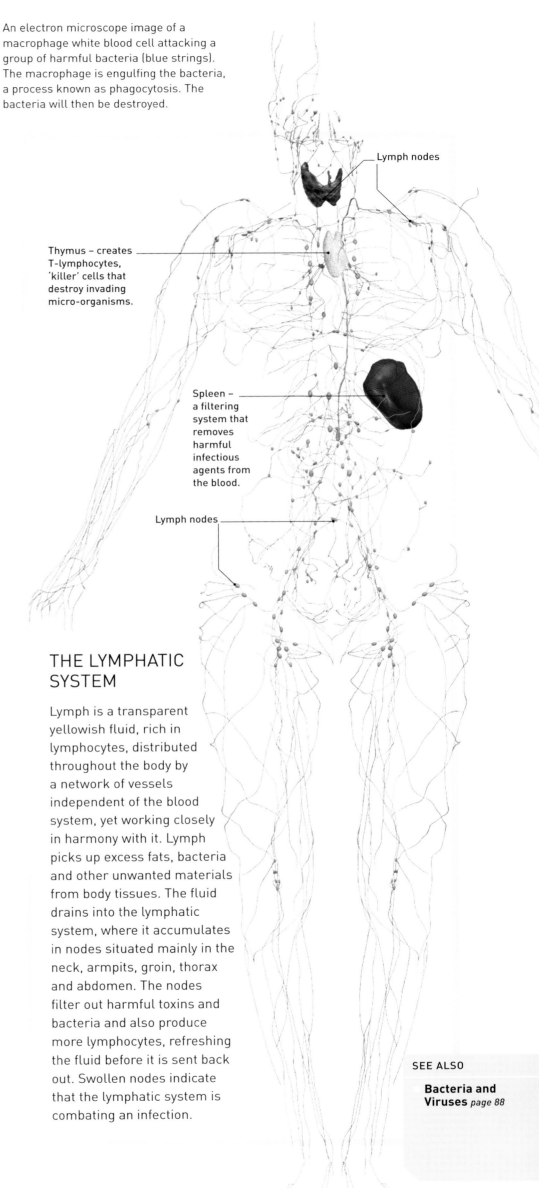

Lymph nodes

Thymus – creates T-lymphocytes, 'killer' cells that destroy invading micro-organisms.

Spleen – a filtering system that removes harmful infectious agents from the blood.

Lymph nodes

Identifying the enemy

The so-called 'B-lymphocytes' produce antibodies, proteins shaped specifically to lock onto antigens, characteristic molecules on the surfaces of pathogens. This is essentially a chemical flagging system that picks out invaders so that other elements of the immune system will be triggered to attack them. When the invasive threat recedes, the antibodies continue to exist in the body: a lifelong guard against recurrence of that particular infection. Each antigen must be countered by a specific antibody. The proper molecular responses have to be learned and then remembered by the immune system. A common medical procedure is to introduce a vaccine, an artificially modified pathogen, into the bloodstream in such a way that its antigen triggers the creation of appropriate antibodies, while the adapted pathogen itself presents no serious danger. The immune system is then prepared against any future incursions of the natural and genuinely harmful version of that pathogen. A small number of suitably primed B-lymphocytes will reproduce rapidly and generate a swarm of antibodies if the pathogen is encountered again. Diseases such as influenza or the common cold are difficult to counter because these pathogens are fast-mutating viruses that come in so many varieties (strains) that no one vaccine can encompass all the possibilities. On the other hand, polio, measles, bubonic plague, tuberculosis and many other once-common diseases, both bacterial and viral, have been held in check by vaccination programmes.

Antibodies lock onto pathogens like remorseless warning beacons, and in many cases can neutralize toxins produced by the invaders, or block them from entering the cells in bodily tissues – but they cannot destroy pathogens outright. That task is conducted by phagocytes, and also by T-lymphocytes, produced by the thymus and sometimes known as 'T cells' or even 'killer cells'. These destroy cells in the body that have been taken over by viruses. This drastic but necessary process strips the viruses of resources that they need in order to multiply (viruses cannot reproduce except by hijacking cells).

THE LYMPHATIC SYSTEM

Lymph is a transparent yellowish fluid, rich in lymphocytes, distributed throughout the body by a network of vessels independent of the blood system, yet working closely in harmony with it. Lymph picks up excess fats, bacteria and other unwanted materials from body tissues. The fluid drains into the lymphatic system, where it accumulates in nodes situated mainly in the neck, armpits, groin, thorax and abdomen. The nodes filter out harmful toxins and bacteria and also produce more lymphocytes, refreshing the fluid before it is sent back out. Swollen nodes indicate that the lymphatic system is combating an infection.

SEE ALSO

Bacteria and Viruses *page 88*

The brain and nervous system

We do not yet know how the brain works, but we can watch it in action. The properties of blood alter according to the amount of oxygen it carries. Brain cells absorb oxygen when activated. Modern scanners identify regions associated with particular kinds of mental activity.

MAGNETIC RESONANCE IMAGING (MRI) – a powerful magnetic field temporarily aligns all the atomic nuclei in the body in a particular direction, like trillions of little compass needles. While they remain aligned, a brief radio pulse is transmitted, causing the nuclei to spin out of alignment for a moment. When the radio pulse is switched off, the nuclei swivel back in line, and as they do so, they emit tiny radio pulses of their own. The MRI scanner then maps the outgoing signals, which are characteristic for each type of tissue.

Positron emission tomography (PET) – follows the progress of a weakly radioactive positron-emitting tracer chemical injected into the bloodstream. When the tracer reaches active areas of the brain, the positrons knock into nearby electrons, generating weak gamma rays that can be detected by the scanner. PET is ideal for observing areas of the brain that become activated during particular kinds of mental processes.

The building blocks of memory

Memories are essentially patterns of neurons, individual cells of the brain and nervous system that fire in unison every time one of them is activated. When a neuron is stimulated to give out a sufficiently strong electrical signal, it provokes its neighbour to do the same. Chemical receptors inside the neighbour emerge onto the surface, making it particularly prone to fire again. This is known as short-term potentiation. All that is required is for the first neuron to send another signal, no matter how weak. If that signal never arrives, the neighbour's potentiation fades after a few hours or days and the receptors are reabsorbed. On the other hand, if the first neuron does fire again, a chemical bond is created between the neurons, making a long-term potentiation. From now on, every time one neuron fires, so will the other. The first elements of a memory pattern have been created. Whenever a linked pair of neurons are triggered, their strong collective signal pulls other neurons into an emerging pattern, and so on. Repetition of a memory pattern

THE NERVOUS SYSTEM

The human body contains many billions of nerve cells. The main structures of the brain alone account for 100 billion. The total number of nerves far exceeds the number of stars in the entire Milky Way galaxy. The right side of the human brain controls the left side of the body, while the left side of the brain controls the right side. At any given moment, only about five per cent of brain cells are activated, but different areas of the brain are called into action for different purposes, and the distribution of that five per cent proportion constantly changes. Nervous impulses are transmitted at a top speed of 200 miles (320 km) per hour: impressive, but still three million times slower than an electric current traveling through a copper wire.

Axon terminals – transmit the electro-chemical signals across a synapse, the gap between the terminal on one neuron and its equivalent terminal on the next.

Myelin sheath – insulates the axon, increasing signal transmission speed.

CLEVER BUILDING BLOCKS

The fundamental building blocks of the brain and nervous system are neurons, nerve cells that transmit signals between each other at up to 200 miles (320 km) per hour. The signals are a combination of electrical impulses and chemical neurotransmitters that mediate the links. Each neuron consists of a cell body with branching dendrites that receive signals from other neurons. A thin, slender structure called an axon allows signals to be passed to other neurons, often over long distances. Until recently, neurons were considered as 'simple' interlinked relays, but it now seems that they conduct a stunning amount of signal processing on their own account.

Dendrites – bring information to the cell body.

The axon – carries information away from the neuron's cell body. Bundles of axons are known as nerves.

The cell body – (soma) contains the neuron's nucleus.

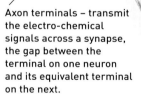

▲ Myelin surrounding nerve fibers performs a similar function to the plastic tubing around electric wires.

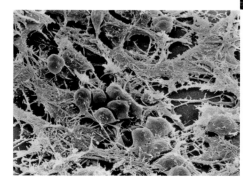

◀ Neurons (blue) among a maze of dendrites and axons that create the connections.

THE BRAIN

This densely packed cluster of neurons and connective tissues is merely the most obvious 'thinking' part of the nervous system, but in truth the mind and body are interconnected. The brain accounts for two per cent of body weight but absorbs 20 per cent of the body's total energy budget.

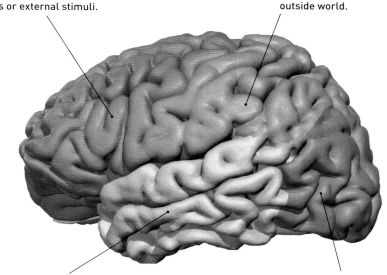

Gyrus – a characteristic fold in the structure of the cerebrum.

Cerebrum – The largest structure of the brain, containing the cerebral cortex (the outer layer) and an inner core divided into regions known as lobes.

Cerebellum – controls balance and aids coordination of bodily movements.

Sulcus – the clefts or grooves associated with a gyrus fold.

Frontal lobes – are the control centres for our personality, also enabling problem-solving and focussed attention on tasks or external stimuli.

Parietal lobes – process sensations, such as touch and vision, to create a sense of the body's physical relationship with the outside world.

Temporal lobes – are associated with language skills and the recall of non-verbal information, such as music and drawings.

Occipital lobes – are the centre of our visual perception, including our ability to recognize colours and track moving objects.

makes it increasingly permanent, while patterns that are not 'fired' sufficiently often will tend to fade. Some patterns disintegrate in moments. Others last a lifetime.

With the exception of instincts, all memories involve the hippocampus (a claw-shaped structure deep in the heart of the brain) and the limbic system, the unconscious emotional centre. All sensory impressions about the outside world are routed from the cortex into the hippocampus, where they leave a fleeting pattern of neural activity. Any stimulus backed up by an emotional response leaves a slightly longer-lasting pattern, because the limbic system alerts the hippocampus that such events are more significant.

In the course of a day, millions of new memory patterns will have been processed by the hippocampus. Important memories will survive for up to three years. Trivial ones soon fade. The vast majority of events that happen across the span of a human lifetime are unavailable for recall, because they are not recorded. A 'lifetime of memories' is more like a heavily edited series of highlights.

Procedural thinking – physical coordination skills for riding a bicycle, making a golf swing and playing the piano are rehearsed repeatedly until they are securely registered in the cerebellum and putamen, after which they are accessed unconsciously. Performers and athletes know that 'doing' is often more useful than 'thinking', because conscious awareness can interrupt the unconscious flow of skills from procedural memory.

Spatial thinking – the hippocampus is a central processing area for all kinds of memory, but the right hippocampus also specializes in spatial and navigational information: for instance, the layout of houses and offices or the street layouts in a familiar city. Brain scans of cab drivers have revealed that their hippocampal regions are slightly enlarged, because complex spatial route mapping is so much a part of their daily lives.

Episodic thinking – the recollection of a past event brings to mind countless impressions of sight, colour, noise, emotions, facial cues and semantic associations, all retrieved from widely scattered areas of the brain. Episodic memory is experienced consciously

when the frontal cortex retrieves these components and weaves them into a 'reliving' of an event. Such memories are often described as being like scenes from a movie. In fact, most episodes are recalled as a series of frozen snapshots. It is not possible to remember the sensation of time passing.

Thinking in words

There is no specific 'language module' in the brain, but the left hemisphere does contain an area devoted to understanding what we hear, and another that helps create our replies. Wernicke's Area is the 'input' module. It absorbs raw sound information passed from the auditory cortex, recognizes raw sounds as distinct words and attaches meanings to them. Broca's Area delivers 'output', processing words retrieved from memory by Wernicke's Area, applying the appropriate grammar to the word order and passing muscle instructions to our vocal cords, tongue and mouth so that the words can be spoken aloud.

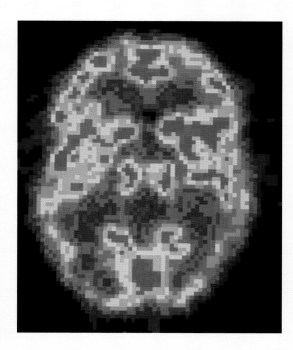

Dreaming It's one of the greatest mysteries: why do we dream? Possible explanations range from sorting out the day's sense impressions and memories or dealing with emotional issues, to random and unimportant neuronal firings. Dreams activate the sensory areas of the brain, including those that process vision and hearing. The vividness of dream life compels us to think that they must have some usefulness.

The senses

Seeing, hearing, smelling, touching and tasting: these are the five main senses by which we accumulate awareness of the outside world. Other senses, such as balance and acceleration, or the feel of our own arms and legs in relation to the rest of our body, demonstrate that we can sense far more than just those five traditional categories.

Vision

The light-sensitive photoreceptor cells of the eye are contained in the retina. They are divided among two types: rod and cone. Rod cells are more sensitive to light than cone cells. They absorb and respond to all frequencies of optical light, delivering a simple 'on' or 'off' signal that the brain interprets as monochrome, lacking in specific colour information. The rod cells make up for this deficiency by being especially good in dim conditions, such as at dusk or on moonlit nights. The cone cells, on the other hand, are primed to absorb only specific frequencies (colours) of light. Each cell will absorb and respond only to red, blue or green. Overall, there are more than 130 million photoreceptors on the retina, yet only about a million synaptic connections lead from the retina to the much thicker optic nerve that sends accumulated visual stimuli to the brain. Clusters of up to 200 rod cells may share just one connection to the optic nerve, while each colour-sensitive cone cell usually has its own direct link. Rod cells are swift and approximate indicators of light and dark, and sudden movements that cause changes in light intensity. Humans, in keeping with other mammals, benefit from fast, generalized warnings of dangerous shapes

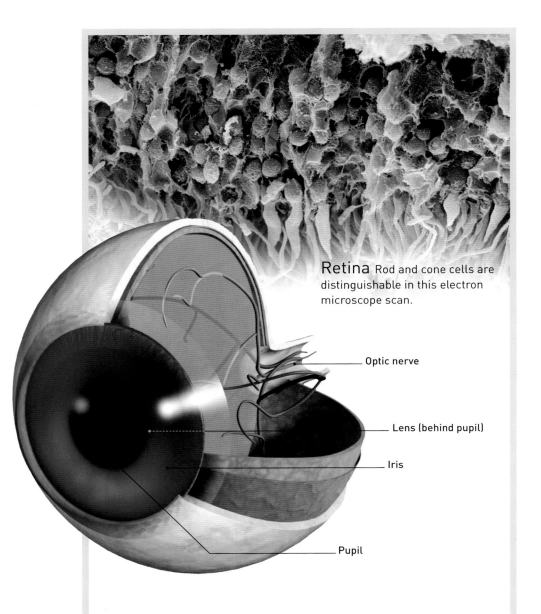

Retina Rod and cone cells are distinguishable in this electron microscope scan.

Optic nerve

Lens (behind pupil)

Iris

Pupil

THE EYES

Each eye is essentially a camera, with an iris to control the exposure by varying the amount of light that enters, and an array of sensors. The human eye is often described as a marvel, but in some ways it is flawed. For instance, many of the blood vessels that supply the retina are on the front surface, partially degrading its sensitivity.

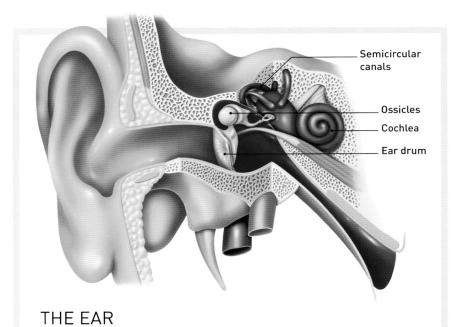

Semicircular canals

Ossicles

Cochlea

Ear drum

THE EAR

The human ear can detect sound frequencies raging from 16 vibrations to 20,000 vibrations per second. Certain noises made by an elephant are too low in frequency for us to discern. Anything higher in frequency than a dog whistle will also be impossible to detect.

Inner ear Tiny hairs sense the movement of fluid in the semicircular canals, acting as a natural 'gyroscope.' The brain combines signals from the inner ear with other sense impressions (especially visual information about the horizon) to determine the body's orientation in space.

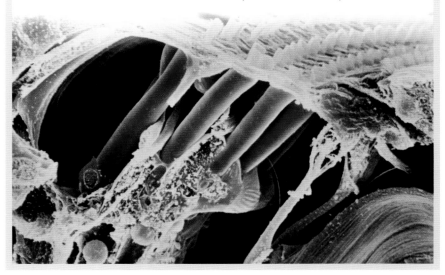

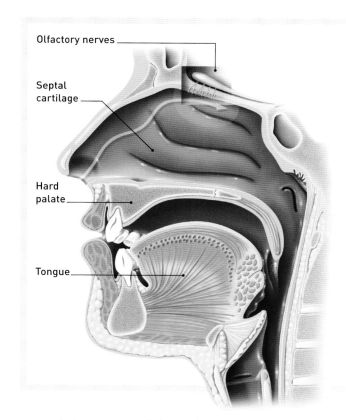

Olfactory nerves

Septal
cartilage

Hard
palate

Tongue

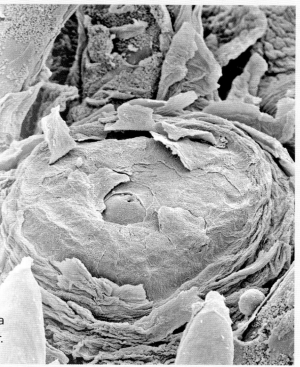

Taste buds near the surface of the tongue allow us to perceive bitterness, saltiness, sweetness and sourness: distinctions valuable for fruit-eating primates. A fifth recently discovered category, 'savory', responds to the taste of cooked meat.

THE NASAL PASSAGE

It is, in fact, our sense of smell that makes food taste so good. Odour molecules from each mouthful travel through the passage between the nose and mouth to olfactory receptor cells at the top of the nasal cavity, just behind the bridge of the nose. Proof of our dependence on smell comes when the nose is blocked with mucus as the result of a cold, causing food to lose much of its flavour.

around them, even if the information is unspecified. The colour-sensitive cone cells are suited for more leisurely and detailed visual processing.

Rod cells are widely scattered across the retina, while cone cells are densely packed in and around the fovea, the small area on the retina where light entering through the lens of the eye comes to the sharpest focus. The fovea occupies only one-tenth of one per cent of the retina's total surface area, yet it contains ten per cent of the total number of photoreceptors and axons (connectors to the optic nerve). Just below the fovea is its qualitative opposite, the 'blind spot'. This where the optic nerve connects physically with the retina. If you stare at a chessboard without shifting your gaze, you will notice some squares simply vanishing. This is because the incoming light from those particular squares comes to a focus on the blind spot, and there are no photoreceptors there to respond.

Hearing

The outer ear is shaped like a cup to direct sounds toward the tympanic membrane, more commonly known as the eardrum. The ossicles, a mechanically linked series of three small bones in the inner ear, transfer vibrations from the eardrum to the oval window, a membrane similar in some respects to the eardrum, that transmits the vibrations yet further along the chain, into a fluid-filled chamber, shaped like the spiral shell of a snail, and called the cochlea. The incoming vibrations from the ossicles push against a membrane known as the oval window. The vibrations then pass from this membrane into the fluid, acting upon membranes on the inner walls of the cochlea that have tiny hair bundles stretched between them. The width and thickness of the membranes varies from region to region within the cochlea, and accordingly each area resonates at different frequencies from the others. The hair bundles are attached to synapses on the auditory nerve, which sends signals to the brain from those membranes that have been activated. In this way, the ear can distinguish different sounds, from the low-pitched, low frequency rumble of thunder to the high-pitched, high-frequency whine of a mosquito's wings.

Other structures inside the ear work in conjunction with visual and other stimuli to give us a sense of balance. There are three

looped chambers in the inner ear, positioned at right angles to each other. These 'semicircular canals' are fluid-filled, and each has at its base a bulbous sensitized area called the ampulla, lined with hair cells. While the membranes in the cochlea are attuned to vibration, the ampullae register the shifting of the entire mass of fluid in the semicircular canals. The brain then registers the nerve impulses from each of the three ampullae to determine the head's inclination or acceleration in three spatial planes, in almost the same way that a gyro platform works in an aircraft to measure its orientation relative to the horizon. Sometimes the sensory information from eye and ear fails to agree. If you are aboard a boat at sea that rocks and sways in a swell, the semicircular canals will register moment-by-moment signals of movement. Meanwhile your brain interprets the far horizon as 'fixed'. This apparent clash of data may cause you discomfort and perhaps nausea: a cue for you to try, if possible, to stay still for a while and reconcile your body's discordant relationship with the outside world.

Taste and smell

Of all our senses, smell is the most evolutionarily ancient. Yet, in comparison to other mammals, we seem to have lost a great deal of sensitivity in favour of visual and auditory processing. Nevertheless, our olfactory receptors will respond to at least 300 odour molecules just so that we can tell the scent of a rose from that of a honeysuckle. Most people can discriminate several thousand different odour molecules.

Touch

There are four different types of touch receptor in the skin, located mainly within the dermis. Meissner's corpuscles are sensitive to light touch, while Pacinian corpuscles respond to pressure and pain. Merkel's discs are sensitive to displacements of the skin surface. They respond most strongly when small points indent the skin, and respond more sluggishly to gentle curves or flat surfaces. This is how we discern the different textures of objects. Ruffini endings are sensitive to the stretching of skin. This feedback helps us to sense and then adjust the positions of our fingers in order to produce the desired grip or action.

The endocrine system
The brain and nervous system send electrical messages to control the body. The endocrine system also plays a significant role, but by using messenger chemicals called 'hormones' rather than by electrical signals.

HORMONES ARE SECRETED by endocrine glands, and then circulate indiscriminately through the bloodstream; but the cells, tissues and organs they eventually reach will respond only to the particular hormones that are supposed to affect them. The endocrine system influences not just our physical body, but our thoughts and emotions too.

In conjunction with the nervous system, the endocrine system monitors bodily functions. The output of hormones rises or falls in response to the chemical changes that they induce elsewhere. This feedback control loop creats a phenomenon known as homeostasis, which keeps the body operating within an incredibly narrow optimum range of temperature, blood pressure, water balance and glucose concentration. Hormones from certain endocrine glands also control slower and longer-term events in the body, such as the growth of a person from childhood into adulthood and full sexual maturity. Other endocrine reactions happen almost instantly. When triggered by nervous signals from the brain, adrenal glands secrete a hormone that heightens the body's preparedness for swift, urgent action against possible dangers.

Pineal gland – located in the middle of the brain, secretes melatonin, a hormone that helps to regulate the wake–sleep cycle.

Hypothalamus – a region in the lower central part of the brain, this is the primary link between the endocrine and nervous systems. Nerve cells in the hypothalamus control the pituitary gland.

Pituitary gland – located just under the hypothalamus, this is often considered as the 'master gland.' It regulates many different functions, from skeletal growth during childhood and early adulthood to sexuality, milk production and giving birth.

Thyroid gland – determines the extent of bone growth in children and young adults, and regulates body temperature and weight by controlling the rate at which individual cells in the body burn fuels from food to produce energy.

Pancreas – secretes digestive enzymes and hormones, including insulin, which is essential for maintaining a steady level of glucose food energy in the blood.

Adrenal glands – at times of urgent stress or excitement, a rush of adrenaline primes the body to respond with a more rapid heart rate, quicker breathing and muscles tensed for action.

A coloured electron microscope image of follicles in the thyroid gland. Each follicle has a cell wall layer (green) around a roughly spherical chamber in which the thyroid hormones are synthesized.

Gonads – the testes and ovaries are responsible, respectively, for sperm production in men and egg production in women. Testes secrete testosterone, a hormone governing male sexual development and behaviour, while ovaries produce oestrogen, which is involved in the development of female sexual features.

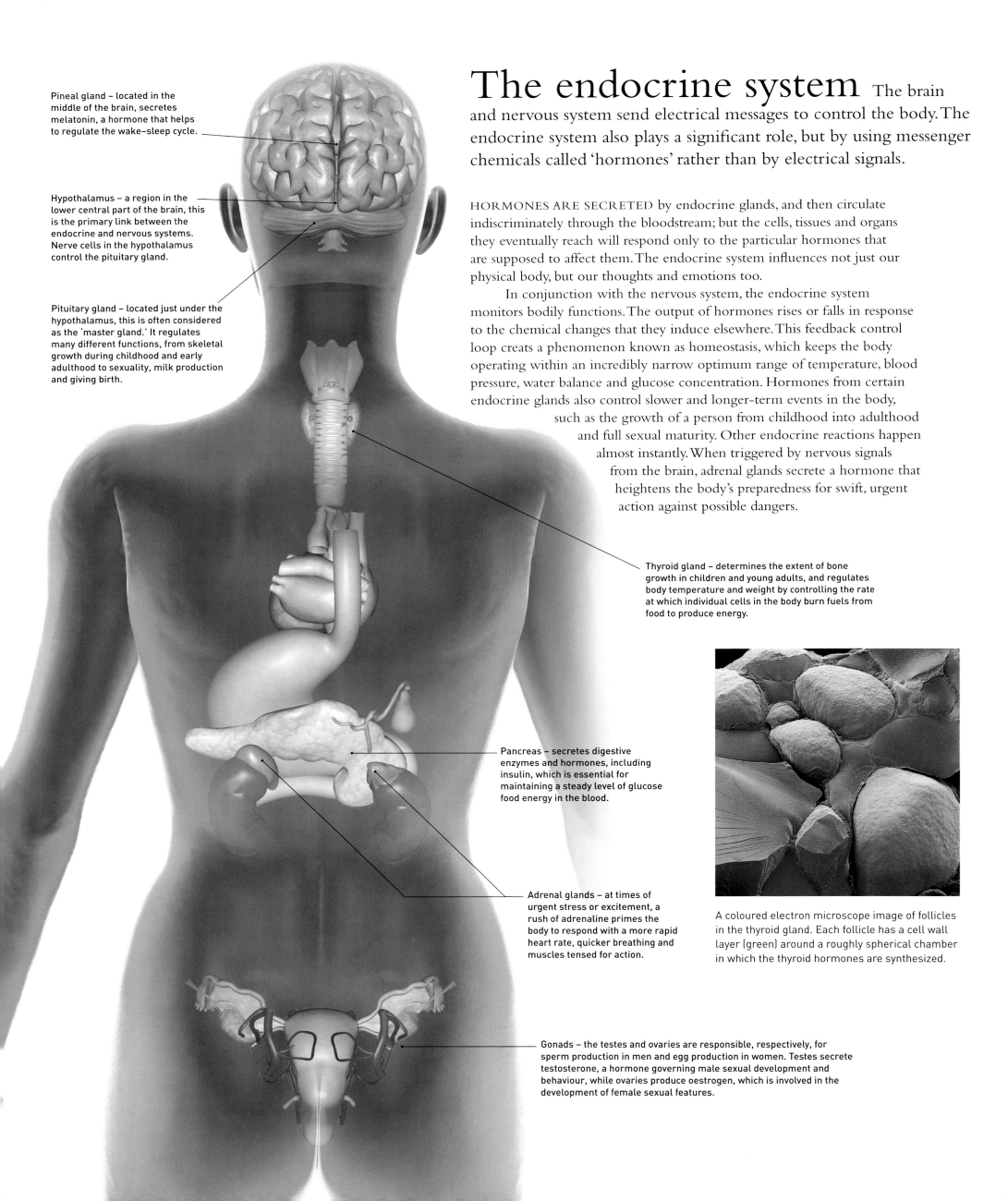

Reproductive system

There are six billion humans on the planet. The birth of babies is commonplace, yet when we participate in that process, we cannot help but think of it as one of the most miraculous events that can happen.

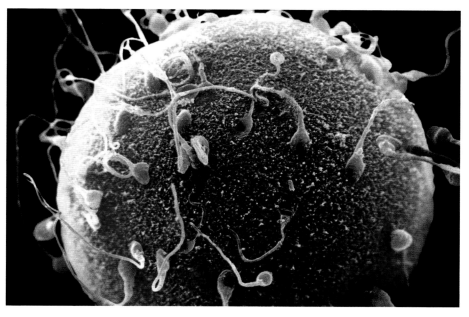

Sperm struggle to penetrate the ovum and achieve fertilization. Only one sperm will succeed. The instant it does so, the ovum will block any further attempts from other sperm. This process has evolved to ensure that only a healthy sperm can get in.

FOR CONCEPTION to occur, a man's sperm must meet a woman's egg and combine with it. Sperm cells are gametes produced in the testes, and eggs are female gametes produced in the ovaries. Just as for all other mammal species, human fertilization happens inside the female's body. A man must ejaculate semen into a woman's vagina to transfer sperm to her. This is the clinical explanation for love-making: a process that has more than merely mechanical significances in human relationships.

Women have two ovaries containing female gametes, or 'eggs'. Once a month, sexually mature women release a single egg into the Fallopian tube where it may be met by a sperm to be fertilized. A healthy woman will release around 400 eggs during her years of sexual maturity, a time in her life spanning anywhere from 30 to 40 years. Only a few eggs are likely to be fertilized in that time. Women have been known to have more than a dozen children in all, but the average is usually somewhere between one and seven children. On fertilization, the combined material of an egg and a single sperm cell becomes a zygote, which now contains genetic information from both parents. Within just a few hours of conception, the zygote undergoes cell division. Then it progresses into a muscular chamber called the uterus, or 'womb', whose main function is to nourish the zygote as its cells continue to divide as it grows into an embryo. A surrounding membrane, the placenta, provides the embryo with blood, oxygen and nutrients from the mother, while removing toxins and carbon dioxide. An umbilical cord connects the embryo to the mother's bloodstream. After forty weeks – nine months – the embryo (by now in the 'foetal' stage) is mature enough to leave its mother and enter the world.

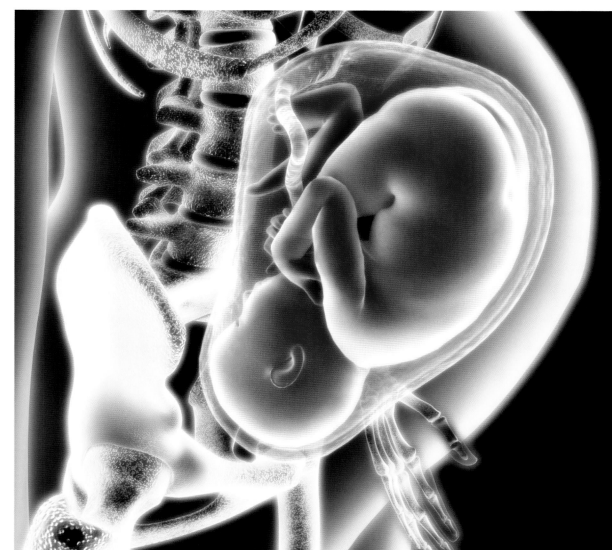

REPRODUCTION

The growth and development of a human embryo from the moment of fertilization and into a baby ready to be born takes, on average, 280 days, or 40 weeks. For ease of reference, this gestation (pregnancy) period is divided into three three-month phases, known as trimesters.

First trimester
Basic growth of the brain, spinal cord, the heart and intestinal tract. Buds that will become arms and legs develop. The heart begins to beat after three weeks.

Second trimester
Major organs are formed by the beginning of the second trimester, and the foetus begins to kick and move, and respond to stimuli such as the sound of the mother's voice.

Third trimester
The lungs continue to develop and the foetus begins to breathe amniotic fluid. Bones fully develop and eyelids open and close. The head turns downward in preparation for birth.

Emotions

What does it really mean to become angry, to be afraid, to get stressed? We think of emotions as a product of our brains, but the 'feelings' that we experience are generated by the body.

ALL STIMULI FROM THE OUTSIDE WORLD (sights, sounds, touches and smells) are routed to various areas of the brain by the thalamus, a central switching area. From here, the stimuli are split between two different paths. One way winds through the cortex, where information can be assessed in detail, consciously. The other route is much shorter, bypassing the cortex and heading straight into the amygdala. If the amygdala detects something alarming in a stimulus, it will fire several milliseconds before the conscious mind has received the same information. This is why we jump unthinkingly at a sudden noise, and only moments later start to wonder what it might have been. The amygdala is not concerned with detailed processing and often fires at the slightest provocation.

Butterflies in the stomach

The conscious mind becomes aware of physical changes in the body triggered by unconscious emotions. We associate these bodily changes with 'feelings' such as anger or anxiety. A sudden increase in heart rate, rapid breathing, sweaty palms, a hot flush to the face, even the tingling of hairs on the back, all provide physical clues about unconscious emotional states.

The most basic emotions are generated by the limbic system, the brain's deeply buried core. Visual and auditory stimuli are all registered by the amygdala (the 'fear centre') which unconsciously detects anything that seems threatening or out of place: an unexpected movement, a strange sound. The hypothalamus then triggers the release of adrenaline and other stress hormones into the bloodstream. These, in turn, provoke increases in muscle tension, heart rate and breathing. The digestive tract is partially shut down, creating that characteristic feeling of 'butterflies' as the stomach is contracted to squeeze blood out of its lining and into the muscles and other organs where it is more urgently needed. Meanwhile, the thalamus stimulates the release of certain neurotransmitters (acetylcholine and noradrenaline, for instance) to heighten communication between neurons and increase mental alertness.

The conscious mind becomes aware of all these physical responses, and recognizes that something is wrong. This anxiety feeds back to the amygdala as a new alarm stimulus, this time coming from inside the brain rather than the outside world. The resulting 'feedback loop' creates a constant interplay between mind and body. When the threat recedes, the frontal cortex sends calming signals to the hypothalamus, which in turn damps down stress hormone levels. The amygdala detects this, and also stops sending out alarm signals. The conscious mind eventually suppresses the unconscious fear responses.

Stress

Strong emotions place a physical strain on the body. The heart beats faster and harder than normal, the digestive system is hindered from delivering nutrients and muscles become overtensed. In the short term, these discomforts are balanced by the increased prospects of escaping from a serious threat, but eventually the body needs to relax, restore its tissues and return to normal.

Long-term fearful emotions are usually known as 'stress'. They arise when perceived threats don't go away. Stress can be caused by overwork, exam pressures, on going financial problems at work, failed relationships and bereavement. Even positive events in life, such as meeting a new partner or playing competitive sports, can cause stress, but in these cases we tend to relish the heightened stimulation.

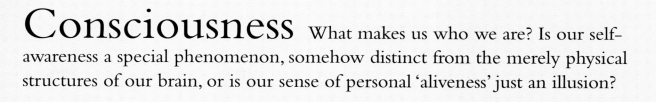

Consciousness
What makes us who we are? Is our self-awareness a special phenomenon, somehow distinct from the merely physical structures of our brain, or is our sense of personal 'aliveness' just an illusion?

THE WORD 'CONSCIOUSNESS' is used in many different ways. We are conscious of our surroundings and make a conscious effort to do well at our studies. We 'lose consciousness' when we fall into a deep sleep. We talk, also, of doing many things unconsciously, like riding a bicycle or hitting a baseball. Consciousness is most easily described as the faculty that allows us to be aware of our own existence and to think about our own thoughts.

Consciousness is difficult to define scientifically. Many theorists insist that consciousness is a biological information process, with the brain acting as a complex computer made from neurons and axons instead of microchips and wires. Most current research assumes this to be the case, even if the 'software' is difficult to unravel. Others say there is a difference between the physical material of our brains, and the nonmaterial consciousness which allows us to know that we exist. Consciousness cannot be understood because it is not part of the physical world. This is the concept adopted by people of faith.

Perhaps the most unsettling idea is that consciousness might not really exist. It could be just a retrospective memory replay of events that happened moments ago, generated by the brain to help us cope with the narratives of our lives. Experiments have demonstrated that we only become aware of our supposedly conscious decisions several seconds after unconscious processes have set them in motion.

An 'emergent' property

Many insects, such as ants and termites, live in huge colonies containing millions of individuals. A single ant responds to its surroundings or its fellow ants. Put those ants together, however, and a sophisticated system emerges. Some scientists call it a collective intelligence. A single ant, with its tiny brain, cannot know very much about what is happening to the colony as a whole, but when all the millions of ants work together, each doing their own little bit, the colony acts as though it had an intelligent mind. It is amazing to see ants working together in huge teams to gather food or build complex nests, as though 'someone' was controlling them. In a similar way, human consciousness may be an 'emergent property' arising from the collective action of billions of unconscious brain cells.

Can computers become conscious?

Since the advent of electronic computers in the 1940s, many scientists have speculated that, since our brains are essentially bio-electrical computers, it must one day be possible to create artificial consciousness in other kinds of computer. Could they be right?

There is a difference between knowing about something and actually experiencing it. That difference is what separates consciousness from other kinds of thinking. We read in a cookery book that a tasty ripe apple should be green with a blushing red patch. This is 'data' that help us pick the best apples when we go to the shop. But that knowledge is not the same as experiencing the red and green for ourselves once we have the apple in our hand. When the colours come alive in our minds, or when we recall, later on, what those colours looked like, we are experiencing 'qualia', the most intense forms of conscious awareness.

A well-programmed computer can learn to spot ripe apples from unripe ones by measuring the wavelengths of light bouncing off them, but could such a machine ever 'experience' the greenness as we can? Qualia are the greatest challenge to explain. It may be that colour sensations and other such vivid qualia (a favourite song, the smell of frying bacon, the taste of chocolate) cannot be translated into dry factual computer knowledge. We might be able to build sophisticated robots, but we don't yet know how to make them think and feel the way we do.

PLANT CLASSIFICATION

Plants are organisms whose way of life depends on chlorophyll, a compound that collects sunlight to power the synthesis of food. If an organism does not contain chlorophyll, it is not a plant.

Plants

Plants are photosynthetic, multicellular organisms, usually (although not always) reproducing sexually, but all containing chloroplasts and cellulose cell walls, and all lacking the ability to move from one place to another under their own power.

Plant classification can be very difficult. Species can resemble each other so closely, only an expert can tell them apart. Plants can also sometimes interbreed across species, producing 'hybrids'. This cannot occur in the animal kingdom, where the very definition of the word 'species' is that an animal can only mate and breed with another of the same species.

Depending on which of various classification systems are used, a plant expert may find that, for instance, palm trees are more like blades of grass than other trees, or that a little wild strawberry plant has more in common with an apple tree than a geranium. One characteristic unifies the plant kingdom. Without exception, they exploit energy from sunlight to manufacture food. Five main groups (phyla) account for almost all plant species: green algae, mosses, ferns, conifers and angiosperms.

Conifers

Conifers including pine trees, firs, spruces, cedars, junipers and yew, never have flowers, typically have needle-shaped leaves and reproduce from seeds, usually clustered in a cone-shaped array (such as a pine cone), that falls to the ground. Yew trees and junipers grow berries that are eaten by birds, who distribute the seeds.

■ **600 species**

Angiosperms

Angiosperms grow their seeds inside an ovary embedded in a flower. Once the seeds are fertilized, the flower falls away and the ovary swells to become a fruit. Most angiosperms are dicots. Their seeds have two parts, called cotyledons. These supply food for a young plant as it sprouts. Most trees, shrubs, vines and flowers belong to this group of at least 200,000 species, as do most vegetables, legumes (peas and beans) and fruit-bearing plants.

Monocots are angiosperms whose seeds do not split into two cotyledons. They stay in one piece as the embryonic plant begins to sprout. Around 30,000 plants are monocots, including orchids, lilies, irises, palms and the grasses that grow on lawns and in fields. Monocots are a vital source of nutrition in the human food chain, supplying us and the animals we eat with grains such as wheat, oats and corn, and fruits such as dates and bananas.

■ **200,000 species**

Ferns

Ferns are vascular, transporting fluids through their bodies, but reproduce from spores rather than seeds. They are among the most evolutionarily ancient plant species.

■ **12,000 species**

Mosses

Mosses are non-vascular. They cannot transport fluids through their bodies. Instead, they must rely on moisture in the immediately surrounding environment to facilitate the movement of nutrients. Though often disregarded by us in favour of pretty flowers and impressive trees, mosses are important. They lay the foundations for other plant growth and help prevent erosion by binding soil. Mosses reproduce by spores and never have flowers.

■ **24,000 species**

Algae

Algae are a very diverse group of organisms that are neither exactly animals, nor precisely plants. Many are capable of animal-like movement, but all of them are plant-like in that they use photosynthesis to gain energy from sunlight. Many algae are single-celled entities too small to see with the naked eye. Some multicellular algae, such as kelp, grow very large.

■ **100,000 species**

FUNGI

Fungi exist in a class of their own. They are not plants because they do not directly harness sunlight as a source of energy. Instead they digest nutrients outside their bodies by releasing enzymes into the surrounding environment, and breaking down organic matter into simpler compounds that they can absorb. They reproduce by releasing spores from a fruiting body, usually called a mushroom. These are scattered into the air to be distributed in the breeze. Most fungi recycle decaying organic matter into nutrients that can be exploited by other organisms.

■ **100,000 species**

Trees

If a plant lives for many years rather than just for a single season, and if it has a strong central stem, or trunk, protected by a tough outer bark, from which many branches sprout, then it is a tree. There is no clear dividing line between trees and shrubs except how tall they grow, and how we decide the meaing of 'tall'.

The largest tree in the world is the sequoia, a conifer found in the western United States, also known as the giant redwood. It is an evergreen, maintaining a canopy of leaves all year round. When mature, it reaches a height of about 380 feet (116 metres). Sequoias can live for up to 2,000 years. However, this span seems brief in comparison to that of the 'Methuselah tree', a bristlecone pine in the White Mountains of California. One example germinated (sprouted from its seed) just over 4,840 years ago; and this is merely the single oldest tree as defined by the 'tree rings', successive layers of vascular tissues in the trunk accumulated with each passing year. The oldest known tree root is that of a 9,550-year-old spruce in Sweden. None of the modest-sized spruce trunks extending from it have lived for longer than about 600 years, but this spruce renews itself by periodically extending new trunks from its root system.

Trees in autumn

As winter approaches and opportunties for photosynthesis are reduced 'deciduous' trees withhold fluids from their broad, colourful leaves and draw the nutrients back into the body of the tree. The leaves turn brown – often making a lovely display as they do so – and they then fall to the ground as dry husks. Deciduous trees conserve energy by coming into leaf only when sunshine is readily available. The 'downside' is the need to grow fresh, large leaves very quickly for the summer. By contrast, many tropical species keep in leaf all year round because winter never threatens them; and conifers keep their small, thin leaves all through the coldest seasons, allowing photosynthesis to continue even during the brief hours of winter sunlight while minimizing the nutrient requirements for each leaf. Conifers also avoid the energy expenditure of growing an entirely new canopy of leaves every spring.

The Giant Sequoia is found only in western Sierra Nevada, California. It grows from a seed no larger than a grain of wheat. If left undisturbed, it can live for 2,500 years.

Tree rings

The study of tree rings is known as dendrochronology. A cross-section of a tree trunk usually shows a distinct pattern of concentric rings, each showing the tissues grown by the tree during the space of one year. The growth occurs in the cambium, a thin, continuous sheath of cells between the outer bark and the inner wood. Very large, old trees are detailed 'diaries' of climate change. Variations in the thickness, coloration and chemical concentrations in each ring yield clues about specific conditions many decades, or even centuries, ago. For instance, a ring can reveal whether or not a particular year experienced a hard winter or an arid summer.

SEE ALSO

■ **The Tree of Life**
page 103

PLANT REPRODUCTION

Animals expend a great deal of energy on sex, often travelling vast distances to find mates, but flowering plants tend to be immobile. They rely on indirect contact with partners for reproduction.

THE 'MALE' PARTS OF A FLOWER, the stamens, are tipped by anthers which produce pollen grains, the plant equivalent of male sperm in animals. The pistil is the 'female' part of a flower, containing the ovary, the style (a tubular structure that extends from the ovary) and the stigma, where pollen from another flower's anther, carried in on the wind, or more likely delivered by a pollinating insect, makes first contact. The pollen grain then extends a tube that makes its way down the style and into the receiving flower's ovary. Inside here are the ovules, each of which contains a single egg cell. When the pollen tube makes contact with an egg, a seed begins to grow. On maturity the seed is dispersed by wind or animal transport – or by becoming part of a seed-bearing fruit, such as a berry, that is eaten by animals. The fleshy pulp of a fruit is digested but the hard seeds are expelled in animal droppings. They land on the ground and germinate as seedlings.

Insects such as bees and butterflies are essential to the life cycle of most flowering plant species. Startlingly precise physical mechanisms have evolved to deposit pollen on the flanks of visiting insects, and capture pollen when the insects visit the next flower. Without the intervention of insects, pollen would not be transported, and the future existence of over 230,000 flowering plants would be threatened. Over the last decade, significant declines in honey bee populations, known as colony collapse disorder, have caused widespread concern.

Under an electron microscope, pollen grains reveal themselves to be unique for each species of flower that generates them, with an evolved design suited to whichever method of dispersal they favour. Grains carried by insects often clump together in sticky packages whenever an opportunity for a ride presents itself. Wind-borne grains are extremely small, dry and light, like the finest talc powder, and travel alone.

Most pollen grains have a hard outer shell, the sporoderm, which is difficult for animals to digest. The sporoderm is so durable that examples can be found in fossil deposits millions of years old. However, there are some essential weak points in the armour: small openings, or pores, that allow the interior proteins and amino acids to interact with the flowers that receive them. (Pollen drifting in the air can also inadvertently interact with the human immune system, causing an allergic reaction known as 'hay fever'.)

▼ **The cocklebur** is typical of plants whose seeds catch in the fur of passing mammals to ensure a wide distribution.

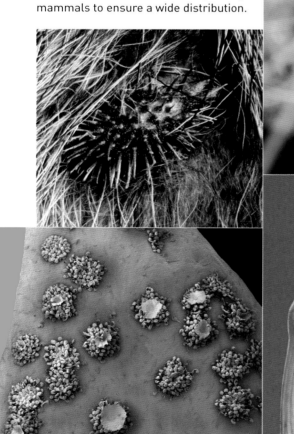

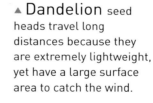

▲ **Dandelion** seed heads travel long distances because they are extremely lightweight, yet have a large surface area to catch the wind.

◄ **Sycamore** seeds have evolved an efficient aerodynamic structure designed to keep them whirling in the air for as long as possible once they have been dropped from their parent tree. Longer flight times increase each seed's chances of finding a landing spot where it will not have to compete for resources with the parent tree.

▲ **The underside** of a fern leaf, showing spore-containing clusters, or 'spori'.

ASEXUAL PLANT REPRODUCTION

Plant and fungal spores contain both male and female reproductive capacities, and so do not depend on complicated pollination machinery to bring about fertilization from outside themselves. They are 'asexual'. Spores ejected by the parent plant must land in a warm, moist and shaded area before developing further. Each spore has a very small chance of success. A parent plant maximizes the chances by releasing many thousands of spores, often in puffy clouds as fine as dust. A fortunate spore will split, forming two identical cells in a small, heart-shaped structure known as a prothallus. This extends root-like hairs (rhizoids) to secure itself to the ground. After several weeks, male and female reproductive organs develop, and self-fertilization occurs. The resulting embryo grows into a new spore-producing plant, and the cycle begins anew. The advantage of this strategy is that it takes less energy to produce spores than to grow flowers and make seeds. The disadvantage is that self-fertilization limits the possibilities of genetic variation between one plant generation and the next. Consequently, only primitive species such as algae, mosses and ferns still rely on spores.

The male organ of a flower, tipped by an anther, that generates and releases pollen grains.

Corolla The whorl of petals, usually brightly coloured to attract pollinating insects.

Calyx The outer petal-like shell that protects budding flowers, then opens as they bloom.

Pistil Collective name for the female parts of a flower: the stigma that receives pollen, the supportive stalk called the style, the ovary and the ovules containing eggs.

BRIGHT BLOOMS

Bees cannot distinguish the red end of the visible light spectrum. They perceive these colours as essentially black, an absence of light. They can see green, yellow, purple, blue and beyond, into the ultraviolet frequencies just outside the limits of normal human vision. Many pollen-bearing flowers have markings that reflect or absorb ultraviolet in distinct patterns. The prettiness of a flower's colouring as appreciated by us is irrelevant to a bee.

PHOTOSYNTHESIS

Plants, algae and certain species of bacteria perform an everyday miracle, generating complex food energy from sunlight, water and a couple of simple gases in the atmosphere.

PLANT LEAVES ABSORB carbon dioxide from the atmosphere and water is drawn up through plant roots. These simple ingredients are harnessed to create glucose at the rate of millions of molecules every second, using energy derived from sunlight to power the reactions. The glucose then forms the basis for other more complex molecules, such as carbohydrates, nucleic acids and proteins necessary for building leaves, flowers and cellulose, the tough, indigestible structural material that gives rigidity to plant cell walls.

Absorbed photons of sunlight boost the energy of electrons inside light-absorbing molecules of chlorophyll, the green pigment that characterizes all plants. A complex electrochemical sequence splits water into hydrogen ions, free electrons and oxygen, exploiting energy-transporting adenosine triphosphate (ATP) molecules for the next phase, the 'dark reaction', which is not dependent on sunlight. In another complex process, energy is then derived from the ATP to power the synthesis of glucose, using absorbed carbon dioxide as the primary chemical source.

The waste product of photosynthesis is oxygen, expelled through stomata, tiny mouth-like pores on the outer surfaces of leaves. That oxygen is what we and most other animals breathe to live. In turn, animals exhale carbon dioxide as a waste gas. Plants then absorb that carbon dioxide for yet more photosynthesis, and the cycle endlessly repeats. Respiration, the process of actually using the glucose for plant metabolism and growth, is the chemical opposite of photosynthesis, exploiting oxygen and delivering carbon dioxide and water vapour as waste products.

Red and blue wavelengths of light are the most effective for photosynthesis because they have the right energy to make chlorophyll molecules respond. Most plants reflect unwanted green light back out into the world. This is why leaves tend to be green, although some may appear red or purple because of accessory pigments, called carotenoids, that exploit certain wavelengths of light that are not so easily absorbed by chlorophyll.

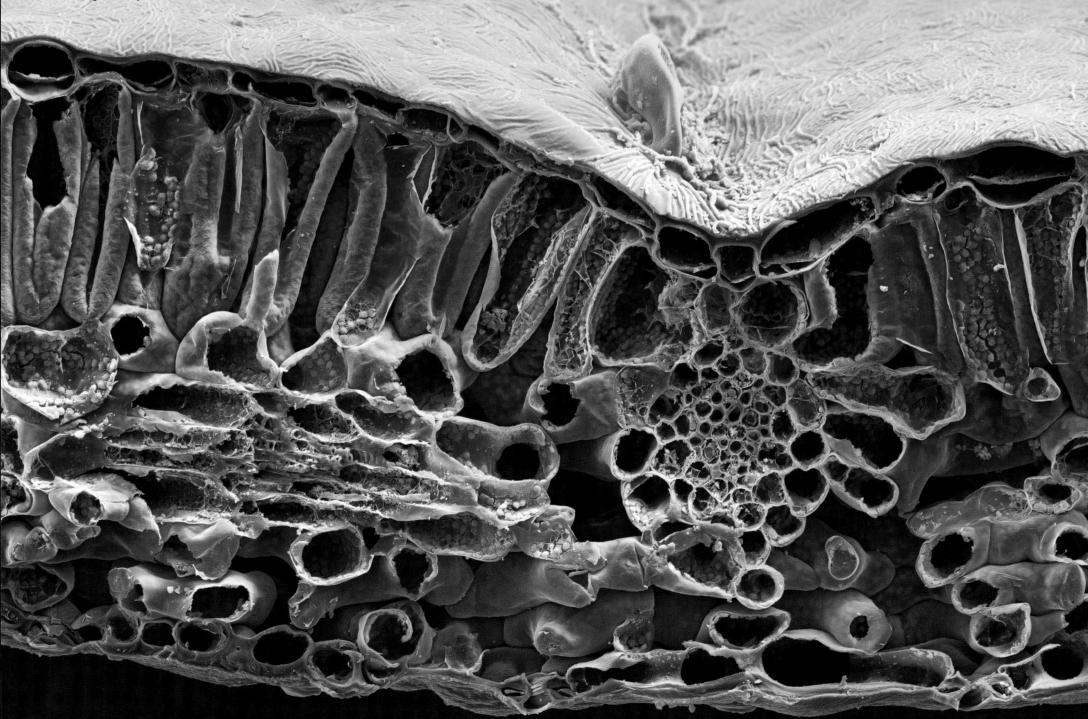

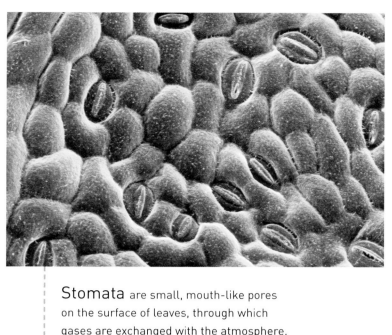

Stomata are small, mouth-like pores on the surface of leaves, through which gases are exchanged with the atmosphere. Each is surrounded by a pair of specialized guard cells, which open and close the pores in response to environmental cues.

Leaves are the principal sites of photosynthesis, but they are consumers of energy as well as manufacturers of food. In winter, when sunlight for photosynthesis is scarce, 'deciduous' plants withdraw nutrients from their leaves and discard them.

Upper epidermis

Palisade parenchyma

Spongy parenchyma

Xylem

Phloem

Upper epidermis

Vein

Oxygen

Carbon dioxide

FOOD FROM SUNLIGHT

Most plants produce more glucose than they immediately need, and store it in the form of starch and other carbohydrates. The primary food sources for humans and other animals are those same carbohydrates, derived either from eating plants or from eating animals that eat plants. Photosynthesizing organisms produce about 170 billion tons of carbohydrates per year: 30 tons for every person on the planet.

Stem The main axis of a plant, often branched, carries the weight of the leaves, flowers and reproductive structures and serves as a conduit for water and nutrients. Water is drawn upwards through chains of tube-like cells called xylem tissue. Sugars and other organic compounds are transported via phloem tissue from the leaves to all other parts of the plant.

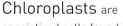
Water

Xylem tissue

Phloem tissue

Nutrients

Roots absorb water and minerals from the soil. The surface area is increased by ever finer branching and the growth of tiny root hairs on the outer surfaces.

Chloroplasts are specialized cells found in all photosynthesizing organisms, containing the chlorophyll pigment required for photosynthesis. Approximately half a million chloroplasts are packed into each square millimetre of a leaf. Chloroplasts also contain parenchyma, loosely packed tissue cells with thin cellulose walls.

SEE ALSO

- **The Cell** *page 81*
- **Plant Reproduction** *page 132*

THE CARBON CYCLE

Carbon is the fourth most abundant element in the universe, and is essential to life on Earth. In fact, it is one of the defining characteristics of life, because its presence or absence helps define whether a chemical is part of the organic (living) or inorganic (non-living) world.

CARBON IS FOUND IN THE INVISIBLE GAS carbon dioxide and in solids such as limestone, wood, plastic, diamonds and graphite. Wherever we find materials or natural deposits that have had some interaction with the natural organic world, we find carbon. Even something as apparently artificial as plastic is derived from hydrocarbons found in natural fossil fuel deposits.

The carbon cycle illustrates this element's movements between the land, the atmosphere and the oceans, and also takes into account its complex relationship with the deepest realms of the Earth's crust.

In geological terms, the migration of carbon from within the crust to the surface may take millions of years. It can be facilitated by volcanism and erosion, or by human activities, such as drilling for oil and gas. The biological phases of the carbon cycle can happen in a matter of hours, minutes or microseconds – in other words, during every moment that animals and plants, living or dead, absorb or release carbon into the surrounding environment. Other chemical elements necessary for life – nitrogen, sulphur and phosphorus, for instance – also circulate in natural cycles.

From living things into the atmosphere

Every time that an oxygen-breathing creature such as ourselves breathes out (exhales), a puff of carbon dioxide gas is released into the atmosphere. Many animals and plants also expel methane (CH_4), another carbon-bearing gas.

From plants into animals

Animals that eat plants, or animals that eat the plant-eaters, absorb the carbon directly or indirectly from the original plant material.

From the atmosphere into plants

In the atmosphere, carbon is attached to oxygen in carbon dioxide (CO_2). During plant photosynthesis, carbon dioxide is absorbed from the air and split. The carbon is absorbed into the plant, while the oxygen is expelled.

From plants and animals into the ground

When plants and animals die, their tissues decay, bringing the carbon into the ground. If successive layers of decay products build up over long time spans, and are subsequently buried by additional geological processes, the carbon can become trapped underground for millions of years in the form of fossil fuel deposits.

From fossil fuels to the atmosphere

When humans burn fossil fuels to run factories, heat their homes and power their vehicles, most of the carbon in those fuels is expelled into the atmosphere as carbon dioxide gas generated by combustion. Each year, 5.5 billion tons of carbon is released from the burning of fossil fuels.

From sea water to the ocean floor

Over long timescales, carbon is removed from ocean water when the shells and bones of marine animals and plankton collect on the sea floor. The carbon in these dead husks accumulates in chalk and limestone deposits.

From the atmosphere into the oceans

Atmospheric carbon dioxide dissolves in sea water and in freshwater lakes and rivers, creating weak solutions of carbonic acid.

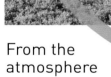

Water vapour rising into the air above
a tropical rainforest is just the most obvious
and visible expression of the close relationship
between plants and the surrounding atmosphere.

ECOSYSTEMS AND FOOD CHAINS

There is a constant interplay between living organisms and the non-living world around them: the rocks and water, the gases in the atmosphere and energy from the Sun.

ECOSYSTEMS ARE INTERDEPENDENT COMMUNITIES of plants, animals and microscopic organisms that inhabit specific physical environments. Biomes consist of many broadly similar ecosystems, defined by the predominant environment and especially the principal types of vegetation. Rainforests and arctic tundra are biomes on vast scales, as are the world's oceans, while marshlands and river estuaries are highly localized ecosystems. An organism's particular way of life within an ecosystem is called its niche. This takes into account where the organism lives (its habitat), how it interacts with other organisms and how it nourishes itself.

An ecosystem's non-biological constituents include the character of the landscape, the minerals in the soil, the climatic conditions, the water supply and, most important of all, the available sunlight. Two major forces link these non-living components with the living ones: the flow of energy and the cycling of nutrients. Energy and nutrition pass between different organisms in an ecosystem in specific pathways. Sunlight and atmospheric gases are captured and converted into stored energy by plants, which also absorb nutrients from the soil. The plants are then eaten by herbivores, which in turn may be eaten by carnivores. The dead and decaying organic matter from these biological dramas is deposited on the ground, where it nourishes countless worms, fungi and microorganisms. Many of the breakdown products from these decomposing organisms (collectively known as saprotrophs) then become part of the soil's nutrient supply, and so on.

Organisms are classified in an ecosystem according to how they fit into trophic levels, or 'food chains'. For example, plants will almost invariably be the primary producers of food, while herbivores are primary consumers and secondary producers. A carnivore that eats herbivores is a secondary consumer and a tertiary (third-level) producer of food. From one trophic level to the next, the original raw energy from the sunlight captured by plants is depleted to a fraction of its original value because organisms convert and exploit so much of it to metabolize and conduct their lives before they, in turn, are consumed. Many billions of blades of grass will feed a herd of several hundred zebras, which in turn provide nourishment for a few dozen lions. The energy stored in the body mass of a lion population is insufficient to support any higher trophic level. Lions, therefore, are the top of their particular food

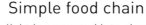

Simple food chain

Sunlight is converted into glucose within green plants. These are ingested by herbivores, which in turn are predated by carnivores. Each stage in the cycle depletes the total energy available for the next stage.

Trees are massive and long-term repositories of carbon accumulated from the atmosphere over years, decades or, in some cases, centuries. Whenever a patch of woodland is cleared by burning, all the trapped carbon is released back into the air in a few hours.

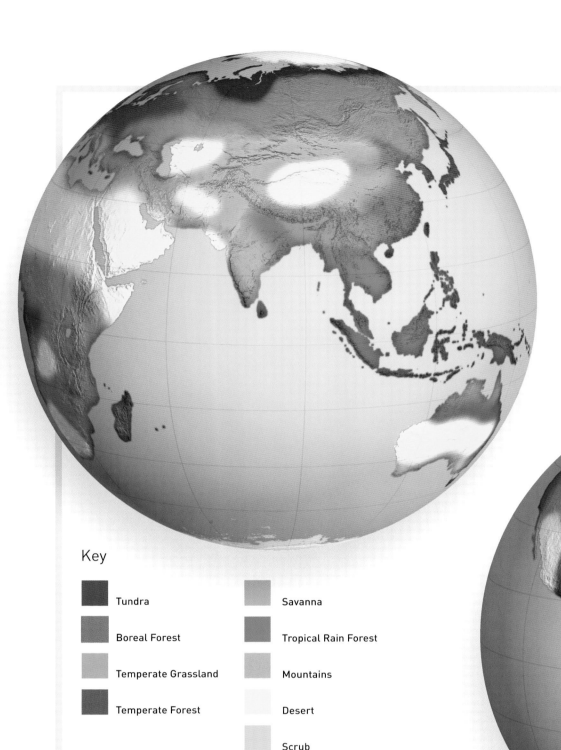

THE WORLD'S BIOMES

The Earth has many different large-scale regional environments known as biomes, each with climates varying in temperature, moisture, sunlight levels and other factors. A biome is characterized by the distinct life forms living in it, and the complex relationships between interdependent organisms. Freshwater and marine biomes vary in salt content but are physically linked. The oceans contain trillions of sunlight-absorbing plankton, which account for 70 per cent of global photosynthesis. Forests, and especially those in tropical climates, contain almost incalculable biological diversity.

Key

- Tundra
- Boreal Forest
- Temperate Grassland
- Temperate Forest
- Savanna
- Tropical Rain Forest
- Mountains
- Desert
- Scrub

chain. Omnivores, animals with a varied diet of meat and plants, complicate the picture by simultaneously occupying different trophic levels. The best analytical technique is to focus on the principal sources of food that any given organism relies upon. The overriding principle of food chains is that they tend to be pyamid-shaped, with the top of the pyramid occupied by the smallest populations.

The human factor

All ecosystems are sensitive to the slightest change in any one of their constituents, such as water supply or reductions to soil nutrient levels. Seemingly unimportant events, such as a slight increase in the acidity of sea water, causes widescale disruptions to oceanic life. Humans are the principal cause of very major disruptions, not just to to ecosystems but to entire biomes.

Consider, for instance, the business of eating a hamburger or a lamb chop, as seen from our privileged position at the top of the global food chain. There are six billion humans. Approximately three billion of them regularly eat meat as part of their diet, especially those living in industrialized nations. One livestock animal typically

can provide a meal for twenty or thirty people. Even so, a global population of 40 billion livestock animals, including cows, pigs, sheep, goats and chickens, has to be maintained to satisfy our taste for meat. Often land has a dual use, supporting livestock in some years and crops in others. It takes 40 per cent of the total land to capture enough sunlight in the grass that nourishes the animals and grows the cereal crops that feed us. As demand for grazing land increases, vast areas of forest with a rich diversity of wildlife are being cleared to make way for simpler ecosystems based on farm stock. Human ingenuity, allied to better knowledge about how ecosystems and biomes function, may help to restore the lost balances in the future, but it will not be an easy process so long as society's needs continue to conflict with those of nature.

SPA

SPACE

On Christmas Eve, 1968, the crew of the Apollo 8 lunar spacecraft gazed in wonder through the tiny windows of their capsule and photographed something that no human eyes had ever witnessed before: our world rising above the horizon of another. A few months later, a group of environmentalists with little interest in space exploration used a similar NASA photograph of the Earth, as seen from an immense distance, on the cover of *The Whole Earth Catalogue*, a gentle riposte to the excesses of technological society.

Moon-bound astronauts and counterculture publishers could hardly have seemed further apart, but in the late 1960s a 'paradigm shift' swiftly transformed our collective understanding of Earth's place in the universe. Today, any one of us can conjure up in the mind's eye that beautiful, haunting image of a fragile and lonely blue ball adrift in the infinite void. According to Apollo 8 astronaut Bill Anders, humanity had flown 'all the way to explore the moon, and the most important thing we discovered was the Earth' bright dots of light in the night sky might be other suns, and even that more worlds like ours could exist; yet none doubted the Earth's primacy in the cosmos.

Around 1,870 years ago, a Greek mathematician called Ptolemy, based in the Egyptian city of Alexandria, believed that the Sun, stars and planets orbited the Earth. He devised a sophisticated and useful mathematical description which held sway for the next 1,400 years. Islamic scholars took up his work, and eventually, as Christian dogma took hold across medieval and early Renaissance Europe, it became not just absurd but dangerous to suggest that the human realm could be anything else but at the centre of all existence.

By the 16th century, astronomers still had great respect for Ptolemy as a brilliant pioneer of their science, but as measurements and timings of motions in the night sky became more accurate, many movements of astronomical bodies refused to fit into his framework. Errors accumulated in Ptolemy's scheme. A better theory of the heavens was needed. In 1610, Galileo Galilei directed one of the earliest telescopes towards Jupiter. He saw its moons, which was stunning in itself. Of even greater significance was the way that he saw sunlight illuminating Venus, sometimes full-on and at other times obliquely, just as is the case with our own moon.

From these observations, Galileo claimed that the Sun could not be orbiting the Earth. Rather, the Earth, and all other known planets, had to be orbiting the Sun. This could only mean that the Earth that God had made was not the centre of the universe: an idea quite literally unthinkable to the Church. He spent the rest of his life in danger of torture and execution for heresy. We, on the other hand, think of the universe in the light of the paradigm shifts that Galileo and other space explorers have granted to us. Science, faith and society alike have made epic adjustments. What might be the next shifts in our viewpoint when the next generation of astronomers and space explorers reports back to us?

THE SOLAR SYSTEM

We think of our Sun and its planets as a special region of space. In fact
there is no real distinction between the Sun's realm and the surrounding
vastness of the galaxy as a whole.

NEARLY 98 PER CENT of our solar system's mass is concentrated in
the Sun. Eight planets, Mercury, Venus, Earth, Mars, Jupiter, Saturn,
Uranus and Neptune, travelling in near-circular orbits, account for
most of the rest. They are confined within a flat disc-shaped region
of space, the plane of the ecliptic, approximately 4.9 billion miles
(8 billion km) across. All but Mercury and Venus have other, much
smaller worlds, called moons, orbiting around them. Moons range
in shape and scale from about the size and roundness of our Earth's

familiar moon, to jagged chunks of rock just a few miles wide.
More than 140 moons have been discovered so far.

A ninth world, Pluto, is so small it does not count as a
proper planet, and is so far away from the Sun that it takes 248
Earth years to complete an orbit. Its maximum distance from the
Sun is a staggering 4.5 billion miles (7.4 billion km) – but the
Sun's gravity continues to reach across a sphere of influence at
least 37 trillion miles (60 trillion km) across. Scattered islands of

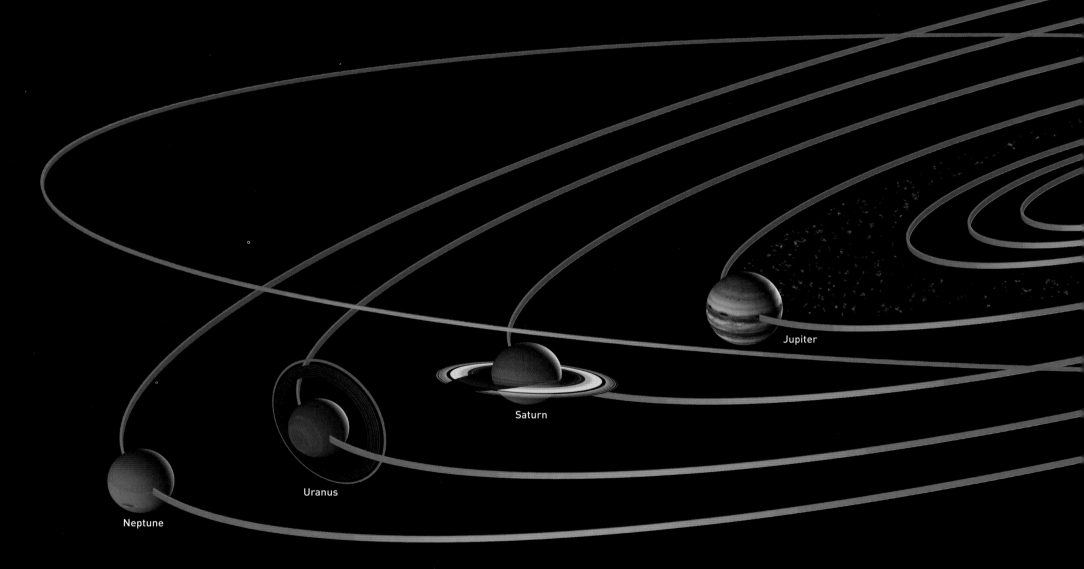

Jupiter

Saturn

Uranus

Neptune

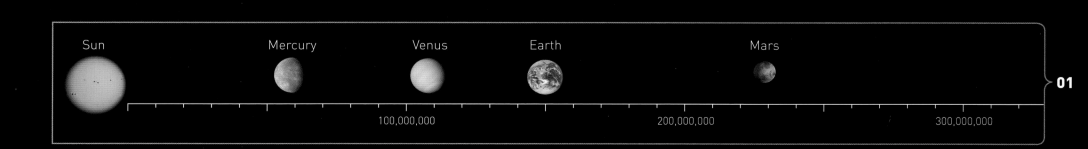

Sun	Mercury	Venus	Earth	Mars

100,000,000   200,000,000   300,000,000

dust, gas and cometary chunks of ice roam this dark perimeter. Light from the dwindling Sun travels for three years before it glints, faintly, on these last, lonely outposts of the solar system. From here, the Sun's influences cannot be told apart from those of the two hundred billion other stars whose collective gravity binds the Milky Way galaxy together.

Worlds of rock and gas

As the solar system first began to form, some 4.5 billion years ago, the heat radiating out of the new Sun blew away the hydrogen molecules in the surrounding accretion disc, so that the regions closest to the Sun became, by default, richer in the scarce heavier chemical elements like iron and silicon, while the outer regions of the disc, where the new Sun's radiation was not so intense, were able to hold on to the more widely available hydrogen. This explains why the inner planets of our solar system are small, rocky and dense, while the outer worlds are mainly giant spheres of gas, dominated by hydrogen.

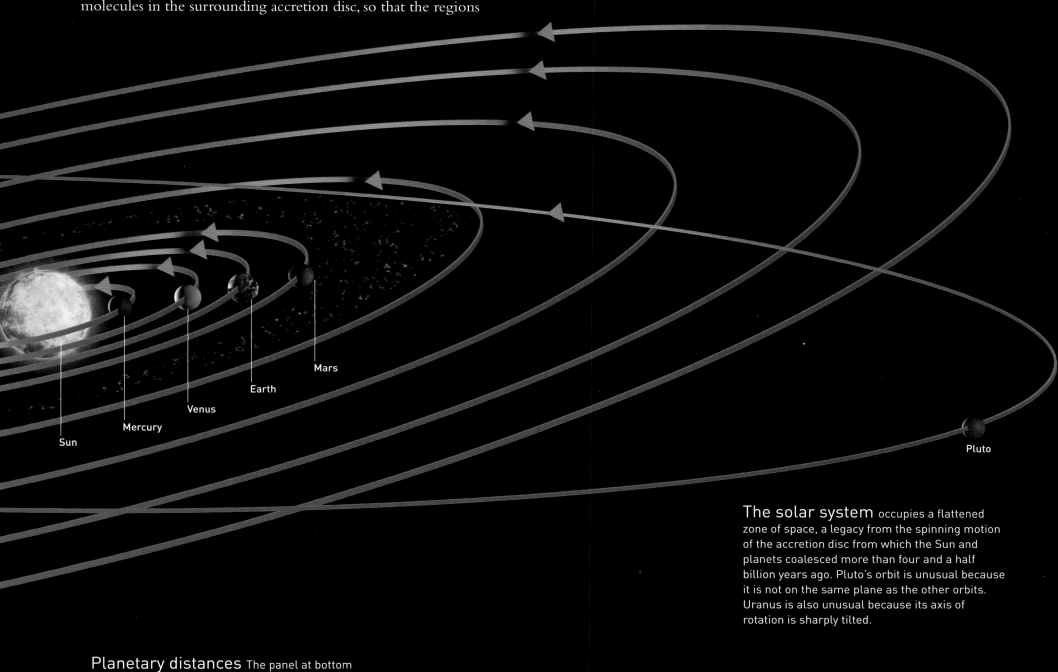

Sun

Mercury

Venus

Earth

Mars

Pluto

The solar system occupies a flattened zone of space, a legacy from the spinning motion of the accretion disc from which the Sun and planets coalesced more than four and a half billion years ago. Pluto's orbit is unusual because it is not on the same plane as the other orbits. Uranus is also unusual because its axis of rotation is sharply tilted.

Planetary distances The panel at bottom left shows the average distances (in kilometres) of the inner planets from the Sun. The entire length of the left hand panel is used as a scaling unit (01) to convey the immense distances of the outer planets shown on the right-hand panel.

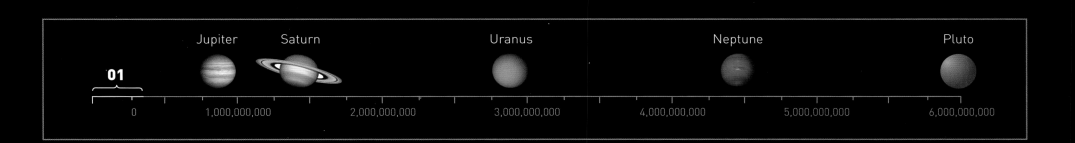

	Jupiter	Saturn	Uranus	Neptune	Pluto

01

| 0 | 1,000,000,000 | 2,000,000,000 | 3,000,000,000 | 4,000,000,000 | 5,000,000,000 | 6,000,000,000 |

THE PLANETS

There are nine planets in our solar system, and 146 moons – or are there?
New moons are still being discovered, while one planet can also be thought
of as a failed star, and another's status is questionable.

Mercury

This heavily cratered world is only slightly larger than the Earth's moon, and in a similar way it rotates around its axis quite slowly relative to its 'year'. A year on Mercury (the time taken for it to complete one orbit of the Sun) lasts 88 Earth days, while a Mercurian 'day' stretches for nearly 59 Earth days. The daylight side of the little planet is superheated because of its unprotected exposure to the Sun, but there is no atmosphere to transfer heat to the night side, where temperatures plunge to hundreds of degrees below freezing.

Venus

Inappropriately named for the ancient goddess of love, this unfriendly world is permanently clouded by a dense carbon dioxide atmosphere. None of its surface features are visible through conventional telescopes. Radar scans reveal energetic volcanism and mountains deformed by heat. The atmosphere traps heat from the Sun so that a runaway 'greenhouse' effect has taken hold, making this a hellish world where ground temperatures are high enough to melt lead. Venus is certainly not as lovely as its name suggests. Even so, we can learn a great deal by studying this most extreme example of global warming.

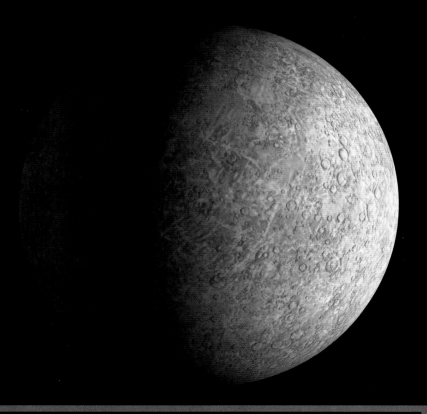

MERCURY FACTS

Average distance from the Sun
36 million miles (57.9 million km)

Equatorial diameter
3,032 miles (4,879 km)

Rotation about its axis
58.6 Earth days

Orbital period
88 Earth days

Gravitational field at surface
0.38 of Earth's

Surface atmospheric pressure
0

Mercury is airless and covered with craters, somewhat like the Earth's moon.

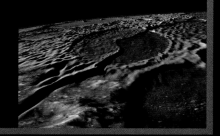

VENUS FACTS

Average distance from the Sun
67.2 million miles (108.2 million km)

Equatorial diameter
7,521 miles (12,104 km)

Rotation about its axis
243 Earth days

Orbital period
224.7 Earth days

Gravitational field at surface
0.9 of Earth's

Surface atmospheric pressure
92 Earth atmospheres

The surface of Venus is hot enough to melt lead. The noxious atmosphere consists mainly of carbon dioxide.

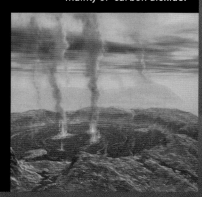

Sun

Mercury　Venus　Earth　Mars　Jupiter　Saturn　Uranus　Neptune　Pluto

PLANETARY SCALES

The planets in their order of orbits from the Sun, shown according to
their relative sizes. The distances between them are not to scale.
If Jupiter were hollow, it would have enough space for more than 1,300
Earths. It is twice as massive as all the other planets combined. The
Sun could hold a million Earth-sized worlds.

Earth
It would be more appropriate to call
our home world 'oceania' rather than 'Earth'. Only 29 per
cent of its surface is dry land. A lucky set of circumstances
makes this planet hospitable to life. It occupies an orbit
that is not so close to the Sun that temperatures reach too
high, nor so distant that they plunge too low for biology to
function. A dense atmosphere protects the planet's surface
against excessive ultraviolet radiation, while an abundance
of water creates a vast realm in which the chemistry of life
can be sustained. Are these circumstances unique, or do
countless similar worlds exist in the universe?

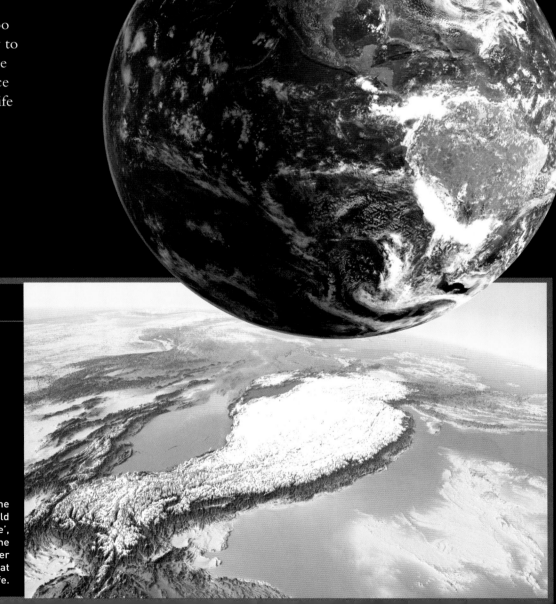

EARTH FACTS

Average distance from the Sun
93 million miles (149.6 million km)

Equatorial diameter
7,926 miles (12,756 km)

Rotation about its axis
23 hours, 56 minutes, 4 seconds

Orbital period
365 days, 5 hours, 48 minutes

Gravitational field at surface
1 ('1g')

Surface atmospheric pressure
1 Earth atmosphere

The Earth is the
only known world
with a 'biosphere',
a zone between the
crust and the outer
atmosphere that
supports life.

THE MOON

Our nearest neighbour in space is so close that astronauts were able to reach
it on six different occasions between 1969 and 1972, after journey times of
less than three days. Yet we are still not sure how it was formed.

THE MOON'S ORBIT is inclined by five degrees to the the plane
of the ecliptic, suggesting that it was captured by the Earth's gravitational field some while after the Earth was formed. A further clue
lies in the moon's density, as revealed by the unexpected weakness of
its gravitational field relative to its size. The moon is considerably less
dense than the Earth because it lacks a heavy iron core. Clearly it did
not coalesce from exactly the same balance of materials in the solar
system's accretion disc that made the Earth.

The best explanation for this is somewhat dramatic. When
the Earth was less than 100 million years old, and while its crust
had barely begun to harden, another newly formed planetary body
almost the size of Mars collided with it. The energy released by this
cataclysm was hundreds of times greater than during the asteroid
impact that wiped out the dinosaurs 65 million years ago. The
Earth's still fragile crust was disrupted, and the Mars-like planet was
completely shattered. Its debris then orbited the Earth, intermingled
with a considerable proportion of wreckage from the Earth's own
crust. Gradually this ring of rubble coalesced into a new world,
the moon.

Mutual tidal forces between the Earth and the moon have
slowed the moon's orbit around its own axis so that it keeps one face
towards the Earth at all times. People talk of the 'dark side' of the
moon, but it is more accurate to call it the 'far side'. It receives just
as much sunlight as the familiar face we always see. In full daylight
the moon's surface can reach blistering temperatures of 100 degrees
Celsius, while at night (which lasts fourteen Earth days) it plunges to
minus 180 degrees Celsius.

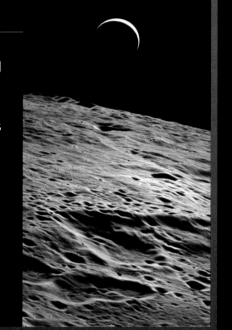

MOON FACTS

Average distance from the Earth
238,850 miles (384,400 km)

Orbital inclination to the ecliptic
5.145 degrees

Equatorial diameter 2,159 miles
(3,475 km)

Equatorial circumference 6,783
miles (10,916 km)

Gravitational field at surface
0.166 that of the Earth

Rotation about its axis 27.3
Earth days

Lunar day 655.72 hours

The moon is pockmarked with craters from countless asteroid
impacts, as if at some point it was the victim of some particularly
terrible violence. In fact most of its craters were accumulated only
gradually, throughout 4.5 billion years of lunar history. In those same
4.5 billion years the Earth, too, has been smashed into countless
times. The difference is that wind and water, combined with a
tectonically restless crust, have obscured all but a few of the Earth's
craters, while the moon, a relatively static and totally airless world,
has preserved most of its scars.

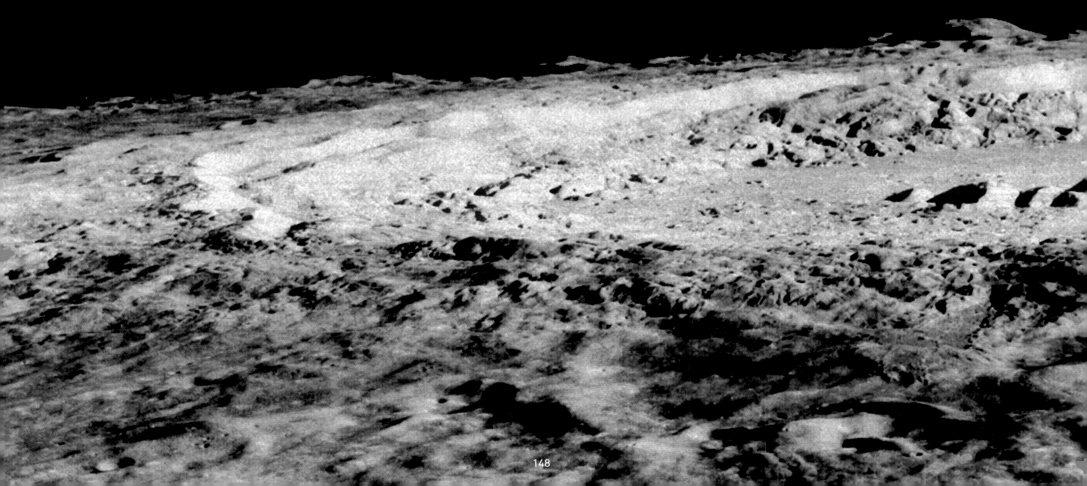

Far side of the moon The face that is always turned towards the Earth is markedly smoother than the so-called 'far side', where thousands of craters pockmark the surface.

The familiar face Tidal forces between the Earth and the moon have slowed down the moon's rotation around its axis, so that one side remains always pointed towards the Earth. It is wrong to call the moon's far side the 'dark side'. Overall, it receives just as much sunlight as the face that is turned towards us.

SPACE EXPLORATION

There is a limit to what we can discover about space using telescopes alone.
In the last half century we have despatched dozens of robot probes to all the
worlds of the solar system, and landed humans on the moon.

THE SPACE AGE BEGAN on on 4 October 1957 with the launch of Russia's tiny satellite, Sputnik. So much has happened since that momentous day, and many dreams of science fiction writers have come to pass. We have been to the moon, and created a permanent space station in Earth orbit. Nearly five hundred men and women from dozens of nations have flown into space, while robotic probes have orbited, or flown past, all planets except Pluto, and most of the solar system's many moons as well, returning a wealth of information and countless thousands of stunning images. Orbiting space telescopes are investigating the deepest reaches of our universe, and their results are available for all of us to access on the internet. Closer to home, Earth-orbiting weather satellites and communication relays have changed our world beyond recognition in less than two generations. Space technology has helped transform our planet into an incessantly chatting global village.

There have been many epic human achievements in space, punctuated by terrible tragedies that have claimed the lives of 17 US astronauts and four Russian cosmonauts. Some of the most wonderful technologies have been realized, and others remain unbuilt. Rocket flight was born in a dangerous time of 'Cold War'

nuclear stand-off between Soviet Russia and the United States, during which intercontinental missile technology from both sides was adapted for reaching beyond the Earth's atmosphere in a bravura show of industrial and cultural competitiveness. Today those nations are just two among many allies in an increasingly international and cooperative adventure in Earth orbit and beyond – so far at least, a peaceful one, although secret military satellites still orbit the Earth, conducting unknown tests and observations.

Before this decade is out, traditional national space agencies will cede much of their operational territory to private companies. Fee-paying passengers will experience suborbital flights aboard privately funded rocket planes and capsules built by a new generation of engineer-entrepreneurs with an unstoppable passion for space. In the next fifty years, it is likely that many hundreds of people will gain access to private space stations in orbit – and some will fly to the moon.

Mars remains a more distant target for human explorers, at least for our generation. On paper, most of the engineering for a Mars ship seems feasible. Building one will require more cash than today's governments or private industries can contemplate.

TIMELINE

1957
4 OCTOBER Russia launches Sputnik, the first artificial satellite, into orbit on the tip of a converted R-7 intercontinental ballistic missile, causing great concern in the USA.

1958
31 JANUARY America's first satellite, Explorer 1, makes one of the most important discoveries of the space age. Physicist James van Allen's instruments find radiation belts surrounding the Earth.

1961
12 APRIL Russia launches the first human space traveller, Yuri Gagarin, into orbit in a ball-shaped capsule called Vostok ('East').

1961
5 MAY Alan Shepard becomes the first American in space. His Mercury capsule escapes the atmosphere for 15 minutes before returning to Earth, splashing down in the Atlantic.

1967
27 JANUARY Ed White, Virgil Grissom and Roger Chaffee are killed when the first three-man Apollo lunar capsule catches fire during a standard simulation to test communications equipment.

1967
23 APRIL Vladimir Komarov is launched aboard Soyuz 1, Russia's equivalent to Apollo. The parachutes become entangled during reentry. Komarov is killed when the Soyuz hits the ground.

1969
20 JULY Apollo 11 astronauts Neil Armstrong and Buzz Aldrin land on the moon, while colleague Michael Collins remains in orbit aboard the mother ship.

1976
20 JULY The first of two Viking robot probes lands on Mars to search for microbial life. The results are not encouraging, but many scientists remain hopeful that primitive life will eventually be found on Mars.

▼ The US Space Shuttle first flew into space in 1981, and has been a 'workhorse' for NASA astronauts for 30 years.

▲ A total of twelve men walked on the surface of the moon between 1969 and 1972.

▼ The Mars Pathfinder landed at Chryse Planitia on 4 July 1997. The crumpled fabric is from the gas-filled landing bags which deflated soon after touchdown. The mission's wheeled rover Sojourner is visible in the distance.

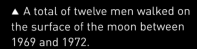

▲ Astronaut Ed White becomes the first American to walk in space on 3 June 1965.

◄ The International Space Station is the world's most ambitious engineering project, with modules, experiments and components from 16 countries.

1981
12 APRIL Space Shuttle Columbia flies to orbit, beginning the shuttle era. The mission is commanded by veteran Gemini and Apollo astronaut John Young, with co-pilot Robert Crippen.

1983
27 JUNE Sally Ride is NASA's first female astronaut to reach orbit, serving as flight engineer during a Challenger space shuttle mission.

1986
28 JANUARY Space Shuttle Challenger explodes 70 seconds after launch, killing all seven crew members and plunging NASA into crisis. A flaw in a solid rocket booster detonates the main fuel tank.

1989
25 AUGUST The Voyager 2 probe skims just 1,850 miles (3,000 km) above the cloud tops of Neptune and beams back images of Triton, a strange multicoloured moon with glaciers of frozen methane and ice 'volcanoes'.

1990
24 APRIL The Hubble Space Telescope is launched into Earth orbit aboard NASA's space shuttle Endeavour. Despite early problems with its instruments, it quickly became one of the most successful scientific instruments in history.

1998
20 NOVEMBER Zarya, the first module of today's vast and complex International Space Station, is launched into orbit by a Russian Proton rocket.

2005
14 JANUARY Europe's Huygens probe successfully lands on Titan, Saturn's largest moon, in one the most challenging space missions ever attempted.

2010
22 MARCH Virgin Galactic celebrates the inaugural test flight, within the Earth's atmosphere, of a giant carrier plane with a smaller suborbital spacecraft slung under its wing – prelude to what could be a new era of private space enterprise.

Mars

The 'Red Planet' has preoccupied us for more than a century. Fantasy writers and scientists alike have speculated about the possibility of life on this world. Modern space probes have revealed a cold rocky wasteland, with no aliens.

Scans taken from orbit reveal the presence on Mars of ancient river beds and sedimentary soils. Scientists still hope to find some microbial life underground – or at the very least, fossil traces from long-dead creatures. Mars did once have a much denser and warmer atmosphere than today, along with plenty of liquid water. Unfortunately, over billions of years, much of the atmosphere has escaped into space because of the planet's weak gravitational field, leaving a dry and frozen world soaked in harmful ultraviolet radiation from the Sun.

Mars has some of the most dramatic terrain in the entire solar system. For instance, there are vents or 'calderas' of four colossal volcanoes. The greatest of them, suitably named Olympus Mons, covers an area equivalent to Arizona, is capped by a caldera that could swallow the entire island of Hawaii and climbs 17 miles (27 km) into the Martian sky. Mount Everest, Earth's tallest peak, reaches less than half that height. The other dominant features don't climb, they plunge. To insult the reputation of Arizona once again: tourists flock to see its most impressive geological scar, the Grand Canyon, a gorge 220 miles (350 km) long and 15 miles (24 km) wide in places, and something over a mile (1.6 km) deep.

The biggest trench This three-dimensional image, based on Mars orbiting satellite radar data, shows Melas Chasma, one of the main canyons forming part of Valles Marineris, the largest canyon system on Mars, or indeed anywhere else in the solar system.

On Mars this would count as the merest scratch. Valles Marineris, a tangled network of canyons, wraps its way around the planet for thousands of miles. The principal trenches are more than 125 miles (200 km) wide in places, and their steep walls extend 4 miles (7 km) below the crust of the surrounding plains. These landscapes are on such a grand scale, they can properly be appreciated only from space. The slopes of Olympus Mons actually have a very gentle incline when viewed from ground level, while the walls of Marineris are so far apart that the opposing faces often cannot be seen at the same time.

The largest Martian feature is, at first glance, the least obvious. The major volcanoes, the Marineris trenches and large areas of rifts and fractures are associated with the Tharsis Bulge, a vast region where the planet's sphere was pushed out of shape by the internal pressures of magma. This molten rock beneath the crust pushed Tharsis outwards like a blister. The great quartet of volcanoes was fed by the blister's hot interior. The magma's journey towards these volcanoes may have formed an underground channel whose crustal roof eventually fell in to create Marineris.

Is there life on Mars?

In 1976 a pair of NASA Viking robot landers tested the Martian soil for signs of alien bugs, but the results were not very exciting. Most planetary scientists agree that life on Mars is unlikely today, but may have thrived many millions of years ago, when the climate was warmer and wetter. Mars may yet have some surprises in store.

The two moons of Mars, called Phobos and Deimos, are just ragged lumps of rock, probably stray asteroids captured by the Martian gravity field.

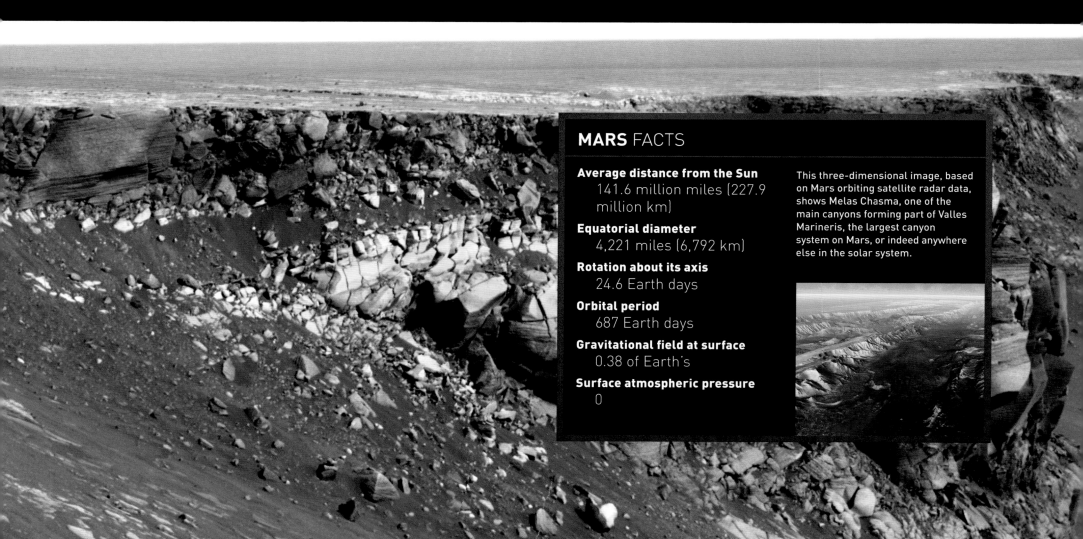

MARS FACTS

Average distance from the Sun
141.6 million miles (227.9 million km)

Equatorial diameter
4,221 miles (6,792 km)

Rotation about its axis
24.6 Earth days

Orbital period
687 Earth days

Gravitational field at surface
0.38 of Earth's

Surface atmospheric pressure
0

This three-dimensional image, based on Mars orbiting satellite radar data, shows Melas Chasma, one of the main canyons forming part of Valles Marineris, the largest canyon system on Mars, or indeed anywhere else in the solar system.

ASTEROIDS AND METEORITES

In the 340 miles (550 million km) of space between the orbits of Mars and Jupiter lies the asteroid belt, where a vast mass of rubble circles the Sun in a diffuse and chaotic band. The Earth has been smashed into by rogue asteroids many times before. It is bound to happen again some time in the future.

MORE WORLDS than we see today condensed out of the solar system's accretion disc, but at least a few of them developed orbits around the Sun that were too elliptical (egg-shaped). At some point in the distant past, their paths intersected and they smashed together, creating a swarm of rubble. Each chunk is known as an asteroid. Some asteroids may be the remains of an ancient planet that was unlucky enough to stray too close to Jupiter. Tidal forces from the mighty gas giant tore the smaller world apart.

Scientists tend to group asteroids into two main groups, based on how they appear in infrared telescope images. The lightest-looking asteroids are rocky bodies rich in iron and nickel. They resemble lunar rocks. The darkest asteroids contain high quantities of carbon. Nearly 200 asteroids have been classified as potentially hazardous by the observers who track them. Some of these might, one day, be pulled away from the asteroid belt by gravitational influences within the solar system. If so, they could end up on a collision course with Earth. Given the long history of ancient and extremely violent impacts, we would be foolish to assume that they could never happen again.

Asteroids Ceres and Vesta compared for scale against continental Europe. These two asteroids, relics from the earliest period of solar system formation, are the largest known members of the Asteroid belt. Ceres is so nearly spherical, it has recently been reclassified by astronomers as a 'dwarf planet.'

Meteorites

Meteors are small asteroids that drift towards the Earth and fall through the atmosphere at great speed. If they are large and dense enough to survive their fiery descent and reach the ground intact, they are classed as meteorites.

Some meteorites are made almost entirely of iron. This suggests that they originated in an ancient planet whose molten interior was iron-rich. Then, in the cold of space, the small blobs of scattered iron cooled very quickly and solidified. Meteoric iron is unlike any iron found on Earth. It has a distinct and regular crystalline structure, called the Widmanstätten pattern, which can easily be seen when the iron is sliced and polished.

The next most common form of meteorites are the stony-irons, derived from the shattered inner crust of destroyed planetesimals. Finally, the most common kind of meteorites are stony, very rich in silicate minerals, and containing only small flecks of metal. These originally came from the outermost crust of planetesimals. Many of these stony meteorites are called chondrites because they contain 'chondrules', tiny fragments of magnesium, iron, silicon and oxygen compounds fused into distinctive glassy spheres.

The chondrules were formed near the young Sun, in the surrounding accretion disc of gas and dust, and then became incorporated into planetesimals. Our Earth has been so drastically volcanized, smashed into, melted and remelted by geological activity that any traces of original chondrule material has long since been obliterated. Chondrites inside stony meteorites show us the oldest examples of solid material in the solar system that we have ever encountered.

SEE ALSO

■ **The Solar System**
page 144

Jupiter

At the dawn of the solar system, the Sun was not the only competitor for the dust and gas in the surrounding accretion disc. The massive hydrogen-rich gas giant that we now know as Jupiter nearly became a star in its own right.

The Sun absorbed most of the hydrogen and helium from the solar system's accretion disc before the supply simply ran out. Jupiter did not quite achieve the high temperatures and pressures at its core that a true star needs. Had it been able to sweep up materials from the disc for a little longer, growing to just seven times its current size, it could have burst into light and become the junior partner in a binary star system.

Jupiter has 16 significant moons with widely differing features. The surface of Io, the third largest moon, is in permanent volcanic disarray. The tidal forces generated by Jupiter's gravity are so great that Io's crust can never settle. The crusts of Ganymede, the largest moon, and Callisto, the second largest, are less turbulent, but the crustal patterns frozen into place on these worlds are very strange.

JUPITER FACTS

Average distance from the Sun
483.8 million miles (778.6 million km)

Equatorial diameter
88,846 miles (142,984 km)

Rotation about its axis
9 hours, 54 minutes

Orbital period
4,331 Earth days

Planetary mass
318 times that of the Earth

Major constituents
hydrogen and helium

Jupiter's largest storm, the Great Red Spot, has raged continuously for at least 300 years.

EUROPA

Europa, the fourth largest moon of Jupiter, is especially fascinating. In August 1996 the Galileo space probe beamed back detailed images of its icy surface. The crust is cracked because the surface melts and reconstitutes itself at intervals, like floating pack ice in an arctic ocean that freezes into place during winter. Scientists think that a huge ocean of fluid water exists just beneath the ice. Could this indicate Europa's suitability for life? Even without sunlight, organisms in the subsurface ocean could be sustained by heat from hydrothermal vents on the ocean floors.

Cracks and grooves on the surface are caused by the restless movements of huge ice sheets, possibly covering a deep liquid water interior.

Saturn

Similar in composition to Jupiter, Saturn's famous distinguishing feature is its complex ring system, consisting mostly of water ice and grains of dust. Close-up space probe images reveal braided rings, ringlets and 'spokes', dark features that circle the planet at different rates from the other rings, like eerie race cars going round a track. The ring system extends hundreds of thousands of miles from the planet, yet the vertical depth is typically only a few tens of metres.

The most fascinating of Saturn's 18 major moons is Titan. Twice the size of our moon, it has an atmosphere that is so dense that we cannot see through it with conventional cameras. Nitrogen is the main constituent, but it also contains water ice and hydrocarbons, such as methane. Although probably unsuited for life, Titan may be a 'pre-biological' world where the basic chemical ingredients are in place. The surface consists of rock and ice interspersed with lakes of liquid methane.

Uranus

At first glance one of the blander-looking planets, Uranus is a dynamic world with some of the brightest clouds in the outer solar system, and its own faint ring system. The atmosphere is mainly hydrogen and helium, with a small amount of methane and traces of water and ammonia. Sunlight is reflected from Uranus' cloud tops, which lie beneath a layer of methane gas. The planet's blue-green colour results from methane absorbing the red portion of the sunlight that strikes the planet, allowing the blue-green to reflect back into space from the cloud tops and pass through the upper layers of atmosphere unimpeded. Most of the planet's mass is contained in a large, icy core.

SATURN FACTS

Average distance from the Sun
890.8 million miles (1,433.5 million km)

Equatorial diameter
74,897 miles (120,536 km)

Rotation about its axis
10.7 hours

Orbital period
10,747 Earth days

Axial tilt
26.7 degrees

Diameter of ring system
155,000 miles (250,000 km)

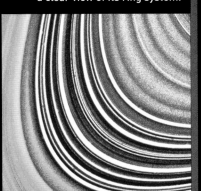

The 26-degree tilt of Saturn's axis allows astronomers on Earth to get a clear view of its ring system.

URANUS FACTS

Average distance from the Sun
1,784.8 million miles (2,872.5 million km)

Equatorial diameter
31,763 miles (51,118 km)

Rotation about its axis
17 hours, 12 minutes

Orbital period
84 Earth years

Axial tilt
97.8 degrees

Main constituents
Hydrogen, helium and methane

The north pole of Uranus has 42-year-long periods of daylight or darkness.

THE OORT CLOUD

Billions of small icy chunks drift at the outermost margins of the Sun's gravitational influence. Occasionally, the gravity of other nearby stars disturbs the orbit of one of these bodies, causing it to streak into the inner solar system as a so-called 'long-period' comet.

Neptune

Neptune, a similar world to Uranus, orbits the Sun once every 165 years. Unlike all the other planets, it is invisible to the naked eye because of its extreme distance from the Earth. It was first seen through a telescope in 1846. Astronomers were looking for it at the time because the available mathematical data predicted that it must exist, or else the equations governing the movements of the other, already known planets in the solar system (especially Uranus) would be incorrect.

Pluto

For so long considered the ninth planet of the solar system, Pluto is now considered to be a 'dwarf planet.' It may not even be completely spherical, being too small to possess a strong gravitational field. It is the only significant body in the solar system not yet photographed in detail or visited by a space probe. We know very little about it. Scientists think that it may be a captured comet, or an icy planetesimal left over from the earliest formation of the solar system. Pluto's orbit is elliptical (egg-shaped) rather than near-circular. As a consequence it reaches closer to the Sun than Neptune for 20 years out of its 249-year orbit.

NEPTUNE FACTS

Average distance from the Sun
2,793 million miles (4,495 million km)

Equatorial diameter
31,763 miles (51,118 km)

Rotation about its axis
16 hours, 6 minutes

Orbital period
164 years

Average temperature
−196 C

Latest planetary status
The outermost planet

Neptune's atmosphere merges into a liquid region of water, methane and ammonia.

PLUTO FACTS

Average distance from the Sun
3,647 million miles (5,870 million km)

Equatorial diameter
1,485 miles (2,390 km)

Rotation about its axis
6 Earth days, 9 hours

Orbital period
248 years

Gravitational field at surface
0.06 of Earth's

Latest planetary status
Classified as a 'dwarf planet'

Pluto's tiny moon Charon seen above the horizon of the only world in the solar system not yet scanned by space probes.

COMETS AND
THE OORT CLOUD

We often see thin, bright streaks in the sky. These momentary flashes are caused when the Earth in its orbit passes through diffuse clouds of dust and ice particles drifting in space: the debris from old cometary tails.

WHEN DUST GRAINS FROM A COMET'S TAIL collide with the Earth's upper atmosphere at colossal speed, they burn for a few seconds and then they are gone. The so-called 'meteor showers' are as insubstantial as sprites. Every year astronomers enjoy a particularly well-known display, the Perseid shower, which peaks in intensity around mid-August with faithful regularity. This shower has been traced to a comet which last swept across the Earth's orbit in 1862, leaving a slight memory of its tail in its wake. Eventually the tail will dissipate, and with it, the beautiful Perseids.

Most comets – and there are vast numbers of them – roam a vast spherical zone far beyond the orbit of Pluto, a zone that reaches one third of the distance to the next nearest stars. This 'Oort Cloud' is named after the Dutch astronomer Jan Hendrik Oort, who predicted its existence half a century ago. Comets appear to be the frozen remains of countless small-scale accretion events during the birth of the solar system. They are light and insubstantial, with almost no gravity. They did not pull in enough additional material from the accretion disc to become protoplanets or protostars.

Very occasionally the Sun pulls a stray comet towards the centre of the solar system. It then sweeps a long and lonely elliptical orbit, occasionally passing close enough to our Earth for astronomers to take notice. Even more occasionally than that, a comet passes close enough for us to see its glowing tail in the night sky. Comets that interact with the solar system repeatedly, at regular intervals, drift in a disc-shaped realm beyond the orbit of Neptune – but closer to us than the Oort Cloud – known as the Kuiper Belt.

Some comets sweeping through the solar system have been observed by space probes. If these occasional specimens are any reliable guide, comets in general are irregular lumps of ice and dust ranging in scale from a few metres to tens of miles in diameter – all depending on how one defines the size of a comet.

The main constituents of the core, the 'nucleus', consist of water ice, carbon dioxide ice and silicate dust grains. These loosely compacted snowballs are so delicate that solar radiation shreds their outer layers and creates characteristic glowing tails of ionized particles. Many comets contain simple organic molecules, such as ammonia, formaldehyde, methyl cyanide and other hydrocarbons. Comets falling onto the young Earth probably contributed some of the essential building blocks of life.

Cometary impacts may be rare, but the consequences can be dramatic when the nucleus, rather than just the dust and ice from the tail, strikes the atmosphere. As recently as 1908 a comet impact levelled hundreds of square miles of uninhabited Siberian forest in the Tunguska region. Although the comet turned to vapour long before it hit the ground, the explosive air burst as it did so was massively destructive. If that event had occurred over a city, it would have killed as many people as an atom bomb.

Comet McNaught photographed here in January 2007 was the brightest comet visible to the naked eye in more than 30 years. It is classed as a 'non-periodic' comet, meaning that it will not pass through the inner solar system again for at least the next 200 years.

SEE ALSO

■ The Early Environment
page 18

STARS

Stars of particular 'classes' live and die in different ways. The spectrum of light that
any given star emits gives us a reliable guide to its behaviour and ultimate destiny.

ASTRONOMERS USE A STANDARD REFERENCE system called
the Hertzsrpung–Russell diagram to categorize individual stars. The
diagram plots the surface temperatures of certain types or 'classes' of
star against their brightness (luminosity), measured in terms of how
much total energy they emit per second. Obviously the brightness of
a star seems to dwindle the further away it is from us. By including
corrections to account for the distances, the 'real' brightness of stars
can be established. Our Sun makes a convenient yardstick.

Most stars, including ours, fall into a narrow band within the
Hertzsrpung–Russell diagram, called the main sequence. Older stars
belong to the upper right side of the diagram, among the dimming
giants and supergiant – although blue supergiants start out their
lives that way, burning their fuels very fast because of their immense
mass and internal energy. Only one in a thousand stars is a blue
supergiant, but they are pretty obvious to us in the night sky. Their
brightness compensates for their scarcity. The best known example
is Rigel, in the constellation of Orion. It is 20 times larger than the
Sun, and 60,000 times brighter.

The mass of a star in its prime of life determines what happens
to it after its main sequence phase. Stars the size of our Sun turn
hydrogen into helium in their cores, but eventually the hydrogen

runs out and the core can no longer generate enough outwards
radiation to balance the inward pull of gravity. The centre of the star
shrinks while the outer layers expand. This makes the star cooler
overall, and it becomes a red giant. Eventually the energy generation
fades almost completely and the star collapses to a white dwarf.
It may even be that white dwarfs eventually dim yet further, to
become black dwarves, but that final fade-out would be so slow
that we may never be able to prove that it actually happens.

That's the average stellar biography, but if a star is one of those
rare examples more than four or five times the mass of our Sun, a
different fate lies in store. It will finish its main sequence lifetime
with a very rapid collapse of its core. The protons and electrons in its
atoms undergo a terrible transformation, leaving a core composed
entirely of neutrons and exerting a very powerful gravitational field.
The outer parts of the star are eventually hurled away in a violent
explosion, and the star becomes a supernova. Needless to say, blue
supergiants invariably end their short, furious lives in a supernova.

At the other end of the extreme, stars that started life very
much smaller than our Sun may just dim over time to become
unremarkable brown dwarves, emitting so little light as to be
almost invisible to our telescopes.

1 A nebula, an interstellar cloud of gas, ice and dust, from which new stars coalesce.

2 Blue Supergiant stars burn fast and hot, collapsing into black holes after just a few hundred million years.

3 Stable, long lived yellow dwarf stars such as our Sun are 'average' in their size and luminosity.

4 White dwarf stars can be as small as the Earth yet with a mass as great as the Sun.

5 A yellow dwarf compared with a red giant, such as our Sun will become at the end of its life.

6 A supernova, the instant when a star explodes, scattering its outer layers into space.

7 A supernova remnant from an exploded star.

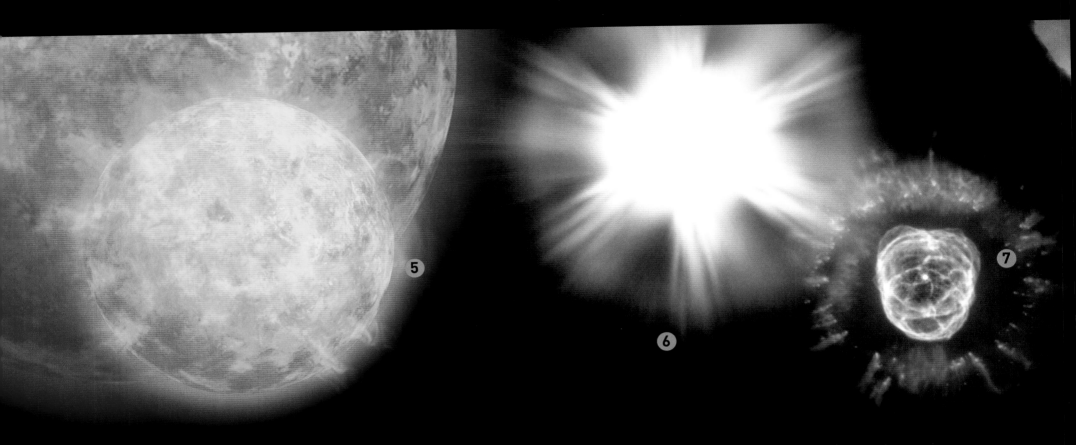

Stellar classification

The lower track (the main sequence) shows the evolution of stars similar to our Sun. After all the hydrogen is burnt, the star increases its diameter and becomes a red giant. Eventually the outer layers are shed, exposing the helium-rich core of the star which becomes a white dwarf. More massive stars (upper track) undergo a red supergiant phase and then a supernova explosion which may leave behind either a black hole or a neutron star. White dwarfs (lower left) are stars that have contracted to become hotter but dimmer. AB Doradus C (lower right) is one of the coolest and least massive stars yet discovered. It is known as a brown dwarf.

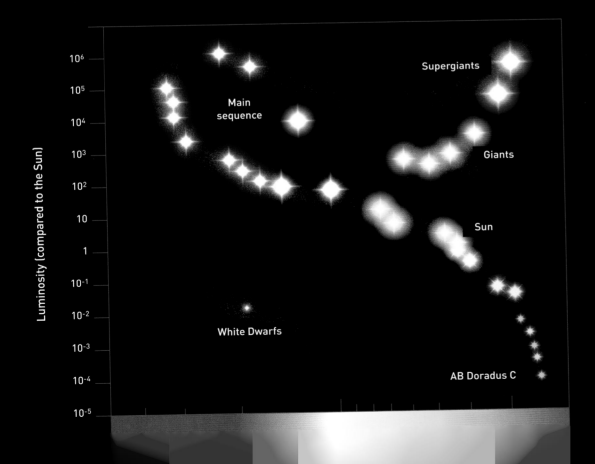

Luminosity (compared to the Sun)

10^6
10^5
10^4
10^3
10^2
10
1
10^{-1}
10^{-2}
10^{-3}
10^{-4}
10^{-5}

Main sequence

Supergiants

Giants

Sun

White Dwarfs

AB Doradus C

SEE ALSO

GALAXIES

Within the universe as a whole, many billions of 'island universes' exist in the form of huge masses of stars loosely held together in distinctive patterns by their collective gravitational force.

WHENEVER ORBITING OBSERVATORIES such as the famous Hubble Space Telescope point their instruments towards a distant region of space that appears featurelessly black on first inspection, a long exposure of the extremely faint light reveals a mass of galaxies. There are perhaps 100 billion galaxies scattered throughout the visible universe, but this is just a rough estimate of a figure that has yet to be tested and confirmed. The most distant galaxies ever photographed are as far as 10 billion to 13 billion light-years away. Because their light has taken so long to reach us, we see them as they were when they – and the universe itself – were still young.

Galaxies are distributed unevenly in space. Some drift in splendid isolation with no close companions. Others form strange pairs, orbiting each other, or in some cases, collidng and mingling. It seems incredible, but collisions between stars are extremely rare because of the inconceivably vast distances between them all.

Many galaxies are found in groups called clusters, typically millions of light years across. A cluster may contain from a few dozen to several thousand galaxies. Clusters, in turn, are grouped in superclusters. On even grander scales, galaxies tend to accumulate in a tangle of filaments surrounding relatively empty regions of the universe, known as voids. One of the largest structures ever mapped is a network of galaxies known as the Great Wall. This structure is more than 500 million light-years long and 200 million wide.

Individual galaxies are usually in the form of spirals or ellipses. A spiral galaxy bulges in the centre, where most of its stars are concentrated. The rotation of the entire galaxy causes outer stars to be dragged along in the gravitational tide as spiral arms. The Milky Way is a spiral galaxy, and our Sun resides near the end of one of its arms. The galaxy turns a full circle once every 220 million years, and our Sun has travelled around the centre about 20 times since the solar system's birth 5 billion years ago.

Elliptical galaxies can be flat discs or near-spherical globes, depending on their size, and the extent to which slow or fast rotation affects their shape. Certainly they rotate much more slowly than spiral galaxies.

All galaxies emit energy in the form of visible light and other kinds of electromagnetic radiation, from radio waves, to infrared, visible light, ultraviolet, X-rays and gamma rays. This energy comes from the heat of the stars, and massively violent events such as supenova explosions. A small percentage of galaxies emit tremendous amounts of energy, sometimes arising from a highly localized source within the centre. These are known as quasars. They can emit a thousand times more energy than the entire Milky Way. Quasars are mysterious, but it seems likely that they are associated with massive black holes.

Our galaxy from outside

◄ The solar system resides within a spiral arm of the Milky Way galaxy. At night we can see a cross-section of the galaxy, but we can only guess what it might look like from a distance, as in this artist's representation.

Colliding galaxies

► The Whirlpool Galaxy, in the constellation Canes Venatici, is slowly merging with a smaller galaxy, NGC 5195. The Whirlpool is approximately 37 million light years away from us. It is 100,000 light years across and contains the equivalent of 160 billion suns.

SEE ALSO

■ **Our Place in the Universe**
page 12

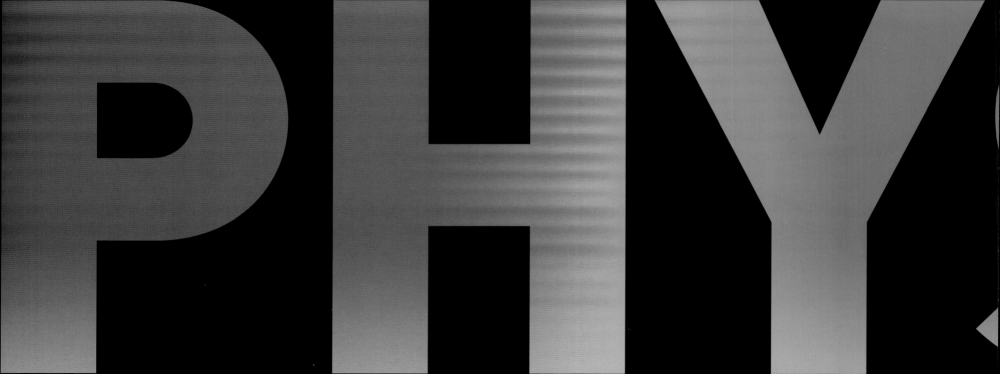

same mathematical laws, we have unlocked many of the secrets of matter and energy and tracked the timeline of the universe to within fractions of a second of its origins. Now we are in thrall to the possibility of a Theory of Everything: a single, elegant equation that could explain all the workings of nature while standing, at the same time, as a final triumph of human ingenuity.

But where do the mathematical laws of physics come from? Why should numbers and equations be so useful in describing how nature behaves? Albert Einstein often said that 'The most incomprehensible thing about the world is that it is comprehensible.' More recently, the physicist Stephen Hawking has asked, 'What is it that breathes fire into the equations and makes a universe for them to describe? Was it all just a lucky chance? That would seem a counsel of despair, a negation of our hopes of understanding the underlying order of the universe.'

Physicists have a love of beautiful equations, and tend to think that they must imply truth. In May 1963, Nobel laureate Paul Dirac, who had predicted the existence of antimatter purely from his calculations, wrote, 'It is more important to have beauty in one's equations than to have them fit experiment. If there is not complete agreement between the two, the discrepancy will get cleared up with further development of the theory.' Einstein was never lost for words on the subject of his fascination for pretty equations. 'It is possible to know when you are right way ahead of checking all the consequences. You can recognize truth by its beauty and simplicity.'

No wonder that so many people think that Hawking and his colleagues are engaged on the ultimate discipline of science. Ernest Rutherford, the gruff New Zealand-born pioneer of atomic research in the early 20th century, said: 'All science is either physics or stamp collecting.' Others fear that prideful physicists have brought us to the brink of disaster. We have harnessed the innermost energies of the atom for power and for war.

One day, it is conceivable that all our cities could be reduced to dust by atomic bombs. All our books could be vaporized in a global firestorm, and every last byte of computerized knowledge would surely be wiped out by the electromagnetic disturbances of this disaster. Fortunately the world is turning away from these weapons, and the risk of nuclear catastrophe has lessened – but just for argument's sake, would such a war be the end of human civilization, or could some of the achievements from the last two thousand years be rescued from the dust and ashes?

Richard Feynman, one of the 20th century's greatest physicists, suggested that we could manufacture dozens of blast-proof tablets in the hope that at least one of them might be discovered by survivors of a future calamity – whatever its origins – and he supposed that these tablets would have space for only one brief sentence of information, perhaps repeated in several different languages, as if on a futuristic Rosetta Stone. He reckoned that a ravaged humanity could eventually deduce afresh all that it needed to know about the material world from one simple description of the relationship between matter and energy.

'All things are made of atoms, little particles that move around in perpetual motion, attracting each other when they are a little distance apart, but repelling upon being squeezed into one another.'

From those few words, all the rest of physics follows.

THE MECHANICS OF PHYSICS

There are six simple arrangements at the heart of almost all mechanical systems. At first glance, some of them appear to make heavy loads as light as a feather. In fact they do not – so why do we use them?

Three simple laws

All the mathematical principles needed to describe the behaviour of mechanical systems were described by Sir Isaac Newton (1642–1727). Even though more than three hundred years have passed since he was in his prime, we have not had to revise his equations at all when dealing with the everyday human-scaled world of machines and physical objects. Newton has given us three fundamental principles:

First law: an object will remain motionless, or move in a straight line at an unvarying speed, so long as no additional force acts on it. Throw a golf ball into an empty region of deep space, where nothing exists to alter its state, and it will simply keep going.

Second law: when a force acts on an object, the object accelerates in the direction of the force. The force and the resulting acceleration are directly proportional. (Force = mass x acceleration)

Third law: every action has an equal and opposite reaction. When a roller skater at rest throws a heavy brick ahead by way of an action, this will cause the skater to roll backwards in reaction.

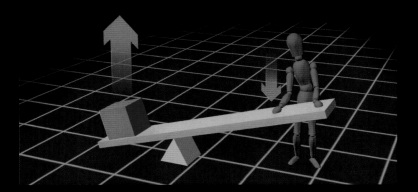

The lever A lever is a rigid bar that rotates around a fixed point, called the fulcrum. If you want to lift the corner of a heavy block of metal off the floor, you might push the end of a long wooden board under it. Near the block end, you rest the board on a solid support that allows it to rotate. Then a small amount of force on the other end of the board will be enough to lift the block. It seems like a magic trick, until we think about what really happens. The block is still just as heavy as ever, and still requires the same amount of upwards force to lift. But the lever allows you to spread the work required over a greater distance when you apply your muscle power to the other end of the board. This reduces the moment-by-moment strain on our arms to a level that is easy to manage.

The length of the lever from the fulcrum to the load is called the 'load arm', while the 'effort arm' is the distance running from the fulcrum to your hand, or whatever else is applying the force. A very simple equation reveals the secret of all levers:

Load arm x load force = effort arm x effort force

The longer the effort arm is in relation to the load arm, the less force on the end of the effort arm is needed to lift the load a set distance off the ground. The trade-off is the ever larger distance that the end of the effort arm needs to move through as the arm's length increases.

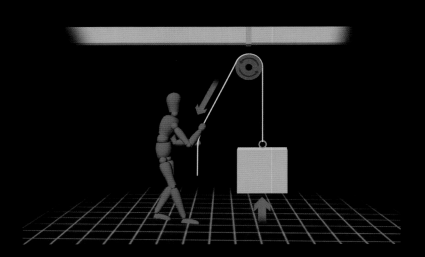

The pulley A little child can lift an elephant off its feet with a suitable pulley system. Just like levers, pulleys spread the necessary work across a distance greater than the distance travelled by the load. The usefulness of levers for lifting loads may be limited by the awkwardness of using extremely long levers, but pulleys use ropes and cables that can be looped around wheels, extending the distance distribution while keeping the machinery as compact as possible.

One rope tied to the top of a heavy load carries the entire weight. Sling the rope around the wheel of a pulley hooked to the top of the load, and now there are two lengths of rope carrying the load, halving the strain on each rope. Each extra pulley added to the system halves the load again, and so on, until the muscle power required to get the load off the ground is negligible. The drawback is that the rope in a pulley system has to be pulled a long way before the load at the other end of the system moves any appreciable distance.

The inclined plane By moving a heavy load up an inclined plane (a ramp), the amount of force required to raise the load a set distance above its starting level is reduced at the expense of increasing the distance forwards that the object is moved. Anyone trying to shift a wheelbarrow full of builder's rubble from the ground to a higher level will use a ramp.

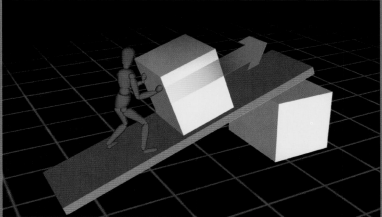

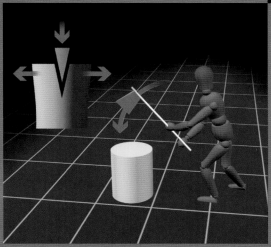

The wedge A wedge is another kind of inclined plane. A force applied to the wide end of a wedge whose narrow end is being pushed into something will redirect the force so that it pushes out against the sides. A wedge can also be conical, like the tip of a nail or the tines on a fork. The narrower (sharper) the wedge, the easier it is to drive it into a gap and push things apart. To split something really wide, the wedge has to be pushed inwards a long way.

The wheel The principal purpose of wheels is to reduce friction between an object – say, a cart full of rock – and the surface that it is moving along. When wheels are attached to the cart, the problem becomes, how to overcome the friction between the wheel and the cart itself. An axle is a wheel within a wheel. Ball bearings between axles and wheels are yet another layer of wheels, reducing friction yet further.

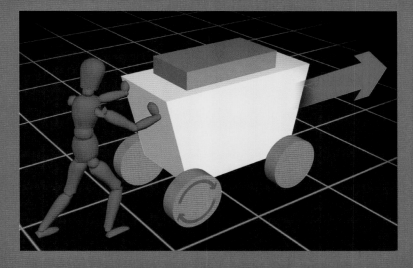

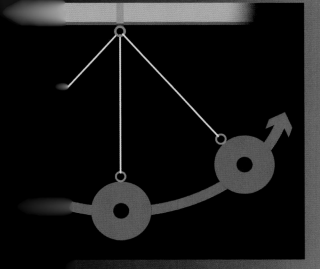

The pendulum As explained by Galileo Galilei, a pendulum is simply a string or rod with a weight at one end. In a given gravity field, such as the Earth's, a pendulum of a certain length always takes the same time to swing from one end of its arc to the other, no matter how light or heavy the load on the end of it. Over time, friction and general energy loss will bring an unpowered pendulum to a halt, but while it moves it reveals fundamental relationships between gravity, mass and time. The end of a pendulum is simply a kind of falling object. A feather and a hammer dropped vertically from the same height at the same time will obey the same principles as if they had each been tied to the end of a pendulum.

The screw A screw converts a rotational force (torque) into a linear (straight-line) force. A screw is basically a wedge or inclined plane compacted into a circular ramp. The vertical distance between two adjacent screw threads is called the pitch. One complete revolution of a screw will pull it into an object by a distance equal to the pitch of that screw. A screwdriver with a handle wider than the diameter of the screw acts in the same way as a lever, reducing the force needed to make each turn of the screw, but at the expense of having to make many turns to drive it in a short distance.

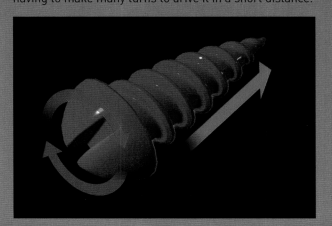

WORK, ENERGY AND FORCE

We all use power and apply force to do work, but what do these terms really mean? They are not really 'things' in themselves, so much as relationships between matter and energy.

ENERGY IS THE CAPACITY to do work. Work is the application of a force over a distance, in the direction of that force. Force is any influence that tries to effect change in physical systems – and it takes energy to apply a force so as to get work done. Notice how these basic concepts refer back to each other? Energy is not a 'stuff' in itself, but it can change from one kind of energy into another, and be precisely measured according to the effect that it has on an object. Another key concept, acceleration, is closely connected with momentum, and there's a crucial difference between speed and velocity. Confused? A great way of talking about all these ideas is to look at a familiar situation where mass and energy are both very much in evidence: on the Formula One race track. Here we see all the phenomena of physics in play.

Sound energy
is the movement of waves travelling through a substance, such as air or water. Sound is produced when a force causes something to vibrate. Then the energy is transferred to the carrying substance (medium) that conveys the sound. The rapid sparking and firing of the pistons inside the race car's engine creates sound waves in such swift succession that our ears and brains interpret them as a continuous high-pitched screech.

Gravitational energy
The higher off the ground and the heavier an object is, the more work it could do if released. When a car rolls down an incline and picks up speed, its gravitational energy is converted into kinetic energy.

Thermal energy
– or heat – is the total kinetic energy from the vibration of atoms within substances. As an object is heated up, its atoms move faster and collide more often. They transfer their kinetic energy to any atoms from another object that happen to be in contact with the heated one. Anyone touching the car's hot engine with an ungloved hand will experience the truth of this.

Nuclear energy
holds together the nucleus of an atom. Vast amounts of this energy can be released if nuclei are split apart, but this only happens under exceptional circumstances. The race car is held together by nuclear forces.

Potential energy
is stored ready for release in the future: for instance, in chemical fuels or electrical batteries. The race car stores most of its energy in gasoline, and in the batteries for its electrical gear and ignition systems.

Radiant energy is the energy of electro-magnetic waves. While mechanical energy can only be transferred when one object or substance comes into contact with another, radiant energy can travel across a vacuum: for instance, the empty space between the Sun and the Earth. The Sun shining down on the race car warms its shell with radiant energy.

Mechanical energy is stored by the tension between one object and another: for instance, a coiled spring compressing or stretching beyond its relaxed state. The spring suspension system of a car alternately absorbs, then releases, mechanical energy to stabilize the car's height above the track.

Electrical energy – for instance in the car's ignition system and monitoring computers, is delivered by electrons moving through wires, and by the magnetic fields surrounding the wires as the electrons flow.

THE ENERGY OF MOTION

Kinetic energy results from any kind of motion of waves, atoms and molecules or objects. A dramatic example is a car crash, when speeding cars come to a sudden, unplanned stop and release all their kinetic energy at once. Most of it is redirected as partial shares of the original energy scattered among the flying wreckage and the shunting of other cars. A small fraction of the total crash energy is converted into heat and sound.

Kinetic energy is just an overall quantity. The individual bits of wreckage have a certain fraction of the energy from the crash, but each also possesses other significant qualities: a specific mass and a particular direction of travel. Velocity is the speed of an object travelling in a certain direction. Mass multiplied by velocity is called momentum. The rate at which momentum changes with time is equal to the net force applied to an object. In the case of the unfortunate car below, momentum has changed extremely fast, thereby delivering sufficient force to do the the work of bending the car out of shape.

ENTROPY AND THE ARROW OF TIME

Our impression of physical events suggests that all the energy behind the noise and bustle of life eventually fades away to nothing. In fact, energy can neither be created nor destroyed. Yet everything eventually falls apart. Why should this be so?

THINK OF TWO BALLS SMACKING INTO EACH OTHER on a pool table. There is a loud 'clunk' as they make contact. Some of the energy of their collision is lost immediately to the air. A faint echo of the clunking noise bounces off the walls of the pool hall. The walls vibrate imperceptibly as they soak up the sound energy, converting it into mechanical energy. The shaking of the walls then disturbs the air again, and a very much weaker wave of sound is retransmitted into the hall.

Meanwhile the pool balls bounce away from each other, carrying a significant proportion of their original kinetic energy in different directions. Friction between the balls and the baize surface of the table eventually brings both balls to a standstill. The friction creates a trace amount of heat, which is then lost to the air circulating around the table. After a few moments, all the energy of the ball's dramatic collision has been evenly distributed across the wider environment of the pool hall. It becomes so diffuse that it can no longer effect any measurable physical change in the hall or any of its tables and balls. But the energy still exists.

Are these balls bouncing off each other after a recent collision, or are they hurtling towards a collision that hasn't happened yet? The equations describing simple systems work just as well backwards or forwards. As the systems become more complex, a distinct direction, the arrow of time, becomes evident, and the equations can only run one way.

Entropy

If an old-fashioned movie of a pool game were made, and the camera stayed focused just on close-ups of the balls, it would be possible for brief moments of the game to be replayed backwards or forwards and still be equally convincing to an audience. From frame to frame, it would be hard to tell which way to run the film for the 'true' version of events. Did the balls collide and fly apart, or did they hurtle towards each other and collide?

The scientific descriptions of simple, individual physical events are completely reversible, but the so-called 'arrow of time' becomes evident when we observe several events in succession. When the footage is reversed, a teacup filmed falling through the air might just as easily be a teacup thrown upwards by an unseen hand, but when it smashes on the floor and becomes a thousand shards of randomly shaped china clay, then suddenly the film can only be screened in one direction in order to make sense. The arrow of time always points forward, towards the dissipation of energy and the breaking down of complex structures into simpler, randomly shaped fragments. The fate of all systems — of everything in the universe, in fact — is to become increasingly disordered as their energies dissipate. This is known as 'entropy'.

On Earth, we have access to ancient trapped solar energy in fossil fuel reserves, and from the Sun itself. Our dissipated energy is constantly replenished. Broken teacups never come back whole, but they can be replaced by new teacups fresh from a potter's glowing hot kiln. This renewability is merely a short sequence from the very much longer 'film' that must climax, some time in the very distant future, in total entropy: not just on Earth, but for the entire universe.

When a ceramic coffee pot smashes on the floor, we know that this is irreversible and the pot cannot be made whole again. We also know that all pots must smash one day. The arrow of time points towards entropy, never away from it.

ELECTRIC CURRENTS

Any flow of electricity creates a magnetic field around it, and whenever an electrical conductor and a magnetic field move in relation to each other, an electric current is generated. But what is electricity?

ATOMS IN CONDUCTIVE MATERIALS contain electrons in their outer shells that are so loosely attached they are free to move around chaotically in the spaces between adjacent atoms. Electrons will travel along a conductor if something at one end pushes them while something else pulls them from the other end. Think of water building up behind a dam as the 'push' and the long drop on the dry side of the dam as the 'pull'. An electrical battery or generator attached to one end of a wire creates a surge of electrons that repel electrons ahead of them, creating a flow of electrons – a current – in the wire. However, a stream of electrons cannot simply reach the end of a wire and stop. It has to flow through a circuit, where the terminating end of the wire comes around to meet the first end. This is why all batteries have two terminals, labelled positive and negative. The electrons travel from the negative terminal, with its excess 'push' of electrons, towards the positive terminal, where there is a deficit of electrons – although, in everyday electrical systems, currents are regarded as flowing from positive to negative: a legacy of ancient misunderstandings.

A wire attached to a battery delivers a flow of current but not much else. It's usual to string the wire with components that do something useful, so that they form part of a more complex electrical or electronic circuit. But even something as insanely intricate as a laptop computer represents just that: a convoluted but unbroken circuit between the two terminals of its power pack.

The potential difference between the negative and positive terminals – the force of water behind the dam allied with the height of the drop on the other side, so to speak – is called the voltage. Electric current is akin to the flow rate of water through a pipe, and resistance can be thought of as the width of the pipe's gauge, with a narrow gauge creating the greatest resistance. A simple equation describes how all these factors interact: $V = I$ times R, where 'V' is the voltage, 'I' is the current and 'R' is the resistance.

If the resistance increases while the voltage stays the same, the current has to drop. If the current increases while the voltage stays the same, then the resistance must have fallen away – and if the current increases while the resistance stays the same, this can only mean that the voltage has been boosted to get those sluggish electrons surging through a reluctant conductor.

An electron, the basic unit of all electric current, has an electric charge. Whenever a stream of electrons moves through a wire, it creates a magnetic field around the wire. Conversely, if a wire is moved through an existing magnetic field, a stream of electrons – an electric current – is generated inside the wire.

Electrons rule Our ability to direct the flow of electrons has shaped our technological life for just over a century. What new forces might we exploit in centuries yet to come?

THE ELECTROMAGNETIC SPECTRUM

A wide range of invisible light energies exists beyond the reach of unaided human senses. They dominate the science and technology of the modern world, and we have discovered how to translate them into light that we can see.

WAVES IN THE ELECTROMAGNETIC (EM) spectrum vary in size from radio waves of several hundred metres long to gamma rays smaller than the nucleus of an atom. All EM waves take the form of intertwined electric and magnetic fields travelling together through space while oscillating perpendicularly to each other. The shorter the wavelength, the higher the energy.

At the gamma extreme of the EM spectrum, the wavelengths are so short and powerful they can smash into atoms and molecules and wreak havoc. Gamma radiation is extremely hazardous to soft biological tissues. At the other end of the spectrum, the longest and most langourously spaced radio waves have so little energy they barely interact with the solid world.

All EM radiation is 'light', even though we can only see a limited range of it through our eyes. The fundamental carrier of EM is the photon, a particle that has no mass but can convey energy: a concept that is hard to reconcile with the notion of EM as spread-out waves propagating through space. Every photon begins its journey when an electron is boosted into a higher, more energetic level around an atomic nucleus by being heated, or by absorbing an incoming photon. The electron eventually falls back to its original state, releasing its excess energy in the form of another photon. The more energy absorbed by an electron in the first place, the higher the energy of the photon it releases.

Infrared (3,000 GHz to 430 THz) Radiated heat energy, emitted by all objects, everywhere, that are not absolutely cold.

10^{-5} Infrared

10^{-4}

10^{-3}

10^{-2} Microwave

10^{-1}

1 Radiowaves

MEASURING LIGHT

Wavelengths are usually expressed in metres, or fractions of a metre, written as powers of 10 for convenience. Extremely short wavelengths are sometimes expressed in nanometres (billionths of a metre). Frequencies are counted in hertz, or one oscillation per second. One megahertz (MHz) amounts to a million oscillations per second, while a gigahertz (GHz) is a thousand megahertz. X-rays and gamma rays are usually expressed in terms of their energy, which is proportional to their frequency.

Radio (up to 3,000 MHz) Whether produced by the Sun and other celestial objects or by our own technologies, radio waves saturate us like an invisible sea, but are generally so lacking in energy that we cannot be harmed by them.

Microwave (3,000 MHz to 3,000 GHz) A term usually referring to any EM radiation with a much shorter wavelength than normally used for radio communications. Microwave photons can be easily absorbed by electrons in the atoms of water, fats and sugars in everyday foodstuffs, causing them to heat up.

PHYSICS

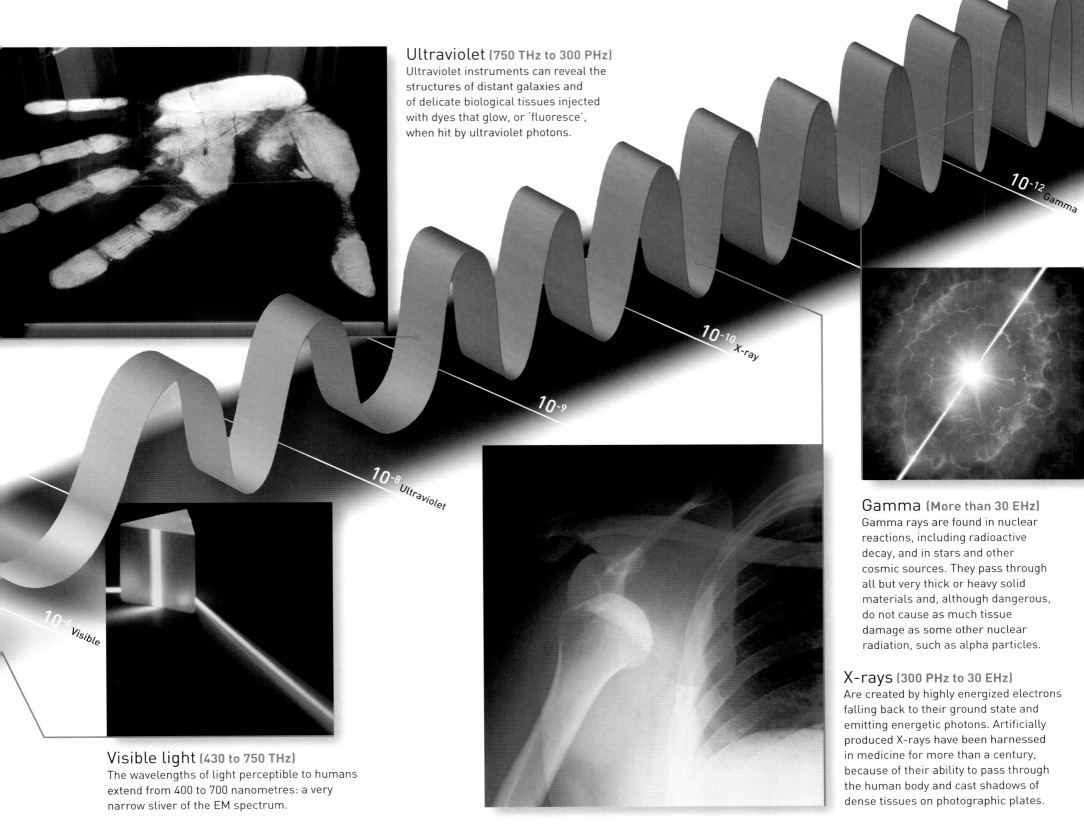

Ultraviolet (750 THz to 300 PHz)
Ultraviolet instruments can reveal the structures of distant galaxies and of delicate biological tissues injected with dyes that glow, or 'fluoresce', when hit by ultraviolet photons.

10^{-12} Gamma

10^{-10} X-ray

10^{-9}

10^{-8} Ultraviolet

10^{-6} Visible

Gamma (More than 30 EHz)
Gamma rays are found in nuclear reactions, including radioactive decay, and in stars and other cosmic sources. They pass through all but very thick or heavy solid materials and, although dangerous, do not cause as much tissue damage as some other nuclear radiation, such as alpha particles.

X-rays (300 PHz to 30 EHz)
Are created by highly energized electrons falling back to their ground state and emitting energetic photons. Artificially produced X-rays have been harnessed in medicine for more than a century, because of their ability to pass through the human body and cast shadows of dense tissues on photographic plates.

Visible light (430 to 750 THz)
The wavelengths of light perceptible to humans extend from 400 to 700 nanometres: a very narrow sliver of the EM spectrum.

Waves or particles?

Low-energy photons, such as radio, are usually thought of as behaving like waves, while higher-energy photons, such as gamma rays, are often described as behaving like particles. Here is where we encounter a puzzling feature of light. Is it a smooth, continuous wave, or a discrete succession of photons?

Wavelengths are infinitely variable, while photon energies are packaged into discrete amounts, or 'quanta'. (Hence the term 'quantum physics'.) The leap between one photon energy level and the next is crisp and absolute, with no fractional levels in between. It is as though the wave description of electromagnetism exists in a world of smooth flowing curves, while the photon description is like the sharp rectilinear treads on a staircase. Scientists work with whichever description of light they need at the time: undulating waves or bullet-like photons.

All the ways of thinking about EM radiation can be related to the others in precise mathematics. Wavelength always equals the speed of light divided by the frequency; and the energy contained in photons is always proportional to the frequency of a wave, with the proportion governed by 'Planck's constant', named in honour of the physicist who discovered it a century ago, heralding the birth of quantum theory. (The Planck number and the speed of light appear to be immutable fixed values set into the laws of nature.)

Wavelength = the speed of light divided by the frequency.

Energy = Planck's constant times the frequency.

The wave–particle ambiguity of EM radiation is hard for us to picture, but the relevant science is one of the most accurate tools of the human intellect. The technologies based on EM dominate modern life, from radio and radar, to mobile phones, microwave cookers, sun lamps, hospital X-ray machines and astronomical telescopes.

SEE ALSO

The Quanum Universe page 180

BEYOND THE SIMPLE ATOM

Most of us have some vague idea of what an atom is like. There is a nucleus with positively charged protons and neutrons with no charge, surrounded by a buzzing shell of negatively charged electrons. At a deeper level, atoms are far more complex than this.

NO VISUAL COMPARISON can really help us understand how small an atom is – approximately one-tenth of one-millionth of one millimetre across. The width of the finest hair is longer than the span of one million carbon atoms stretched out in a row. A cup of sea water contains as many atoms as there are cups of water in all the oceans of the world.

The atom's tiny size is only one of many qualities that we find hard to grasp. Another challenge to our sensory expectations, based as they are on the seeming solidity of the world around us, is that the atom is mainly just empty space. Most of the mass, and all of the the positive charge of an atom, is concentrated in its nucleus. This is surrounded by a cloud of electrons. If we could picture an atom as being the size of a great cathedral, then the nucleus would be like a mosquito suspended in the middle of the cavernous building, and the electrons would be on the scale of microscopic bacteria dotted around the inner walls.

All the gaping space between the nucleus and the electrons is completely empty. If all the atoms in your body could be squeezed down to get rid of the empty volume inside them, you would weigh the same, but would be as small as a grain of salt. On that basis, the entire human race would fit in a bucket. Almost all of us – almost all

of everything everywhere – is empty space. The atom is not a hard-edged 'thing'. It is a ghostly shimmer. The only reason that we do not fall through the floor, like one cloud of atoms passing ghostlike through another, is because of the electrical forces that cause atoms on the outside of our bodies to repel atoms on the surface of the floor, and vice versa.

The 'particle zoo'

Subatomic particles have 'antimatter' counterparts: particles that are just like them, except with opposite electrical charges. There are negatively charged versions of protons, called antiprotons, and positively charged electrons, known as positrons. Matter and antimatter cannot coexist. When they meet, they annihilate each other in a burst of gamma radiation. We routinely manufacture positrons, so that the weak gamma radiation produced on contact with ordinary matter can be harnessed for hospital scanners. There may be regions in the universe where antimatter predominates.

The protons and neutrons in an atomic nucleus are themselves made from even smaller particles, known as quarks. There are six kinds or 'flavours' of quark, each given a whimsical name that acts as a convenient label for particular mathematical characteristics, such

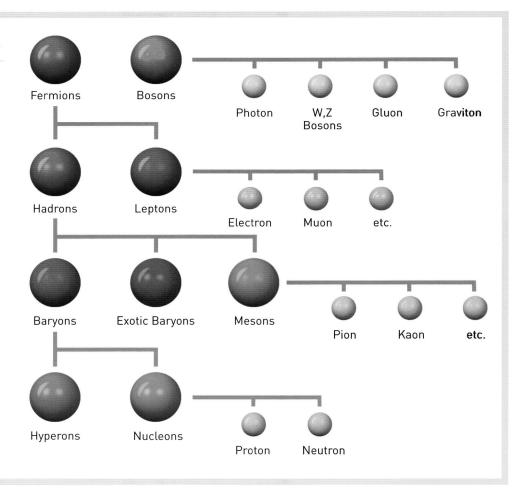

CLASSIFICATION OF SUBATOMIC PARTICLES

All subatomic particles are either fermions or bosons. Fermions are matter particles, and are either leptons or hadrons. Leptons (such as electrons) cannot be subdivided into anything smaller, but hadrons are made from smaller particles called quarks. These combine to make baryons, such as protons and neutrons (nucleons) and hyperons, short-lived unstable baryons. A proton is made from three quarks, each possessing a fraction of a charge: a very peculiar concept. Bosons are force-carrying particles. Gluons and the W and Z bosons hold atomic nuclei together, while photons carry the electro-magnetic force. Gravitons convey gravity, and the Higgs boson is responsible for mass, although these abstract theories have yet to be confirmed by experiment. All matter particles have antimatter versions which usually annihilate on contact. Mesons are very short-lived particles made from one quark and one antiquark.

Fermions | Bosons | Photon | W,Z Bosons | Gluon | Graviton
Hadrons | Leptons | Electron | Muon | etc.
Baryons | Exotic Baryons | Mesons | Pion | Kaon | etc.
Hyperons | Nucleons | Proton | Neutron

as mass, spin and electrical charge. Quarks do not exist on their own, but must be bound up with partner quarks inside protons and neutrons (known as hadrons because they are among the class of particles built from quarks). A proton consists of two 'up' quarks and one 'down' quark, while a neutron is made from one 'up' quark and two 'down' quarks. Electrons are not made from quarks, and cannot be subdivided into other particles. Quarks and other particles inside an atom are held together by the exchange of various force-carrying particles called bosons, including gluons that bind together the protons and neutrons in a nucleus. Photons are the bosons that convey electromagnetic forces.

Particles proliferate as new particle collider experiments at ever higher energies reveal new complexities. Scientists sometimes talk of the 'particle zoo' that they are trying to unravel. At the European Centre for Nuclear Research (known as CERN) physicists from around the world are contributing to the hunt for one particle in particular, the Higgs boson, that – so the theories suggest – is responsible for giving other particles their mass. The accelerators and detectors designed to find this particle are the costliest and most massive instruments ever built for a scientific experiment. Another elusive candidate, the graviton, may be responsible for the interaction between gravity and the individual atoms from which all masses are made.

HOW ATOMS INTERACT WITH ENERGY

The 'ground state' of an electron is its state of lowest energy. There is also a maximum energy that an electron can have. Beyond that, an electron flies away from its atom, leaving a positively charged ion. The energy 'kick' comes from a photon, a packet of electro-magnetic energy. For an electron to be boosted to an orbital shell with a higher energy, it must gain the difference in energy between the orbital it is in, and the orbital to which it is going. It does so by absorbing a photon that contains precisely that amount of energy – or else it derives the energy by colliding with another matter particle. When an atom is in a higher energy shell than its normal one, it is said to be in an 'excited' state. The electron can drop again all the way down to its ground state, releasing a photon equivalent to that difference in energy, or halt on intermediate orbital levels, releasing photons equivalent to just those jumps.

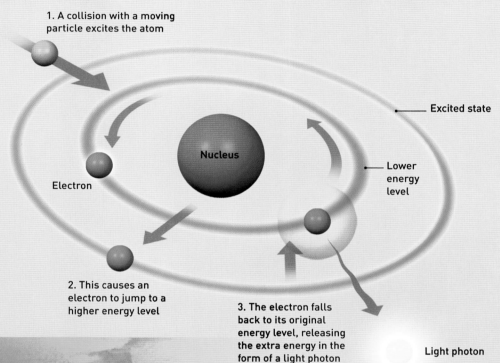

1. A collision with a moving particle excites the atom

Excited state

Nucleus

Electron

Lower energy level

2. This causes an electron to jump to a higher energy level

3. The electron falls back to its original energy level, releasing the extra energy in the form of a light photon

Light photon

▲ A photon of electromagnetic energy is absorbed by an electron, causing the electron to jump to a higher energy level, or 'electron shell'. When the electron returns to its original state in a lower shell, a photon is emitted. The energy of the outgoing photon depends on how high, in terms of shell numbers, the electron is boosted by the incoming energy, and how far it falls back again.

◀ When anything is heated in a furnace, we will always see its glow turning from red to orange and then dazzling white, whatever the object in question is made of. This is because the light energy emitted always comes from the same source: electrons interacting with photons. As the heat increases, the energy of the emitted light photons increases, but always by the same discrete quantum steps between one energy level and the next.

SEE ALSO

Elements and Compounds *page 56*
Tracking the Subatomic World *page 176*

TRACKING THE SUBATOMIC WORLD

Subatomic particles are smaller than the wavelength of light. We cannot see them directly, but we can detect the trails that they leave in their wake.

INSIDE A SMALL SEALED CHAMBER, liquid hydrogen is gently heated to the point where it is on the cusp of becoming gas, but the tight enclosure of the chamber holds it in liquid form still. Then the pressure inside the chamber is eased slightly. When a subatomic particle (an electron, for instance) is fired through the chamber, it smashes into hydrogen atoms in its path, knocking off electrons and leaving positive ions which repel each other. Centred around these islands of perturbation, tiny bubbles of gaseous hydrogen quickly emerge in the liquid. Using an optical microscope, bubble trails left in the speeding particles' wakes can be photographed. Yet we can never see the particles themselves. The trails look very precise through the microscope, but the tiny bubbles that form them are many thousands of times larger than the diameter of the particles whose swift flights created them.

When subatomic particles are made to collide in a particle accellerator, their interactions can be studied. Powerful surrounding magnetic fields deflect positively or negatively charged particles to varying degrees, and the relative curves of their paths reveal their identities, depending on the strength of their charge and their mass. Particles with no charge are unaffected by the magnetic fields and fly straight through the detection chamber. If particles collide with sufficient force, showers of other particles may come into existence,

One of six detector experiments at the Large Hadron Collider (LHC) particle accelerator at CERN, Geneva, Switzerland. It has eight toroids (grey with orange stripes) that generate the powerful magnetic field needed to confine the particles. ATLAS is a broad-range detector that measures all particle types and physical processes that emerge out of extremely high-energy particle collisions at close to the speed of light.

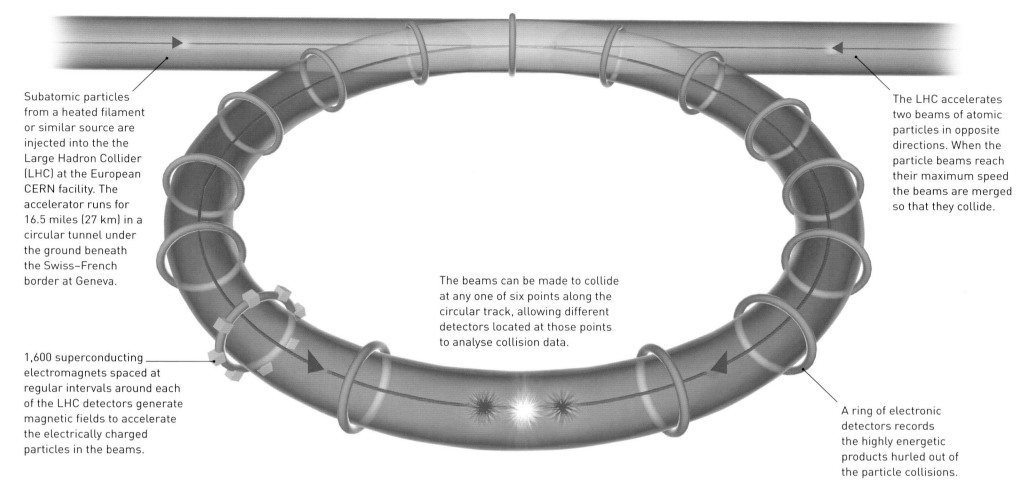

Particle collider The aim of smashing matter particles together at extreme and exceptional energies is to discover the conditions that prevailed in the first few instants after the Big Bang, the explosive event that created all matter and energy 13.75 billion years ago.

Subatomic particles from a heated filament or similar source are injected into the the Large Hadron Collider (LHC) at the European CERN facility. The accelerator runs for 16.5 miles (27 km) in a circular tunnel under the ground beneath the Swiss–French border at Geneva.

The LHC accelerates two beams of atomic particles in opposite directions. When the particle beams reach their maximum speed the beams are merged so that they collide.

The beams can be made to collide at any one of six points along the circular track, allowing different detectors located at those points to analyse collision data.

1,600 superconducting electromagnets spaced at regular intervals around each of the LHC detectors generate magnetic fields to accelerate the electrically charged particles in the beams.

A ring of electronic detectors records the highly energetic products hurled out of the particle collisions.

perhaps with life spans of billionths of a second. They then spiral into non-existence, or decay into other types of particle. The trails are usually captured electronically today, using powerful computers to calculate the likely paths retrospectively, based on the incoming energies and directions of subatomic debris particles that hit the walls of the detector after a collision.

How particle accelerators work

Particles are generated in various ways prior to their injection into a particle accelerator: from a heated cathode, or by smashing one stream of heavy particles into a target material to knock off other particles. Certain particles also emerge spontaneously from radio-active substances. They then travel, through a vacuum, down a long metal tube, the main body of the accelerator. Powerful microwave generators, called klystrons, clad the outside of the tube. They create fast-moving electromagnetic wave fronts inside the tube, which greatly accelerate the particles. Electromagnets running the length of the accelerator keep the particles confined in a narrow controllable beam.

Modern accelerators are huge. The Stanford Linear Accelerator in California, for instance, is 2 miles (3 km) long. The world's largest accelerator, the Large Hadron Collider at CERN near Geneva, propels two streams of particles in opposite directions, cycling them many thousands of times around a circular track more than 16 miles (26 km) in circumference, surrounded by 1,600 electromagnetic arrays. At each pass, the electromagnetic fields around the giant machine are readjusted so that the particles accelerate yet further. Only when they have reached 99.99 per cent of the speed of light are they at last diverted by a shift in the surrounding control fields towards a detector array. Typically, streams of billions of particles are intersected in the expectation that just a few will collide inside a detector chamber so that the results can be recorded. The engineering precisions for the vast machine are daunting. Equipment weighing thousands of tons must merge beams no wider than a human hair.

Tracks showing subatomic particles with different electrical charges passing from left to right through a bubble chamber full of hydrogen nuclei (protons) under the influence of a magnetic field. Several collision events are shown here, with the particles produced by the collisions showing as curved or spiralling tracks. The clockwise-spiralling tracks are produced by electrons, which lose their energies rapidly, causing them to spiral in ever smaller circles.

WHAT IS MASS?

When we step onto the bathroom scales and check our weight, we see how Earth's gravity exerts a downwards pull on the mass in our bodies. But what is mass? Why should the subatomic particles that give mass to all objects be either 'light' or 'heavy'? Mass is one of those qualities that seems perfectly unremarkable until we give it a moment's reflection. In 1964 the physicist Peter Higgs thought that a force-carrying particle (a boson) must be responsible for giving other particles, such as protons and neutrons, their mass. Scientists around the world are now trying to hunt down the 'Higgs boson'. Mass is a quality possessed by all objects in the universe, from specks of dust to supermassive stars. The Higgs boson is often nicknamed the 'God Particle' to signify its potential importance.

NUCLEAR FISSION

The energies within an atom are not yet completely understood, but they
can be harnessed as a source of energy – or of immense destruction.

AT THE HEAVIEST END of the periodic table lies uranium,
with 92 protons and 92 electrons. The rarest naturally occurring
isotope, uranium-235, is massively overloaded with 143 neutrons.
The nucleus is bursting at the seams and ready to split apart at
the slightest provocation, such as the impact of a single additional
neutron. Newspaper reports about the first splitting of nuclei in the
1930s talked of scientists 'smashing' uranium atoms into fragments.
In fact, the gentlest bombardment of uranium atoms with slow-
moving neutron beams causes the split to occur. When a uranium
atom does divide, its exploded fragments consist of two new and
smaller nuclei, roughly equal in size. After the split, there are still
two or three stray neutrons left over, and these travel slowly enough
so that they can slip into the nuclei of adjacent uranium atoms,
upsetting their internal balances, and so forth, in a chain reaction
that is like the splitting or fission of breeding bacteria. One split
uranium atom leads to two more being split, then four, eight,
sixteen, and so on.

Einstein's famous equation

The energy for nuclear fission does not have to be supplied from
outside the experiment. It is already contained in the atoms. The
two nuclei formed by the division of a uranium atom are lighter
than the original nucleus, by about one-fifth the mass of a proton.
Whenever mass disappears, energy is created, according to Einstein's
famous formula $E = mc^2$ (energy = mass times the speed of light
squared). One-fifth of the mass of a proton may seem a very small
amount of matter. On the other hand, the square of the speed of
light is an unimaginably huge number. Thus, atomic fission liberates
vast amounts of energy. The fission of a single uranium atom yields
enough energy to make an entire grain of sand jump in the air. A
small lump of uranium in an atomic bomb can shake all the grains of
sand that make up a city.

When free-flying neutrons are slowed down sufficiently in a
nuclear experiment, they can be induced to stay inside a uranium
nucleus rather than splitting it. This new and highly unstable
artificial isotope is known as plutonium. It is even more prone to
splitting than uranium, and consequently is prized for its potential
use in nuclear power reactors and weapons systems.

◀ **Radioactive fuel rods**
being loaded into a nuclear power
station's reactor core. The reactor
itself is immersed beneath the
water (blue), and lifting machinery
is being used to raise and lower
the fuel rods (centre) into the
core (circular area). Uranium
and plutonium fuel are used to
produce a controlled nuclear
fission reaction. This releases large
amounts of energy from a small
amount of material.

▶ **Hydrogen bomb explosion.**
Mushroom cloud produced by the
detonation of XX-33 Romeo, an
11-megaton thermonuclear bomb, on
26 March 1954. This was one of a series
of six detonations carried out during
Operation Castle in the Bikini Atoll
Proving Grounds in the Marshall Islands
of the Pacific Ocean. XX-33 Romeo was
detonated from a barge on the atoll rim.
It was the third largest test ever detonated
by the USA. Atomic or nuclear bombs work
by releasing the energy in the nucleus of
atoms. Fusion bombs contain isotopes
of hydrogen that are fused together by
heat created in a fission chain reaction.
The fusion releases heat and radiation.

MASS AND ENERGY EQUIVALENCE

An observer monitoring a stationary object would think of it as having a particular mass. Relativity tells us that all measurements depend on the observer's frame of reference (see p.184). Another observer with a different frame of reference might consider the object to be hurtling along at great speed, and would measure its kinetic energy differently. For all observers, the laws of physics are the same. Energy cannot be created or destroyed. It stays in the system. Einstein thought (among many things) about this ambiguous nature of kinetic energy, the accelerations of particles in magnetic fields, and how a particle's mass increases as it approaches the speed of light. He calculated that mass and energy must be different facets of the same thing.

A kilogram of water contains about 100 grams of hydrogen atoms. The mass of the electrons is negligible. The 100 grams consists essentially of protons: particles with mass that can be converted into energy, measured in units called joules. One joule is approximately the energy released if you drop this book onto the floor. That 100 grams' worth of protons is the mass equivalent of 10,000,000,000,000,000 joules: equivalent to dropping every copy of all books that have ever been printed in all of history 10,000 times in succession.

Neutrons

Fission products

Neutrons

Uranium-235

Fission products

Uranium-235

Neutron

A neutron colliding

with the nucleus of a uranium atom causes the nucleus to split into two. In the process, known as 'nuclear fission', more neutrons are released, which then collide with adjacent nuclei, and so on. The process continues exponentially, releasing massive amounts of energy.

THE QUANTUM UNIVERSE

In the human-scaled world, things either 'are' or they 'are not'. Quantum theory tells us that individual atomic particles shimmer in an uncertain cloud of possible states.

WHEN WE MEASURE A PARTICLE, such as a proton or an electron, some specific quality will be observed: in particular, location (where the particle is) or momentum (the particle's mass multiplied by its velocity). But the more accurately we measure one of these qualities, the less we know about the other. Depending on the experiments undertaken, a particle might be found at a particular spot in a detector, or else observed hurtling through an experiment with a particular momentum, but it is never possible to pin down both measurements at once. In plain and simple terms, we can register where a particle is in space, but not be sure of how energetically it is moving through that space, or else we can measure how much of an energetic punch it carries, while having only a vague idea of where it is. Quantum theory treats atoms and subatomic particles as ghostly waves of probability rather than as discrete objects located definitely in both time and space.

Quantum entanglement

If two or more subatomic particles come into contact and then fly apart, they remain in communication. If one particle's state is measured in the laboratory — for instance, its spin — the other 'entangled' particle reacts instantly, registering an opposite spin, regardless of how far away it has travelled. Even entire atoms have been entangled in laboratories. The great Albert Einsetin called this 'spooky action at a distance' and tried to prove that it could not really happen. Just for once, he was wrong. No matter how great the distance between them might be, a pair of entangled particles has to be considered as an inseparable quantum system. Particles separated by cosmic distances may well be entangled because they were crowded together when the universe was young.

It may become possible to send encrypted messages that are useless to anyone who tries to intercept them before they reach their intended destination, because any attempt to read (measure) them mid-stream interrupts quantum entanglement in the 'key' portion of the data that unlocks the meaning of the message. If the rightful recipient gets a jumbled message, it will be obvious that someone has tried to snoop. Quantum entanglement promises much, but *Star Trek*-style instantaneous communication of complex information across vast distances is likely to remain a science fiction dream.

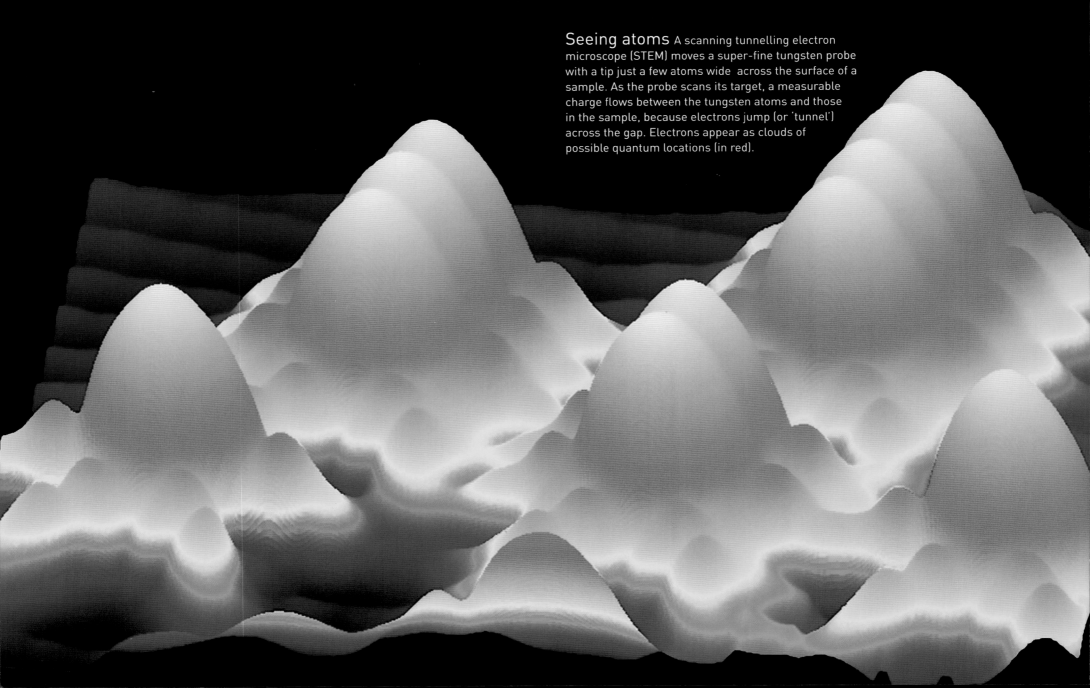

Seeing atoms A scanning tunnelling electron microscope (STEM) moves a super-fine tungsten probe with a tip just a few atoms wide across the surface of a sample. As the probe scans its target, a measurable charge flows between the tungsten atoms and those in the sample, because electrons jump (or 'tunnel') across the gap. Electrons appear as clouds of possible quantum locations (in red).

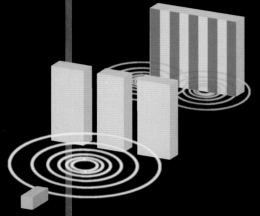

▲ Waves of light approach a pair of narrow openings in a barrier, which splits them into smaller waves on the other side. These interfere with each other, much like ripples on the surface of a pond, creating interference patterns of brightness alternating with darkness on a detector screen.

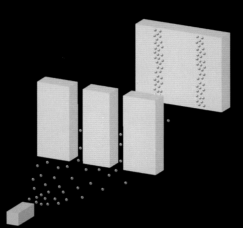

▲ Everyday experience would lead us to suppose that an individual particle of matter, such as an electron, when fired through the barrier, would pass through either one slit or the other, but not both at the same time. Cumulatively they would build up clean, crisp 'shadows' of the slits on the detector behind them, just as if they were machine gun bullets striking a wall.

▼ What actually happens is that the path of each individual electron as it passes through the barrier is unpredictable, but as they keep firing, one after another, all their 'hits' on the detector screen form a wave-like interference pattern. Matter particles can generate self-interference in mid-flight, just as light waves would.

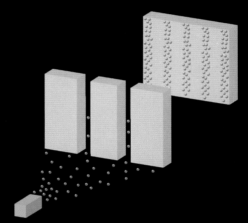

▲ The double-slit experiment proves the dual wave and particle natures of energy photons and matter particles.

▼ So light is both a particle and a wave. One of the central mysteries of physics is that individual matter particles behave randomly, yet collectively they create order and predictability. Where is the dividing line between sheer randomness and the comprehensible world that we humans experience (see p.183)?

WAVE–PARTICLE DUALITY

Imagine two stones thrown into a pond at the same time. Each centre of impact sends circular waves of disturbance towards the other. Inevitably the waves meet and interfere. Where peaks overlap with peaks, the colliding waves reinforce each other and the newly combined peak becomes higher. Conversely, where a peak meets a trough, the combined wave form cancels out at that point and the water becomes flat. The patterns observed are consistent and precise.

When light is shone at a pair of narrow slits on a thin sheet of metal, and the slits are separated from each other by less than the width of a human hair, each arriving light wave is split into two smaller waves, which then interfere with each other just before they hit a detector screen behind the plate. A characteristic banded interference pattern is created. Essentially the screen records the combined behaviour of the waves seen edge-on. This is what we expect from waves. So light is a wave, but what about supposedly solid bits of matter?

When the 'double-slit' experiment is repeated using electrons fired one by one from the same apparatus, a strange thing happens. As more electrons are fired in succession, a wavelike interference pattern builds up on the detector screen. Individual electrons, fundamental particles of matter, apparently pass through both

slits at once. When one slit is blocked off, no interference pattern appears on the screen. Instead, just one neat vertical shadow of the open slit is registered.

How do individual electrons, flying through the space between the electron gun and the slits, 'know' whether or not they are going to encounter one slit or two? With single electrons fired at intervals of many seconds, there is no possibility of one electron interfering with another in mid-flight. Each electron must, essentially, be interfering with itself. It is an astonishingly difficult phenomenon to explain, because we are so used to thinking of matter particles as if they were solid point-like nuggets, like tiny pool balls. How could a pool ball interfere with itself, let alone drop into two pockets of a pool table at once?

There is a disconnect between the words we use to describe conventional experience and the complex mathematics of the quantum world. What's more, our understanding of light energy shows that it can adopt the form of discrete particles (photons) as well as travelling in waves. This 'duality' presents us with a mystery that cannot easily be solved. Our very act of observing matter and energy seems to affect, in advance, what they will do, and how they will appear to us.

QUANTUM UNCERTAINTY AND YOU

It is tempting to imagine that quantum physics is confined to scientists' abstract mathematical equations, but the strangeness of the subatomic realm has an impact on all our lives.

IMAGINE THE FOLLOWING SCENARIO. You are in a crowded airport, much distracted by bustling people and flashing timetable display screens. You check your mobile phone to see if the time is adjusted for local. A cluster of photons, at the very limit of quantum uncertainty, enter the extreme perimeter of the pupil of your right eye. Your retinal cells respond to a glint of light so negligible it is on the cusp of what the eye can register. Unconsciously you swivel your gaze and spot someone also checking their phone, which happens to be a vivid red. The veritable swarm of photons at this most atmospherically penetrative end of the spectrum is unmissable, and draws you further into the scene. He/she looks up, sees you looking in their direction, and smiles.

Result? You marry that beguiling person with the lovely smile and you obtain a house, a hefty mortgage and three children, one of whom eventually enters politics and becomes a respected world leader. But that first glint in your eye was on the cusp of quantum uncertainty, so few were the light photons involved. You could just as easily not have registered it, and not met and married that person. Your bright politically minded offspring would not have been born. On countless trillions of occasions, all of our fates ride on the back of quantum uncertainties at subatomic scales. We are all creatures of Schrödinger's box.

Many quantum theorists state that if subatomic particles exist in 'superpositions' of alternative outcomes, then so must we. Multiple universes split from each other during every human observation of external truth whose outcomes depend on small-scale quantum events. Multiple versions of ourselves exist simultaneously, each experiencing a different large-scale consequence arising from the range of possible subatomic outcomes. The mathematics at the heart of quantum theory seems perfectly convincing to many scientists, but it all depends on how the equations are interpreted. Our everyday impressions of the world reinforce our belief that we have one life, we make one set of choices, and that multiple copies of ourselves surely cannot exist. We have to remember that everyday impressions can be misleading. The Sun, for instance, does not go around the Earth… Just because multiple universes are hard to believe in does not mean that they cannot exist.

Reality 2 Even though the photon of light has caused you to glance up and see the stranger, a similarly fragile quantum indeterminacy within a single neuron in your brain causes you to hesitate a fraction of a second before smiling back. The bond between you and the stranger is never formed. You head into another future in which you do not have children with that other person.

Reality 1 According to the laws of quantum uncertainty, a photon of light reflected from a distant shiny fixture interacts with an atom in your retina, setting off a chain of events that leads you to glance up and spot a handsome stranger. An exchange of smiles between the two of you dramatically alters the course of your life. A single photon has just determined the children that you will have.

Reality 3 The photon of light glancing off the shiny airport display board does not interact with your retina. You continue with your journey and, some time later, meet someone else. You have completely different children from the ones you would have had if you had partnered with the airport stranger. In our daily lives, uncountable numbers of tiny quantum events influence the outcomes of our lives.

Quantum truth?

In quantum physics, the role of the observer is central. If we observe a photon of light interacting with an instrument (such as the human eye), then that very act of observation creates the reality of that quantum event. But what is meant by the term 'observer?' Must an observer be conscious, or even exclusively human? This difficult question haunts quantum science.

SCHRÖDINGER'S CAT

At what point does the weird small-scale world of quantum mechanics impinge on the human-scaled world? A famous 'thought experiment' devised by the physicist Erwin Schrödinger more than seventy years ago still presents us with more questions than answers.

A healthy cat is locked inside a windowless and totally soundproof steel chamber, along with a radiation monitor and a speck of radioactive material so small that perhaps in the course of one hour, one of its atoms might decay and give off a radioactive pulse. If an atom does decay, the radiation monitor detects it and triggers a hammer that smashes a small glass container of lethal gas. The cat has only to get the tiniest whiff of this poison into its nostrils and it will die instantly. On the other hand, there is a precisely equal probability that none of the atoms in the radioactive speck will decay during the course of that hour, and the hammer won't fall. We are not allowed to sneak a look inside the box, nor cheat by installing TV cameras or microphones. So, if this rather cruel system is left to itself for an hour, what can we know about the fate of the cat unless we open the box?

According to the rules of quantum mechanics, the 'aliveness' or 'deadness' of the cat is bound up with the decay or failure to decay of a single atom – and that

process is subject to quantum uncertainty. Therefore the cat is neither alive nor dead, but exists in a potential cloud or 'superposition' of both possibilities at once. This strange scenario demonstrates that we cannot talk about subatomic particles that are neither in one state nor the other, unless we are also prepared to talk about things that are neither in one state nor the other. Taken to its logical conclusion, quantum mechanics suggests a world so much at odds with our ordinary understanding that it simply refuses to make sense: a world in which cats can be both dead and alive at the same time.

RELATIVITY

Whenever we hear the phrase 'Einstein's theory of relativity', many of us imagine something beyond the scope of normal minds to grasp. Actually some of the underlying phenomena are quite simple. We can even observe them in our everyday lives.

IMAGINE YOU ARE ON A TRAIN, and you have momentarily closed your eyes for a brief sleep while waiting for the train to start moving out of the station. A tremendous rushing noise wakes you from your nap, and you notice, to your relief, that your train appears to be on the move again. In fact it seems to be going at full speed. Through your window you see a blur of other windows as your train rushes past another one on the track alongside yours. You can feel the blustering of air between the trains as the mutual shock wave rocks your carriage sideways. Then, with a disappointing suddenness, the other train passes out of view and you realize that your train is exactly where it was before you fell asleep – motionless and still in the station.

To be more accurate, your train is motionless relative to the ground. Obviously it was not motionless relative to the other train, or else you would not have observed that sensation of speed as one train passed the other. Now imagine what the passengers on the other train would have experienced from the restful comfort of their window seats: your train and the station rushing past them.

According to Einstein's view of the universe, everything depends on the observer's relationship with the observed. In our human-scaled world of trains, red lights and earthly landscapes, it

does not take long for befuddled passengers to regain their sense of perspective. However, in the depths of space, no absolute frame of reference exists. There is no 'solid ground' to serve as an unshakeable foundation for all our measurements. If we detect an asteroid speeding towards Earth, then that is merely the conclusion that we draw from our particular perspective. For the alarmed space explorer stranded on the asteroid, it is equally true to say that the Earth is hurtling towards the asteroid.

Now imagine yourself in a high-speed lift, ascending from the ground floor to the penthouse suite of a tall skyscraper. The lift cage accelerates as it ascends. You can feel the floor pushing against the soles of your feet. If you happen to have a good set of bathroom scales with you, you can measure very accurately a slight increase in your weight. From this experiment you discover that the effects of gravity and acceleration on an observer are the same. They cannot be told apart. Later that day, you are in a jet airliner flying at a steady 370 miles (600 km) per hour. There is nothing but darkness outside your window. Nothing seems to be 'rushing past' you. You only know your speed because your captain has just announced it on the cabin speakers, yet you feel completely motionless, and your drink does not spill as you set it on its little plastic tray. Just as gravity is

Frame of reference
The physical phenomena observed by this passenger are measured by comparison with his or her local universe: the interior of the train, the window, the seat, and all the other objects that are 'at rest' relative to that passenger. The train could be motionless, or it could be moving at great (but constant) speed.

WHY TIME SLOWS DOWN
WHEN OBJECTS ARE IN MOTION

Time, space and motion are interconnected. Imagine a clock that counts pulses of light bounced between two mirrors inside a jet flying extremely fast, but at constant velocity. The jet's motion is undetectable to its pilot, for the same reason that people do not spill their drinks on airliners at cruising speed. The light bounces back and forth between the mirrors, and the pilot notices nothing unusual. However, from the point of view of scientists on the ground, observing as the jet hurtles across the sky, the pulses leave one mirror and travel diagonally to the next, because by the time each pulse completes its short crossing from one side of the jet to the other, the receiving mirror will have shifted slightly forward. From the ground's point of view, the pulses travel a long zig-zag path, rather than the short perpendicular one observed by the pilot. Therefore they take longer to complete each bounce. At the end of the experiment, the jet lands and its clock is compared against a similar clock on Earth. Less time has passed for the jet's clock.

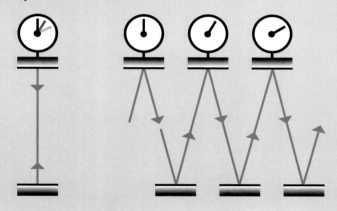

When a lift accelerates and rises, the upwards push of its floor on the soles of your feet is indistinguishable from the force of gravity.

indistinguishable from acceleration, being at rest is indistinguishable from hurtling through space at a steady speed.

Relative to you, the airliner's cabin staff approach with their trolley at 0.3 miles (0.5 km) per hour, walking along the central aisle and towards the plane's nose. Relative to the ground, they are travelling at 370.3 miles (600.5 km) per hour: their walking speed, plus the speed of the plane. Our measurements of the universe depend on our particular situation, or 'frame of reference'. Other observers at other locations will obtain different measurements of this scene. The pilots of another plane flying at 370 miles per hour on a direct collision course would be entitled to interpret your plane hurtling towards theirs at a terrifying 740 miles (1,200 km) per hour.

The head-scratching complications in Einstein's physics are a consequence of one of the 'absolutes' that the universe does exhibit. The speed of light is constant at all times and in all places. If a flight attendant on your plane shone a torch forwards along the aisle as they walked along at 0.3 miles per hour, while the plane continued to travel forward at 370 miles per hour, the beam from the torch would not travel at 370.3 miles per hour faster. It would shine forwards at exactly the same speed as before: a steady 185,057.072 miles (299,792.458 km) per hour. If a spaceship flew away from the Earth at 99 per cent of the speed of light, astronomers would still measure the light from its exhaust flare coming towards their telescopes at full light speed. Wherever we measure the speed of light, it is always the same. In relativity theory, the only way that this can make sense is for something else to change: space itself.

Spacetime

We think of space as having three dimensions: up–down, left–right, forwards–backwards. Objects, such as suns and planets, cats and dogs, occupy particular volumes of three-dimensional space. However, in Einstein's description of the universe, a fourth dimension has to be taken into consideration. *When* does an object occupy space?

Relativity wraps space and time together into four-dimensional 'spacetime'. Time can be stretched out or compressed just like any other dimensional measure, such as length or width. The speed of light stays constant while spacetime bends and stretches around it. The best way of illustrating this complicated idea is to tell the story of two twins and a spaceship.

The 'twin paradox'

Imagine that two astronauts, 30-year-old twins John and James, are the leading candidates for the first mission to another star system, ten light-years away. James is eventually selected to make the round-trip voyage, and sets off in a ship that travels very close to the speed of light. Allowing five years for the time taken to gradually accelerate the ship for the outward journey, and five more to slow it down again for the return trip, it will be thirty years before James comes home, as measured by the very high-quality digital watch that John wears at all times on his wrist.

John stays behind, helping to run mission control. When his twin brother finally returns and hugs him in celebration, John is startled by the digital readout on James' watch, even though John's training should have prepared him for the shock. For John, thirty years have passed, while James' near light-speed adventure means that, for him, less than ten years have passed. While James' ship was accelerating and decelerating he aged at the normal rate, but during the phases of his journey when he was travelling at close to the speed of light, time aboard his ship was compressed relative to time back in mission control. James noticed nothing unusual about his watch during the flight. For him, time seemed to pass as normal. It 'felt' like ten years, both according to his animal senses and his readings of the ship's instruments. Now James finds that, biologically, he is 40 years old while his twin brother, born on the same day as him, is 60.

No such fantastic flights to the stars are yet possible for human beings, but modern computer guidance systems routinely compensate for 'time dilation' effects experienced by digital clocks aboard fast-moving objects such as jet aircraft, rockets and space satellites relative to clocks on the ground. The discrepancies amount to only a few millionths of a second – but they are real, and could cause significant navigational errors if left unadjusted.

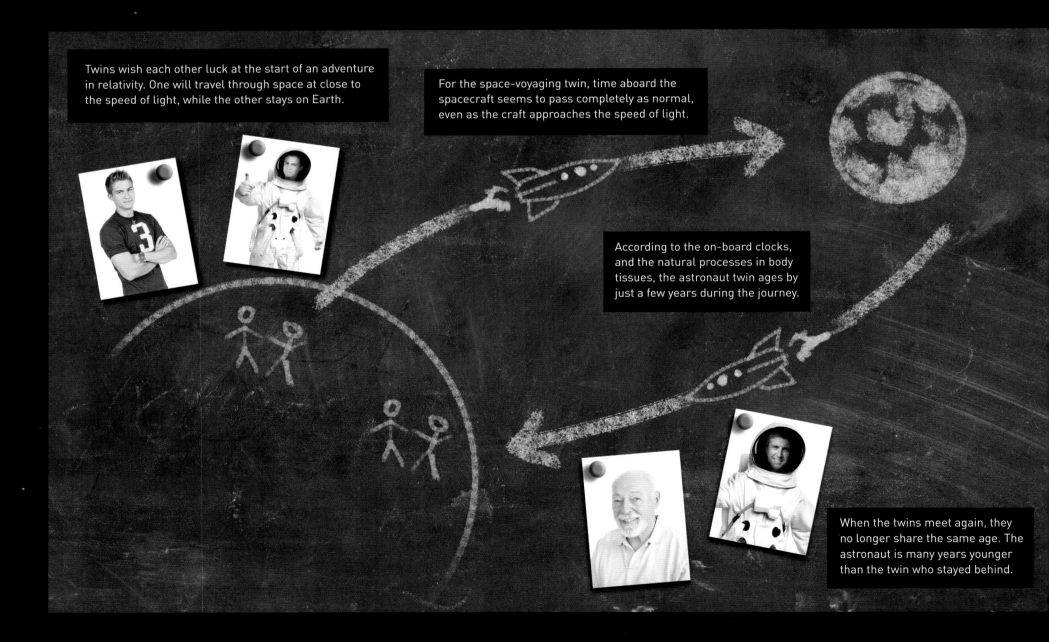

Twins wish each other luck at the start of an adventure in relativity. One will travel through space at close to the speed of light, while the other stays on Earth.

For the space-voyaging twin, time aboard the spacecraft seems to pass completely as normal, even as the craft approaches the speed of light.

According to the on-board clocks, and the natural processes in body tissues, the astronaut twin ages by just a few years during the journey.

When the twins meet again, they no longer share the same age. The astronaut is many years younger than the twin who stayed behind.

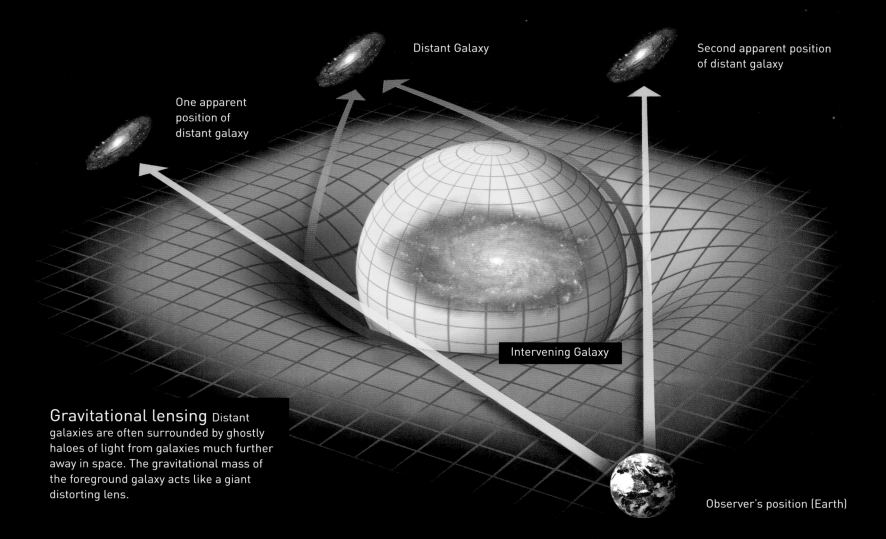

One apparent position of distant galaxy

Distant Galaxy

Second apparent position of distant galaxy

Intervening Galaxy

Gravitational lensing Distant galaxies are often surrounded by ghostly haloes of light from galaxies much further away in space. The gravitational mass of the foreground galaxy acts like a giant distorting lens.

Observer's position (Earth)

Infinite energy and shrinking objects

Time is just one dimension of spacetime. Relativistic effects also cause spatial dimensions to compress along an object's direction of travel. If James' spaceship could travel at the speed of light, its length along the direction of travel would shrink to zero. But no solid object can reach that speed. Relativity also shows that an object's mass increases with its velocity. As James' ship approaches quite near the speed of light, it becomes so massive that no amount of energy available in the entire universe can boost its speed any further. If it could actually reach the speed of light, its mass would become infinite. Light photons can travel at the speed of light because they have no mass. If it were possible to hitch a lift on a photon, no time at all would pass as it traversed from one side of the universe to the other – although, for external observers, its journey would be measured as taking over 13 billion years.

Gravity and spacetime

Most branches of science treat gravity as an invisible force exerted by all objects in the universe, such as galaxies, stars and planets. Relativity treats gravity not as a force but as a distortion in spacetime caused by the presence of mass. When light travels through spacetime, it always does so in an absolutely straight line – but spacetime itself is distorted by massive objects, causing the path of light to appear 'bent'. When the moon eclipses our Sun, we can monitor stars in the sky at the same time as the outer edge of the Sun's disc. The stars immediately adjacent to the disc appear to shift in the sky. This is because the Sun is distorting the spacetime around it. Similarly, and on a far grander scale, telescope observations of distant galaxies often reveal ghostly ring-shaped haloes of light from other galaxies behind the ones that are principally being observed. 'Gravitational lensing' vividly demonstrates the distortion of spacetime.

Spaghettification

The distortion around a black hole is so extreme, gravity will pull much more strongly against the legs of an unfortunate astronaut than his arms. He will be stretched like spaghetti as he falls feet-first into the hole.

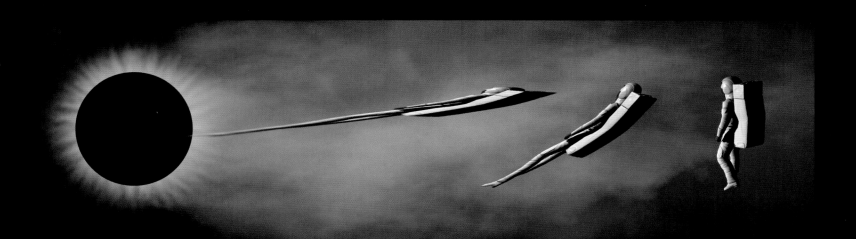

STRING THEORY

In a bid to reconcile the subatomic world with the larger-scaled universe, scientists are reaching for exotic and controversial explanations at the limits of theoretical possibility.

CONVENTIONAL PHYSICS reveals the effect of gravity on large masses like galaxies and stars, planets and people. We do not yet understand how it interacts with individual subatomic particles. Given that everything in the universe is made of particles, gravity must affect them somehow – and arise from them too. The search is afoot for the 'graviton', the particle that carries the force of gravity. So far, we haven't found it. However, we have theorized how it might be generated.

The graviton problem is simplified if we think of all subatomic particles as just the surface manifestations of something deeper. Many physicists now think that all particles of matter (hadrons), and all force-carrying particles (bosons) too, may be generated by extremely tiny vibrating strings of energy. One mode of vibration makes a string behave as an electron, another as a proton, and so on. Best of all, string theory includes a vibration mode to deliver the graviton. At last, gravity can be described subatomically as well as at the cosmic scale. All of physics might soon be tamed so that it appears similar to harmonious music from a single stringed instrument, rather than a bewildering cacophony of noises from an argumentative orchestra. The hope is that a string-based Theory of Everything (ToE) will bind all the laws of nature into one equation.

HIDDEN DIMENSIONS

String theory requires us to believe that multiple extra dimensions can be wrapped up in strings so small we cannot see them. Try to imagine strings as suspended power cables and ants as subatomic entities. From a distance, the cables are one-dimensional lines, and the ants are invisible. But the cables are actually three-dimensional, and the ants crawl 'up' and 'down' as well as 'along'.

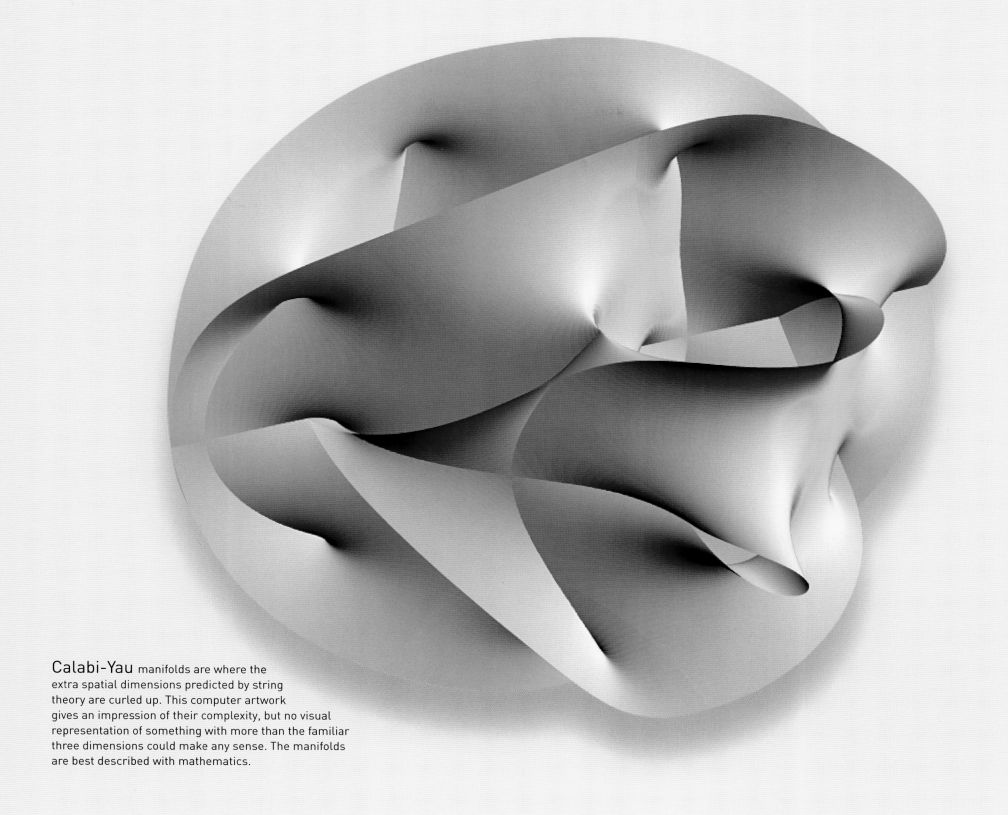

Calabi-Yau manifolds are where the extra spatial dimensions predicted by string theory are curled up. This computer artwork gives an impression of their complexity, but no visual representation of something with more than the familiar three dimensions could make any sense. The manifolds are best described with mathematics.

Strings are much smaller than the smallest subatomic particles. There is not much hope of detecting them (proving their existence) with even the most advanced scientific instruments. Another difficulty is that, while the mathematics of string theory seems quite convincing on paper, it calls for some very weird assumptions. We experience the world in four dimensions: one in time and three in space. Strings supposedly exist in ten, eleven or twenty-six dimensions, and perhaps even more, depending on the specific theory. The hidden dimensions are wrapped up in invisibly tiny bundles, associated with the strings, called Calabi-Yau manifolds. These behave in a way that can be loosely compared to the chambers of a complicated musical instrument, shaping the energy vibrations to deliver the 'notes' we observe, in the form of specific particles. String theory is controversial. Some scientists are becoming frustrated by theories that they cannot test with any observation or experiment. These rebels are looking for an even better idea that can be verified through discoveries as well as equations.

Thinking in tiny dimensions

The idea of wrapping extra dimensions of space into specks so small we cannot see them sounds absurd, but picture yourself looking at a long, thin power cable strung between two high pylons. You may well perceive it as nothing more than a one-dimensional black line etched across the sky. Now imagine some ants crawling on the surface of that cable. For them, this is a completely three-dimensional world with an 'up' and a 'down' as well as an 'across'. Now imagine that those cables are in fact hollow…yet another set of surfaces becomes available for the ants to crawl around on. Meanwhile you, staring into the sky, still see nothing more than a one-dimensional black line. This is a simplistic scenario, yet it does make Calabi-Yau manifolds fractionally less of a strain to think about.

COSMO

OLOGY

In 1905, a five-year-old English girl, Cecilia Payne, saw a meteor shooting across the sky and decided at once to become an astronomer when she grew up. Fourteen years later, as a student at Newnham College, Cambridge, she attended a lecture by the world-famous astronomer Arthur Eddington, in which he explained how his solar eclipse observations had proved Einstein's prediction that massive objects such as the Sun should bend the light from distant stars. Payne tried to get access to the university's telescope, only to find its guardian rushing off to warn his superiors, 'There's a *woman* out there, asking questions!' Payne's career would be dogged by sexism and resistance, yet she somehow managed to make one of the most important discoveries in the history of science.

Payne went to America's Harvard University, where she began analysing the complicated spectrum of light from the Sun, and found that the entire astronomical community was misreading it. The prevailing theory was that stars like our Sun consisted of around 60 per cent iron. Payne believed that the light spectrum told a very different story. In a brave academic paper, *Stellar Atmospheres*, published in 1925, she asserted that the Sun was more than 90 per cent hydrogen, with most of the rest consisting of helium. Even though her text included phrases designed to soften the blow, her male critics were outraged, because they knew, as no foolish woman ever could, that if the Sun were made of hydrogen, it would have burned out long ago.

The fate of scientific arguments is to be settled, one way or the other, by further experimentation and observation. Payne's work was replicated and she was at last heralded as brilliant. Now the path was clear to discover how our Sun, and all other stars, generate vast amounts of energy over billions of years. It is a nuclear process. After Payne, the Sun was no longer quite so mysterious. On the other hand, no one yet knew where it, or anything else in the universe, had come from. Everything was made from atoms. What had made the atoms?

By 1931 it was known that the universe contains galaxies, and that they are all speeding away from each other as the universe expands in all directions. A scientifically trained Belgian-born Catholic priest, Georges-Henri Lemaître, came up with an extraordinary idea, simply by imagining the expansion running backwards to the first moment of time. 'We could conceive the beginning of the universe in the form of a unique atom, the atomic weight of which is the total mass of the universe,' he wrote. Lemaître's highly unstable atom gave birth to the universe 'by a kind of super-radioactive process'. With a brilliant leap of imagination, he had described what we all know today as the Big Bang theory.

These are just two stories from the realm of cosmology, a discipline where the practitioners must first try to imagine the seemingly unimaginable – the universe in its totality – so that scientific observations can then be directed to prove them right or wrong. Modern theories about the origins of existence call for some of the greatest feats of human imagination, from string theory and eleven-dimensional spacetime to alternative reality and infinite multiverses. Now we are on a quest to invent experiments that can test these possibilities. Just as Payne discovered, phenomena that seem impossible to us today may become the commonplace facts of tomorrow.

THE BIG BANG

The universe began at a single instant approximately 13.75 billion years ago, when an infinitely dense speck of energy expanded with great violence in a colossal explosion known as the Big Bang.

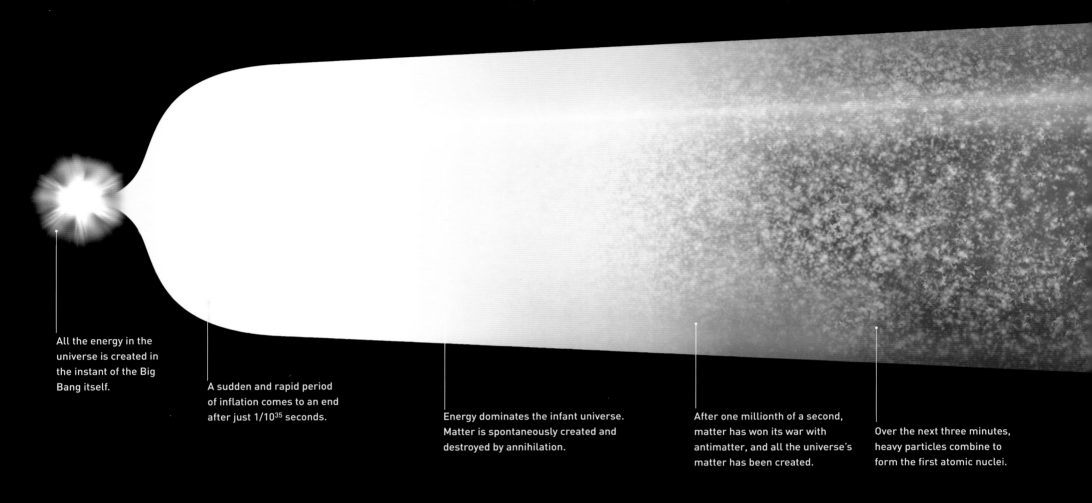

All the energy in the universe is created in the instant of the Big Bang itself.

A sudden and rapid period of inflation comes to an end after just $1/10^{35}$ seconds.

Energy dominates the infant universe. Matter is spontaneously created and destroyed by annihilation.

After one millionth of a second, matter has won its war with antimatter, and all the universe's matter has been created.

Over the next three minutes, heavy particles combine to form the first atomic nuclei.

FOR THE FIRST FEW BILLIONTHS of a second of its history, the universe was concentrated within an infinitely dense and super-hot point, a singularity, smaller than a grain of sand. Within a few more fractions of a second, the furious energies contained in that speck blew it outwards in a gigantic explosion, the Big Bang. From this inconceivably powerful cataclysm emerged all the energy and matter that exists today – and all of space and time, too. After just three seconds, the basic components of matter condensed out of the brilliant storm of energy: the electrons, protons, neutrons and other subatomic building blocks from which the 'stuff' of our familiar world is constructed.

In the wake of these swift and dramatic events, the next 10,000 years were relatively uneventful. The universe was still too hot for anything much to happen except for the continuing, remorseless expansion into a larger and larger space, which that same expansion process actually created as it progressed. Fierce radiation dominated this phase, preventing any of the matter particles from condensing into atoms.

After 300,000 years, as the fireball at last began to cool down to a modest 10,000 degrees Celsius, the subatomic particles were able to link together into complete atoms of hydrogen, helium and lithium, the three lightest and simplest chemical elements. At 300 million years old, the universe's first distinct physical structures emerged when vast clouds of hydrogen and helium coalesced under the force of gravity. These regional variations were the seeds of future galaxies. At yet smaller scales, tightly localized swirls of gas were drawn together into hot, dense spheres. The gravitational forces and internal pressures increased even further, and the spheres reached a critical point, igniting into the first generation of stars.

After 300,000 years, the first atoms form. The number of free particles in the universe falls and space becomes transparent for the first time.

For over 100 million years, matter cools and coalesces in the darkness.

After 200 million years, the first generation of giant stars enriches the universe with heavy elements.

400 million years after the Big Bang, the first galaxies begin to condense.

COSMIC MICROWAVE BACKGROUND RADIATION

This map of the sky charts microwave aftershocks from the Big Bang, dating from a time when stars and galaxies, and even matter itself, had not yet formed. The scattering of very faint signals, billions of light-years across, is the weak remnants of energies that were originally compressed within quantum fluctuations in the first super-hot pinprick of creation. Without these asymmetries in the first moments of the Big Bang, the young universe would have expanded with elegant but sterile evenness. Around those random imperfections, matter condensed into the lumpy and diverse universe we know today.

SEE ALSO

■ **Our Place in the Universe** *page 12*

The big questions
What will happen to the universe?

Will it go on forever, or will it one day come to an end? Is there one universe, or are there many universes? And where did the laws of physics come from? These are just some of the deep questions for which science has no answers – yet.

In the far future, the universe continues to expand from the Big Bang

In the 'Big Rip' scenario, dark energy ultimately overcomes all the other forces, tearing the universe apart.

Unlikely numbers

All the physical events in the universe can be accounted for by just four natural forces: gravity, electromagnetism, the strong nuclear force that holds the nucleus of atoms together and the weak nuclear force that allows radioactive atoms to decay. What would happen if any of these forces were to change, even slightly?

Gravity is such a weak force at small scales that it scarcely counts. However, if the exact strength of gravity weakened by the tiniest degree, the large-scale implications would be dramatic. Galaxies would disintegrate. Suns would die prematurely. The formation of new suns from drifting galactic dust clouds would be impossible. We wouldn't be here, because the cosmos couldn't have produced stars such as the one that warms our Earth. On the other hand, if gravity were a little stronger, then the rate of collisions between stars would be so great that a typical solar system like ours would not survive long enough to produce stable planets. We wouldn't have had a chance to evolve.

What about electromagnetism? If the balance of the electromagnetic force altered in any way, all known chemistry would disintegrate. The same applies to the strong force. As for the weak force, it is tempting to think that we could do without radiation. But then the stars could not shine, and the basic chemical elements of life, carbon, nitrogen, oxygen and so on, could not be manufactured inside them. These examples are just simplifications. Any tiny change in the relationship between the four forces would make existence as we know it impossible.

The Big Bang could easily have produced forces and physical laws very different from the ones we actually find out there. In fact the possible varieties of unstable balances between the forces are billion-fold. Any of these 'poor' balances would have produced a universe incapable of maintaining order and creating life. In fact the odds against our stable, life-friendly universe emerging from the Big Bang were vastly greater than those against winning a national lottery grand prize with your one and only ticket purchase.

This fact leads many cosmologists to speculate that Big Bangs may have happened countless times, not just once, and that consequently we are living in a lucky universe rather than a unique one.

In the 'Modified Big Chill' the universe's expansion gradually grinds to a halt, but can never be reversed.

In a Big Crunch universe, gravity overcomes all other forces, and cosmic expansion goes into reverse.

The Big Crunch itself is a return to the singularity from which the cosmos was born.

In a Big Chill universe, cosmic expansion continues forever, even as the stars become extinct.

THE BIG CRUNCH?

All the galaxies in the observable universe are flying apart from each other. The further away a galaxy is from us, the faster we observe it receding. Its light stretches into longer wavelengths at the red end of the spectrum (the 'redshift'), just as sound waves from a speeding train lengthen when the train hurtles away from an observer. The expansion of the universe is a legacy from the outwards momentum of the Big Bang. Until recently it was thought that, one day, the expansion could slow down, then go into reverse as gravity regains the upper hand. All galaxies would then move towards each other. This could only end one way: in a Big Crunch. The latest data suggest that, far from slowing down, the expansion process is speeding up, powered by an as yet unidentified 'dark energy'.

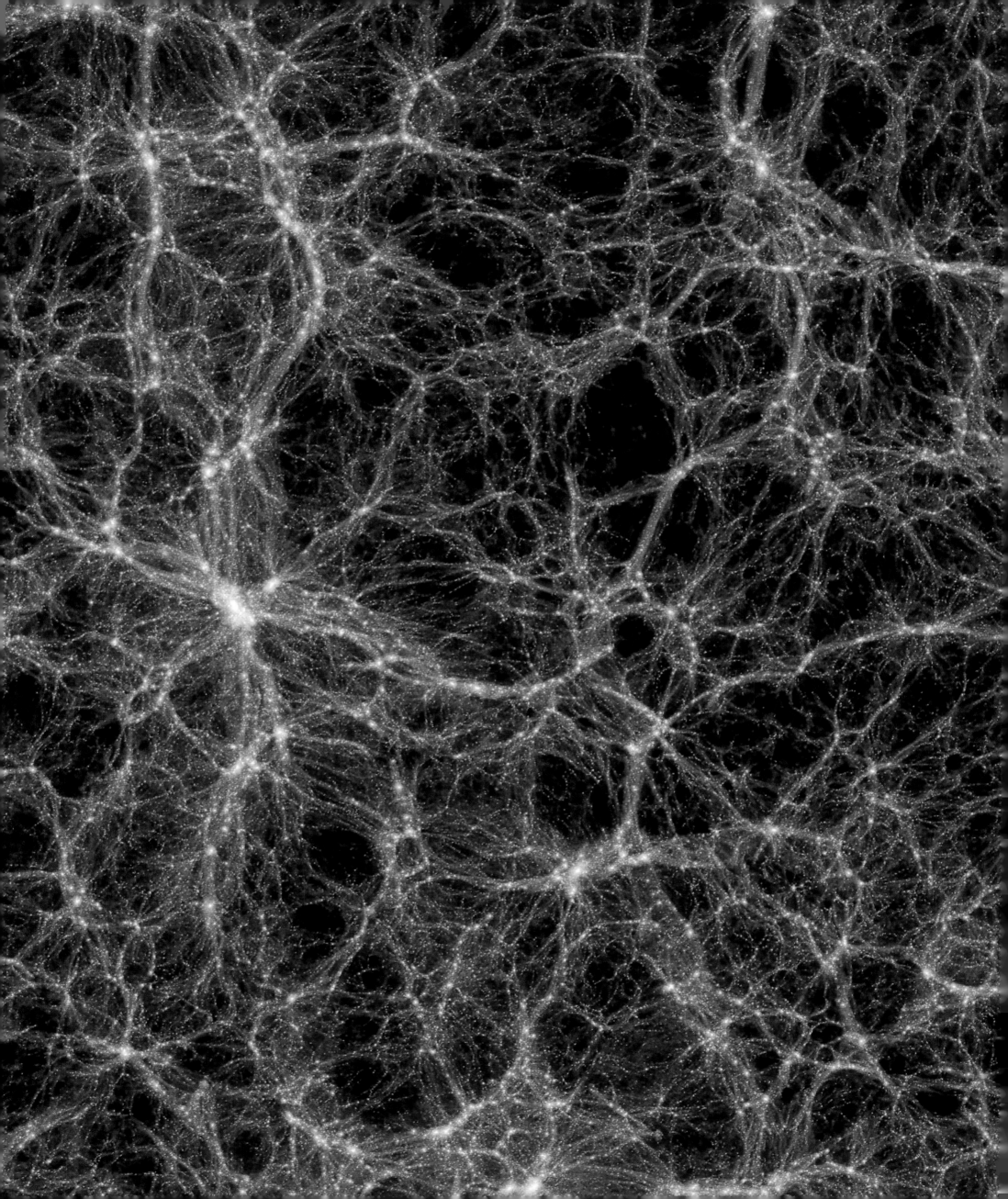

DARK MATTER
AND DARK ENERGY

The trillions upon trillions of stars and countless billions of galaxies that we can observe account for only a small fraction of the universe's total mass and energy. What else is out there?

GALAXIES DRIFT AROUND each other under the influence of their collective gravitational fields, but the total gravity involved is stronger than a simple tally of the mass of galaxies alone can explain. Even the rotations of individual galaxies show that they contain much more mass, or 'dark matter', than all the stars, planets and gas clouds inside them can account for. Dark matter may consist of WIMPs, subatomic weakly interacting massive particles which possess mass, and therefore create gravitational effects, but which otherwise hardly influence normal matter.

From our perspective, light from distant galaxies is bent by the gravity of closer foreground galaxies, and that gravity is generated mainly by dark matter. Astronomers have analysed the shapes of thousands of distant galaxies in selected regions of the sky, and compared the gravitationally distorted shapes against the normal shapes of closer galaxies, to build a map of dark matter distribution in that region. The filaments of dark matter, shown here in red and white, are invisible in reality, but the distorted galaxy images that we can see in our telescopes tend to be stretched along the filaments. This allows dark matter's possible distribution to be calculated.

The rate of expansion of the universe is also accelerating. A 'dark energy' is pushing galaxies away from each other, essentially like an anti-gravity force. Dark matter and dark energy are, so far at least, invisible to our scientific instruments, but they account for more than nine-tenths of the universe.

Dark matter distribution

◄ A supercomputer simulation, made in 2005 by scientists at the Max Planck Society in Germany, shows the distribution of dark matter in the local universe. The frame represents a zone 824 million light-years across. Dark matter cannot be detected by telescopes because it emits no radiation. However, it does seem to contain mass, which in turn exerts a gravitational influence. Galaxies formed in web-like strands focused around filaments of dark matter.

Dark energy

▼ In the late 1990s, observations of very distant supernovae made by the Hubble Space Telescope showed that, a long time ago, the universe was actually expanding more slowly than it is today. So the expansion has not been slowing due to gravity, as everyone thought. Instead, it is still accelerating. The dark energy that powers this cosmic oddity may result from a property of space itself; or else it may be an indication that our current theories of gravity and spacetime are not quite right, and that the legacy of the great Albert Einstein might one day be improved upon, just as Einstein's work improved upon Newton's.

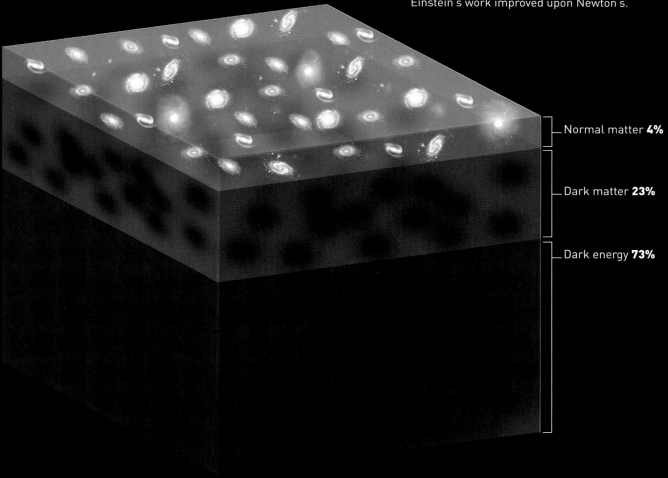

Normal matter **4%**

Dark matter **23%**

Dark energy **73%**

BLACK HOLES AND MULTIPLE UNIVERSES

At the heart of every galaxy sits an invisible monster. The space-twisting forces and inconceivable gravitational energies inside a black hole are so extreme, they reach beyond our current understanding.

WHEN SOME VERY LARGE stars die, they explode with such immense force that material is pushed inwards as well as exploding outwards. The inward-rushing mass becomes so dense it collapses to a pinprick under its own gravity. From this point, any further stray material, gas clouds, and even entire nearby stars that wander too close, are sucked in, increasing the pinprick's mass until it suddenly blinks out of the realm of normal time and space, becoming a dimensionless point of infinitely condensed matter with a truly monstrous gravitational field. Nothing can escape this field. Not even light. Hence the term 'black hole'. These exotic and terrifying objects are the ultimate challenge for science because, by their very nature, they can never be directly seen through our telescopes or measured with instruments. The centres of galaxies are more densely packed with stars than the perimeters, and black holes are more likely to form in these galactic cores because of the relative abundance of material to feed upon. Given time, a black hole could swallow a galaxy. However, some theories suggest that black holes also have a useful aspect: they are a centre of mass around which healthy young galaxies coalesce.

The 'other side' of a black hole may be a 'white hole' giving rise to another universe with its own spacetime dimensions, completely separate from ours. The Big Bang from which our universe was born was a singularity, a dimensionless point of infinitely compressed matter. Black hole singularities also are dimensionless points of infinitely compressed matter. The two singularities, 'black' and 'bang', are equivalent. A black hole can compress a few million stars into a pinprick of infinitely condensed matter, yet it takes only one such pinprick to make an entire universe containing trillions of stars. At least, it does if this theory is correct.

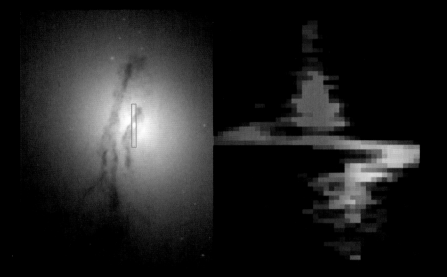

Observing the influence of a black hole

This eerie image from the Hubble Space Telescope (right), taken in 1997, yields compelling evidence for a supermassive black hole at the heart of galaxy M84 (left). It is a spectral line of light frequencies emitted from a fast-spinning disc of glowing gas and other material within the black hole's baleful influence, but not yet quite sucked in. The gas is being spun around so fast that the wavelengths of its emitted light appear from our point of view to be stretched into the long red end of the spectrum or compressed into the short blue, depending on whether the material is rushing away from us or hurtling in our direction. What should have been a vertical set of spectral lines is now crazily distorted.

This is not a 'picture' in any sense that we might normally use that term, yet the image certainly conveys the power of this terrifying vortex. Analysis of the data suggests that M84's black hole may have swallowed the mass equivalent of 300 million Suns since its birth.

MORE THAN ONE UNIVERSE FROM THE BIG BANG?

In one region of the universe at least, a strange force, seemingly from 'outside' the observable universe, seems to be pulling at a cluster of approximately 1,000 galaxies. This is known as 'dark flow'. It is possible that the Big Bang created multiple 'bubbles' of expanding spacetime. Our universe is in one of those bubbles. Cosmologists think that dark flow may result from the influence of another universe upon our own.

▶ Multiple universes

Computer artwork showing funnels that represent several different universes being created at the same time. Each parallel universe may have different physical laws from our universe (central funnel). Some physicists believe that there are an infinite number of parallel universes. The collective name for them is the 'multiverse'.

THE END OF EVERYTHING?

We know that the universe came into being 13.75 billion years ago. Will it go on forever, or must it die? And what will happen to us and our world in the meantime?

BY WEIGHT, our bodies are 10 per cent hydrogen atoms, 60 per cent oxygen and 20 per cent carbon. The last 10 per cent is taken up principally by atoms of nitrogen, calcium, phosphorus, sulphur, sodium, magnesium, iron and copper. All these atoms were created, not in our Sun, but by other stars long since dead. They are not our atoms. They do not belong to us, nor to our bodies. They are just passing through us for a very short while. They have existed for 5,000 million years already, and will continue to exist, long after we are gone, in the soil, then inside microorganisms and plants, and in the air breathed by our descendants. Even at that point, their new chemical adventures will barely have begun, and they will continue to combine and recombine long after the Earth itself has ended its days as a life-giving world.

Our Sun has burned for five billion years, and will burn for five billion more; after which, it will have used up a crucial proportion of its available hydrogen fuel. Eventually the Sun will become an unpredictable monster, prone to sudden nuclear shutdowns and reignitions, expansions and contractions, alternating over several millennia. The Sun will end its days as a red giant – so gigantic that its wayward mantle of gases will swallow up half the planets of the solar system, including the Earth. Everything on our world that lives and breathes will be utterly vaporized in a slow but remorseless firestorm. The grass, the trees, even the toughened lichen that clings to granite will be blasted into atoms. The oceans will boil away to the last drop. The ice caps will vaporize. The sands on every beach in the world will fuse into glass. Mercury and Venus will probably vanish altogether.

If Earth survives the storm, it will remain only as a scorched lump of rock. The Sun's final life-giving service will have been to vaporize the thin sliver of biosphere on the Earth's surface, blasting it into space once more so that the atoms might one day contribute towards new worlds and new forms of life. Perhaps, some day in the far future, some intelligent and curious creature containing a few of our second-hand atoms will wonder where they came from.

The greater ending

Beyond that, we can only wonder if the universe itself will persist forever, or if it, too, eventually will come to an end. All the stars that shine must finally sputter out, and the nebulae that they leave behind become too diffuse to generate new stars. All energy, everywhere, is in the process of becoming more diffuse, random and disorganized. In the 'heat death' scenario, the temperature across the entire universe eventually settles at a few degrees above absolute zero. All matter, the thin and lightless fragments of long-gone structures, is just dust, specks of ice or cold gas. No single spot or zone contains anything so interesting as to constitute an 'event'. The dull dark ghost of our universe persists in this state for ever…Or does it? Perhaps the 'dark energy' that accounts for so much of the universe will continue to feed its dynamics indefinitely? Perhaps black holes in other universes feed new matter and new energy into our universe, in a way that we can as yet only speculate about?

Whatever the possible outcomes, for this planet or for the universe, none of these grand-scale events can conceivably matter to us, our descendants, or even the creatures that we might become some thousands, or even tens of millions, of years into the future. What will count are the decisions that we make during the current, extraordinarily brief spark of time during which our technological ingenuity has become balanced almost exactly against the environmental stresses caused by that same ingenuity. The balance will tip, one way or another, in decades or centuries, not aeons. A new kind of science might be well advised to take into account the vast stretch of opportunity that exists between today and the time when the Sun shines its last. If we think like sentient occupants of an infinite cosmos instead of like nervous beasts scuttling on the surface of a tiny, overcrowded sphere of rock – if we aspire to live as long as our own star continues to shine – we might have a chance, at least, of making it through the next century.

◄ Sun over dying Earth The moon passes in front of the massively swollen Sun as it enters its red giant stage, in about five or six billion years' time. It will expand and engulf the inner planets. Even if the Earth survives the scorching, its barren surface will freeze forever as the Sun collapses into a white dwarf star.

GLOSSARY

Absolute zero The lowest temperature theoretically possible, equivalent to -273.15 degrees Centigrade.

Acceleration The rate of change of an object's velocity. A negative acceleration (slowing down) is called a deceleration.

Acid A reactive chemical compound that, in solution with water, yields hydrogen ions (protons) that attract electrons from other atoms, forming ionic bonds.

Active galaxy A galaxy which releases huge amounts of energy from its centre. The central energy source of an active galaxy probably is a supermassive black hole.

Alloy A mixture of a metal and at least one other element, resulting in a metallic material with certain useful properties derived from the original components. Steel is made from iron and carbon, while bronze is an alloy of copper and tin.

Adipose tissue Fatty, connective tissue in vertebrate animals that serves as an energy reserve and shock absorber.

Agar A carbohydrate jelly made from seaweed, and used as a nutrient for growing microbes in laboratory experiments.

Alkali A chemical compound classed as a 'base' that is soluble in water. Alkalis neutralize acids, and are soapy to the touch.

Allele A variant of a gene that produces different varieties of inheritable traits, such as eye and hair color in animals, or flower and seed colour in plants.

Amino acid An organic compound containing an amino group (-NH$_2$), a carboxylic acid group (COOH), and any of various side groups, and especially the 20 compounds that have the basic formula NH$_2$CHRCOOH, and that link together to form proteins.

Amplitude The measure of energy in waves judged by the height of the wave peaks.

Antimatter For every particle of ordinary matter there is an identical particle of antimatter, but with an opposite electrical charge. When a particle meets its antiparticle, they annihilate.

Astronomical unit (AU) A measure of distances in space, defined by the average distance between the Earth and the Sun.

Atom The smallest particle of a chemical element that can take part in a chemical reaction without being permanently changed. Atoms consist of a positively charged nucleus that binds one or more electrons in motion around it.

Atomic number The number of protons in an atomic nucleus. Protons are not dislodged except by extreme nuclear events. The atomic number is a reliable method of identifying a chemical element.

ATP Short for Adenosine triphosphate, a universal energy carrier for biological systems. Nearly half of the energy content of food is converted into ATP to power tissue growth, muscle work and other physiological processes.

Bacteria Single-celled organisms, and the most widespread form of life on Earth. Bacteria are classed as prokaryotes. The cell is contained within a membrane but the interior is not compartmentalized.

Bile The digestive juice stored in the gall bladder and released into the digestive tract to help absorb fats. Bile contains acids and derivatives of cholesterol.

Biotechnology Manipulation of biology into forms not found in nature, through processes such as gene transfer between species or the production of biochemicals in animals for human consumption.

Carbohydrates Organic compounds consisting of carbon, hydrogen, and oxygen. The two major types are sugars (such as fructose, glucose, and lactose) and starches, found in foods such as wheat and rice.

Carbon The element that defines the chemical properties of life. Carbon is the third most common element in cells, after hydrogen and oxygen.

Catalyst A substance that increases the speed of a chemical reaction, or lowers the energy required to trigger the reaction, without itself being consumed in the process.

Cell The smallest unit of life. Cells are bound by a membrane, and contain all the compounds necessary for life, such as proteins and DNA. Cells are either prokaryotic (simple) or eukaryotic (having a nucleus).

Cholesterol Contrary to myth, this substance is essential to us. It is a soft, waxy lipid found in all complex animals, and is transported around the body by proteins in combinations called lipoproteins. Cholesterol contributes to the production of bile acids and hormones, and plays a key role in the function of cell membranes.

Chromosome Tightly bundled strands of genetic information contained in every cell of the body. During cell reproduction, the strands coil and condense into structures visible under a microscope. Chromosomes assemble in pairs in all cells except the reproductive cells.

Constellation One of the 88 familiar patterns of stars that enable the night sky to be interpreted by navigators and astronomers. For example, the seven brightest stars in the constellation Ursa Major form the 'Plough'. Constellations are just a convenient human invention. Seen from elsewhere in the galaxy, they would look completely different.

Covalent bond A very strong attraction between two or more atoms, formed by the sharing of electrons.

Cytoskeleton A fibrous network that maintains the structure of a eukaryotic cell. Three fibre types perform different tasks. Actin filaments control cell size, while microtubules deal with the internal movement of chromosomes and organelles during cell division. Intermediate filaments adjust the flexibility or stiffness of cells and tissues.

Dark Matter Material in space that is widespread, and responsible for a large proportion of the universe's total mass, yet which does not produce significant light and therefore is extremely hard for scientists to detect.

Distillation A technique for separating components of a mixture based on their different boiling points.

DNA Deoxyribonucleic acid, the molecular material responsible for the transmission of genetic characteristics. DNA is a polymer made from four nucleotides, each distinguished by one of four base structures: adenine (A), guanine (G), thymine (T), and cytosine (C).

Electrical charge A property of certain subatomic particles, such as electrons and protons. that creates forces of attraction or repulsion between those particles. Electrons are repelled by other electrons but attracted to protons.

Electrical current A measure of the transfer of electrical charge per unit time, representing the flow of electrons through a conductive material. The measurement unit is the amp (or ampere) and its symbol is 'I.'

Electromagnetic radiation Waves of electric and magnetic energy, oscillating (vibrating) perpendicularly in relation to each other, and propagating through space at the speed of light. Gamma rays, X-rays, ultraviolet light, visible light, infrared and radio waves are all electromagnetic radiation.

Electrons The negatively charged particles that exist in a cloud around the nucleus of an atom. Electrons are negatively charged, and are 'fundamental' particles that cannot be divided into anything smaller.

Element A substance that cannot be split into other substances. Elements are defined atomically according to the number of protons in the nucleus. There are approximately 102 different elements in nature, and some additional synthetic elements created in laboratory experiments.

Energy The capacity to do work. Work is done by transferring energy from one form to another. For example the chemical energy in the fuel for a vehicle is converted to thermal energy as it burns in the engine. In turn, the thermal energy is converted into mechanical energy.

Enzyme A protein that enables a chemical reaction as part of a cell's metabolism, but without itself being consumed by the reaction: essentially a biological catalyst. While many biological reactions would happen anyway, enzymes increase the rate by a thousand to a million fold.

Eukaryotes Multicellular or single-celled organisms whose large cells have an internal membrane-clad nucleus, along with other discrete structures called organelles.

Fission The splitting of an atomic nucleus after a neutron is absorbed, causing the nucleus to divide into two smaller nuclei, and releasing some of the original mass as energy. Fission liberates yet more neutrons which then collide with other adjacent nuclei, causing an extremely swift 'chain reaction.'

Fluid Any substance that can flow. Often mistaken as being another word for liquid, in fact both gases and liquids are fluids. Window glass is also fluid, even though it flows very slowly.

Force Pushing and pulling influences that make objects move or change shape. A force causes an object to accelerate.

Frequency The measure of how often a repetitive action occurs in a given time, usually measured in hertz (Hz) where 1 Hz equals 1 action per second.

Fusion The joining of atomic nuclei to form a larger nucleus. Fusion powers the Sun and other stars. One day we may be able to exploit hydrogen fusion to provide energy on Earth.

Galaxy A very large cluster of stars in space, typically containing hundreds of millions of stars, and often as many as hundreds of billions. Most galaxies contain black holes.

Gamma rays The shortest and most energetic form of electromagnetic radiation. They are produced by extremely energetic nuclear decay processes, or by the mutual annihilation of matter and antimatter particles. The reverse also occurs, where gamma energy becomes matter. When two gamma particles (photons) interact in the right way, they can produce a matter particle and an antimatter particle.

Gene A particular portion of base pair sequencing within an organism's DNA that transmits specific inheritable characteristics from that organism to its offspring. A gene cannot be divided into smaller units without losing its informational content.

Genome The complete set of genetic information for an organism, including both coding and non-coding sequences, and physically partitioned into chromosomes.

Globular cluster A roughly spherical, localized collection of stars within a galaxy, held together by their own mutual gravity, and containing up to hundreds of thousands of stars.

Glucose The major carbohydrate component in starch and fruit sugars, and the principal source of energy for an organism's cells. Animals derive glucose by processing of food materials, while plants manufacture glucose via photosynthesis.

Haemoglobin An iron-rich protein, found especially in red blood cells, that binds to oxygen and transports it through an animal's body.

Heat Death The possible fate of the universe, in which the temperature everywhere drops toward zero, all stars fade, black holes evaporate, entropy (disorder) increases, and no further energy is available for physical processes.

Higgs Boson A hypothetical particle which may play an important role in endowing matter particles with mass.

Homeostasis The condition where an organism maintains its body temperature, plus the water and salt concentration in its cells, and other important balances, despite the constant flux of physical and biochemical processes within the body. Cellular components such as proteins, membranes, sugars, and nucleic acids are constantly recycled, but the integrity of the organism is preserved.

Hormones Messenger substances synthesized in the body and secreted by the endocrine glands. Hormones regulate the digestive system, bodily growth, appetite and thirst, glucose levels, bodily day and night cycles, menstrual cycles, and the sex drive.

Hydrocarbons Chemical compounds that consist only of hydrogen and carbon atoms.

Inertia The property of an object that resists any attempt to change its state of motion. The greater the mass, the greater the inertia. Even in the weightless environment of space, astronauts have to take care when trying to move large, heavy items of equipment against their own inertia.

Infrared Electromagnetic radiation with wavelengths longer than visible light but shorter than that of microwaves. All warm or hot objects emit infrared radiation.

Inheritance The features of an organism, such as body shape and eye colour, determined by the chromosomes originating in the organism's parents and passed down during fertilization.

Insulin The hormone secreted by the pancreas that maintains the correct glucose levels in the blood stream after the body's intake of food.

Interstellar Medium The thinly scattered material that floats in the space between stars. It consists of gas (mostly hydrogen) and dust. Even at its densest, the interstellar medium is emptier than the best vacuum we can create in the laboratory, but because space is vast, it still adds up to a huge total mass. New stars and planets slowly coalesce from these materials.

Ion An atom or molecule that has acquired an electric charge by either gaining or losing electrons. An atom with missing electrons has a positive charge and is called a cation. An atom with extra electrons is negative and is called an anion.

Isotope One of the different forms in which the same element can occur. One isotope differs from another according to the number of neutrons in its nucleus. Neutrons have little or no effect on chemical reactions, but do become significant during extremely energetic nuclear processes, such as radiation and fission.

Kilogram The international unit of mass, as defined by a platinum/iridium rod amounting to exactly one kilogram of mass, held in a special laboratory in Paris. Future standards may be defined by a specific number of silicon atoms.

Law In scientific terms, a law is a theory that has become particularly well confirmed and well established because of its reliability as a predictive tool. Laws are sometimes revised when more detailed theories replace older ones. For instance, Newton's laws have been revised in modern times to take account of Einstein's discoveries in relativity theory.

Lipids Organic compounds, such as fats, oils and waxes, that cannot be dissolved in water, and which – together with carbohydrates and proteins – constitute most of the structural material of living things.

Macromolecules The especially large and complex molecules typically found within biological systems, such as proteins and nucleic acids.

Mass A measure of the total amount of matter in an object. Weight is just a measure of gravity's influence on an object, which varies according to the planet exerting the gravitational force, but the mass of the object always stays the same, even in weightless space.

Metabolism The sum total of all the chemical processes in cells and living organisms, based on the chemistry of energy extraction from nutrients and the assembly of the building blocks of life, such as amino acids, proteins, sugars and fats.

Mitochondria Organelles inside the cytoplasm of all eukaryotic cells, responsible for converting glucose into energy for the cell. Mitochondria generate most of the ATP molecules responsible for the energy transportation within – or between – cells.

Molecule A chemically unique aggregate of at least two atoms linked to each other by covalent bonds. Almost all conventional matter on Earth is made up of molecules. Individual atoms are rarely found. A molecule is the smallest amount of a compound that can exist and still exhibit the chemical characteristics of that compound.

Momentum The tendency of a moving object to keep moving in the same direction. Increasing the velocity of an object increases its momentum. A heavy moving object will have more momentum than a lighter one moving at the same speed.

Nanotechnology The manufacture of materials at molecular scale by manipulating single atoms. 'Nano' comes from the size of molecules measured in nanometres, or one-billionth of a metre (0.000000001 m).

Neurotransmitter Messenger molecules that convey signals from one nerve cell (neuron) to another within fractions of a second. A neuron releases its neurotransmitters near another neuron's receptors. After the signal has been relayed, the neurotransmitter is reabsorbed by its original host neuron.

Neutron One of the particles in the nucleus of an atom. Neutrons have substantial mass but no electrical charge.

Newton The unit of force. 1 newton (N) is defined as being the force required to give a mass of 1 kilogram an acceleration of 1 metre per second per second ($1m/s^2$).

Newton's Three Laws
First Law: A moving object will continue to move, or an object at rest will stay at rest, unless acted upon by an external force.
Second Law: The force applied to an object produces an acceleration proportional to the mass of the object.
Third Law: For every action, there is an equal and opposite reaction.

Nucleus In biology, the nucleus is the organelle inside a cell that contains its DNA and governs its growth and reproduction. In physics and chemistry, the word refers to the core of an atom, where neutrons and protons are tightly bound, and most of the atom's mass is contained. Nuclei are thousands of times smaller than the atom itself. For example, if an atom were the size of a football stadium, the nucleus would be comparable to a pea, while the electrons would be in just a handful of spectator seats at the perimeter of a stadium comprised almost entirely of empty space.

Occam's Razor Attributed to the 14th century English philosopher William of Occam (or possibly Ockham), who advised against needlessly complicated theories. For example, if a mysterious light appears in a forest, it is simpler, and therefore more likely correct, to theorize that it comes from a farmer's bonfire rather than a flying saucer.

Organelle One of a number of subcellular structures in eukaryotic cells that perform a specialized function. Organelles are separated from the internal fluid (cytoplasm) of the cell by membranes.

Organic chemistry The study of carbon-based compounds. Organic molecules can exist, and be created, without being associated with life, but no living thing yet discovered can exist without organic molecules.

Periodic table A graphical representation of chemical elements according to increasing atomic number, showing the relationships between elements and chemical properties.

Photon A discrete, indivisible packet of energy associated with electromagnetic radiation. Each photon carries energy proportional to its frequency, with the proportion governed by a special number, Planck's Constant.

Plasma In biology, the transparent fluid in which blood cells are suspended. In physics, plasma is a hot, gas-like state of matter consisting of positively charged ions, free-flying electrons and other subatomic particles. Plasma occurs naturally in stars and solar wind, and in lightning and fire.

Polymer A large, very long-chain molecule made by linking smaller molecules (monomers).

Prokaryote A single-celled form of life lacking a nucleus and without internal membrane-bound organelles. Prokaryotes are thought to be the oldest forms of life on Earth, predating the eukaryotes.

Proteins Found in all living things, and existing in a vast variety of molecular configurations, all proteins are amino acid polymers, each with a specific function contributing to the growth, regeneration, reproduction and repair of cells.

Proton One of the particles that make up the nucleus of an atom, and the second largest by mass, after the neutron. Protons are formed from triplets of quarks, and have a positive electrical charge.

Pulsar A rotating neutron star that produces regular pulses of radiation when observed from a distance. A pulse is recorded every time the rotation brings a magnetic polar region of the neutron star into line with observers on Earth.

Qualia A property of consciousness by which we experience vivid yet physically intangible qualities such as sound and colour, taste or pain.

Quantum Mechanics The theory that describes the behaviour of extremely small phenomena, such as atoms and subatomic particles. It is based on the idea that energy comes in discrete, indivisible bundles, called 'quanta.'

Quarks Fundamental subatomic particles that cannot be divided into anything smaller. They are incapable of independent existence, but combine in triplets to form protons and neutrons.

Quasar Meaning 'quasi-stellar', any extremely bright and unusually energetic star-like object located a very great distance away from our galaxy. Quasars are believed to be powered by supermassive black holes dating from early in the history of the universe.

Radioactivity Spontaneous and unpredictable emission of particles or high-energy electromagnetic radiation from the nuclei of unstable atoms.

Red shift If a source of light, such as a star or galaxy, is moving away from us at a significant fraction of the speed of light, then the wavelength of its light will be elongated towards the red end of the spectrum by the time it reaches us. This effect, otherwise known as a Doppler shift, proves the expansion of the universe.

Refraction The bending of a wave as it encounters the boundary between two different mediums: for instance, air and water. A stick dipped in a pond will look as if it is bending sharply. This effect is caused by refraction.

Resistance The extent to which an electrical conductor hinders the flow of an electric current. Its measurement unit is the ohm, and its symbol is 'R.'

Scientific notation A convenient shorthand system for writing very small or very large numbers as a decimal number between 1 and 10, multiplied by a power of 10. For example, 10,000 can be written as to 1×10^4, and 6220,000,000,000,000,000,000,000,000 becomes 6.22×10^{27}.

Singularity A dimensionless point in the heart of a black hole where matter becomes infinitely compressed, and the laws of physics break down.

Starch The major complex carbohydrate of useful energy value derived from plant foods. Starch is a polymer made of thousands of glucose units.

Synapse The specialized tip of a neuron or nerve cell that is used for communication with other neurons or muscle cells.

Theory An explanation for experimental data, confirmed by experimental tests conducted by many different and independent investigators. Theories usually cannot be proven to be correct beyond all doubt. A single contrary experiment can require a theory to be reconsidered.

Thermodynamics The study of heat and other forms of energy. The total amount of energy in the universe stays the same. It changes from one state to another but is never created or destroyed. Heat always flows from hot objects into cold ones, never the other way around. The distribution of energy in the universe becomes increasingly dissipated and disordered over time.

Thermoplastic A polymer that softens or melts on heating, and becomes rigid again on cooling. Polystyrene is a thermoplastic.

Trait A genetically determined characteristic. A trait can be be physical, such as hair colour or leaf shape, or behavioural, such as the tendency for birds to build nests. Traits usually result from several genes acting in combination.

Ultraviolet Electromagnetic radiation with wavelengths longer than that of X-rays but shorter than visible light.

Uncertainty Principle In the human-scaled world, the behaviour of an object can be exactly described and predicted, based on Newtonian mechanics. In the quantum-scaled realm of atoms and particles, the Uncertainty Principle states that it is impossible to know both the position and momentum of a particle. The more accurate one measurement is, the less accurate the other becomes. This is not a failure of science. It is a fundamental uncertainty in nature itself.

Universe The sum of all that exists physically, including matter, energy, physical laws, space and time. The word applies to something whose limits are not yet known. Multiple universes may exist.

Virus The smallest of all organisms, with debatable status as a living thing, because it does not eat or excrete, and depends strictly on different and cellular living organisms to replicate itself.

Voltage The measure of energy available to drive an electric current. Voltage is measured in volts and is represented by the symbol, V.

Wave An oscillating transfer of energy that moves outward from the source of some disturbance (ripples travelling away from a pebble tossed in a pond, for instance).

Wavelength The distance between adjacent peaks or adjacent troughs on a wave form. Varying the wavelength of light changes its colour. Varying the wavelength of sound changes its pitch.

White Dwarf The small super-dense remnant of a star at the end of its life. The surface has a very high temperature and radiates mainly white-hot and ultraviolet light, but the star is only about the size of the Earth: hence the term 'dwarf'.

WIMPS An acronym for Weakly Interacting Massive Particles, subatomic phenomena that have little or no obvious interaction with the electrically charged electrons or protons inside atoms of normal matter, yet whose mass collectively may help account for the total gravity in the universe.

X-rays A type of electromagnetic radiation, second in energy only to gamma rays, that easily penetrates soft tissue, making them useful for medical imaging.

Zygote A fertilized egg resulting from sexual reproduction, and containing two sets of chromosomes, one from the mother's egg and one from the father's sperm.

INDEX

Picture Credits

All images from the **Science Photo Library** with the exception of:
R= right, L=left, T = top; B= bottom; C = centre

12-13: Pikaia Imaging; 17 R: iStockphoto.com; 21: Pikaia Imaging;
22-23: Pikaia Imaging; 24-25 C, TR: Pikaia Imaging; 27 L, T-B: Pikaia
Imaging; 28 C: Pikaia Imaging; 29 B: Pikaia Imaging; 30 TL: Daniele
Pellegrini/GettyImages, BC: David Tipling/GettyImages, BR: Sergio
Pitamitz/GettyImages; 37 L: National Geographic/Getty Images;
38 T, B: iStockphoto.com; 40 L: Pikaia Imaging; 42: Pikaia Imaging;
43 © British Crown copyright 2010 the Met Office; 44-45 (main
image): Pikaia Imaging; 46 BL, BR: Pikaia Imaging; 47: Pikaia
Imaging; 48-49 (main image): Frans Lemmens/GettyImages; 49 TR:
Pikaia Imaging; 51 TR: iStockphoto.com, CL: Istockphoto.com; 56-
58: Pikaia Imaging; 59 L (4th & 5th from top): iStockphoto.com; 62
B: iStockphoto.com; 66 L: Pikaia Imaging; 67 L: Pikaia Imaging; 68
B: iStockphoto.com; 68-69 (main image): ULTRA.F/GettyImages,
CL, BR&L: iStockphoto.com; 70 BRx2: iStockphoto.com; 71 BLx2:
iStockphoto.com, TR: SSPL/GettyImages; 72 B: © Joe Skipper/
Reuters/Corbis; 79: Pikaia Imaging; 80-81: Pikaia Imaging; 82 B:
Pikaia Imaging; 88-89: Pikaia Imaging; 90 BL: Pikaia Imaging; 95
BR: Pikaia Imaging; 99 TR: © Craig Lovell/Corbis; 100 B: Image
Source/GettyImages; 101: Pikaia Imaging; 102-103: Pikaia Imaging;
104 (main image): Image Source/GettyImages; 110-111 (main image):
Tom Brakefield/GettyImages; 111 T: © Louie Psihoyos/Science
Faction/Corbis112-113 (main image): © Paul A. Souders/Corbis;
114: Pikaia Imaging; 115: Primal Pictures Limited, UK; 116: Primal
Pictures Limited, UK; 117 R: Primal Pictures Limited, UK; 119: Primal
Pictures Limited, UK; 121 R: Primal Pictures Limited, UK; 122 L:
Primal Pictures Limited, UK; 123 T Primal Pictures Limited, UK;
135 BL: Pikaia Imaging; 136 (main image): Pikaia Imaging; 138 C:
iStockphoto.com; 139: Pikaia Imaging; 142-143 (main image) Pikaia
Imaging; 144-145: Pikaia Imaging; 146-147 All Pikaia Imaging except
BR: Geo-Innovations; 148-149 All except 148 R: Pikaia Imaging; 150
(main image): Pikaia Imaging; 151 TL: NASA, TR: NASA, C: NASA/
STS-114 Crew; 152 C: Pikaia Imaging; 154-155 All except B: Pikaia
Imaging; 156: Pikaia Imaging; 158-160: Pikaia Imaging; 161: NASA,
ESA, S. Beckwith (STSci) and The Hubble Heritage Team (STSci/
AURA); 166-167 (main image): © William James Warren/Science
Faction/Corbis; 167 BL & BR: Pikaia Imaging; 168-169 (main image):
© Schlegelmilch/Corbis; 169 TR, BR: © Schlegelmilch/Corbis; 170
B: © Erik Dreyer/Corbis, T: iStockphoto.com; 171: Mitchell Funk/
GettyImages; 172 BL: Walter Bibikow/GettyImages, BR: Thierry
Dosogne/GettyImages; 174: Pikaia Imaging; 175 TR: Pikaia Imaging;
177: Pikaia Imaging; 181 C: Pikaia Imaging; 182-183: Pikaia Imaging;
184: iStockphoto.com; 185 L: Pikaia Imaging, R: iStockphoto.com;
186 L, BC: iStockphoto.com, R: Pikaia Imaging; 187: Pikaia Imaging;
188 (main image): iStockphoto.com; R: Pikaia Imaging; 194 (main
image): Pikaia Imaging; 195 BR: NASA/WMAP Science Team; 196-
197: Pikaia Imaging; 199: Pikaia Imaging; 200: NASA/B.Woodgate
(GSFC)/G. Bower (NOAO)

Quercus Publishing Plc
21 Bloomsbury Square
London
WC1A 2NS

First published in 2010

A catalogue record of this book is available from the
British Library

UK and associated territories 978 1 84916 485 6

US and associated territories 978 1 84866 122 6

Printed and bound in China

10 9 8 7 6 5 4 3 2 1

Art Director Nick Clark
Commissioning Editor Slav Todorov
Managing Editor Emma Heyworth-Dunn
Designer Austin Taylor
Illustrator Tim Brown/Pikaia Imaging